D1097841

NOBEL PRIZE LIBRARY

SEFERIS

SHOLOKHOV

SIENKIEWICZ

SPITTELER

Nobel Prize Library

PUBLISHED UNDER THE SPONSORSHIP OF THE
NOBEL FOUNDATION & THE SWEDISH ACADEMY

Giorgos Seferis

Mikhail Sholokhov

Henryk Sienkiewicz

Carl Spitteler

ALEXIS GREGORY, *New York,* AND
CRM PUBLISHING, *Del Mar, California*

CONTENTS

Giorgos Seferis

1963

"For his eminent lyrical writing, inspired by a deep feeling for the Hellenic world of culture"

Illustrated by POSTMA

PRESENTATION ADDRESS

By ANDERS ÖSTERLING

PERMANENT SECRETARY
OF THE SWEDISH ACADEMY

THIS YEAR'S Nobel Prize for Literature has been awarded to the Greek poet Giorgos Seferis, who was born in 1900 at Smyrna, which he left at an early age to accompany his family to Athens. After the Greeks were driven out of Asia Minor and Seferis' home town had gone up in flames, homelessness—ever the fate of an oppressed and scattered people—was to play a decisive role during his adult years in more ways than one. Seferis studied in Paris, then entered the diplomatic service, went into exile with the Free Greek Government when Greece was occupied in 1941, and was moved about from country to country during the Second World War, when he served his country in Crete, in Cairo, in South Africa, in Turkey, and in the Middle East. After six years as ambassador in London, he retired last year and returned to Athens to devote himself entirely to his literary work.

Seferis' poetic production is not large, but because of the uniqueness of its thought and style and the beauty of its language, it has become a lasting symbol of all that is indestructible in the Hellenic affirmation of life. Now that Palamas and Sikelianos are dead, Seferis is today the representative Hellenic poet, carrying on the classical heritage; a leading national figure, he is also acclaimed abroad insofar as his poetry has been made available in translation. Here in Sweden his work was presented thirteen years ago by Hjalmar Gullberg, whose translations included the famous *The King of Asine,* the theme of which has a connection with Sweden because of our archaeologists' successful excavations on this site. Using imagination as a tool, Seferis tries in this poem to penetrate the secret behind a name that is merely mentioned in a verse of the *Iliad.*

When reading Seferis we are forcibly reminded of a fact that is sometimes forgotten: geographically, Greece is not only a peninsula but also a world of water and foam, strewn with myriad islands, an ancient sea kingdom, the perilous and stormy home of the mariner. This Greece is the constant background of his poetry, in which it is conjured up as the vision of a grandeur both harsh and tender. Seferis does this with a language of rare subtlety, both rhythmical and metaphorical. It has rightly been said that he, better than anyone else, has interpreted the mystery of the stones, of the dead fragments of marble, and of the silent, smiling statues. In his evocative poems, figures from ancient Greek mythology appear together with recent events in the Mediterranean's bloody theater of war. His poetry sometimes seems difficult to interpret, particularly because Seferis is reluctant to expose his inner self, preferring to hide behind a mask of anonymity. He often expresses his grief and bitterness through the medium of a central narrative figure, a kind of Odysseus with features borrowed from the old seamen in the lost Smyrna of the poet's youth. But in his hollow voice is dramatized much of Greece's historical fatality, its shipwrecks and its rescues, its disasters and its valor. Technically, Seferis has received vital impulses from T. S. Eliot, but underneath the tone is unmistakably his own, often carrying a broken echo of the music from an ancient Greek chorus.

Seferis once said of himself, "I am a monotonous and obstinate man who for twenty years has not ceased to say the same things over and over again." There is perhaps some truth in this description, but one must remember that the message he feels bound to convey is inseparable from the intellectual life of his generation as it finds itself confronted with ancient Greek civilization, a heritage that presents a formidable challenge to the impoverished heir. In one of his most significant poems Seferis describes a dream in which a marble head—too heavy for his arms, yet impossible to push aside—fell upon him at the moment of awakening. It is in this state of mind that he sings the praise of the dead, for only communication with the dead conversing on their asphodel meadows can bring to the living a hope of peace, confidence, and justice. In Seferis' interpretation the story of the Argonauts becomes a parable halfway between myth and history, a parable of oarsmen who must fail before they reach their goal.

But Seferis animates this background of melancholy resignation with the eloquent joy inspired in him by his country's mountainous islands with their whitewashed houses rising in terraces above an azure sea, a harmony of colors that we find again in the Greek flag. In concluding this brief presentation, I should like to add that the Prize has been awarded to Seferis "for his eminent lyrical writing, inspired by a deep feeling for the Hellenic world of culture."

Dear Sir—In honoring you, it has been a great privilege for the Swedish Academy to pay its tribute to the Greece of today, whose rich literature has had to wait perhaps too long for the Nobel laurels. Extending to you the congratulations of the Swedish Academy, I ask you to receive from the hands of His Majesty the King this year's Prize for Literature.

ACCEPTANCE SPEECH

By GIORGOS SEFERIS

I FEEL AT THIS MOMENT that I am a living contradiction. The Swedish Academy has decided that my efforts in a language famous through the centuries but not widespread in its present form are worthy of this high distinction. It is paying homage to my language—and in return I express my gratitude in a foreign language. I hope you will accept the excuses I am making to myself.

I belong to a small country. A rocky promontory in the Mediterranean, it has nothing to distinguish it but the efforts of its people, the sea, and the light of the sun. It is a small country, but its tradition is immense and has been handed down through the centuries without interruption. The Greek language has never ceased to be spoken. It has undergone the changes that all living things experience, but there has never been a gap. This tradition is characterized by love of the human; justice is its norm. In the tightly organized classical tragedies the man who exceeds his measure is punished by the Furies. And this norm of justice holds even in the realm of nature.

"Helios will not overstep his measure," says Heraclitus, "otherwise the Furies, the ministers of Justice, will find him out." A modern scientist might profit by pondering this aphorism of the Ionian philosopher. I am moved by the realization that the sense of justice penetrated the Greek mind to such an extent that it became a law of the physical world. One of my masters exclaimed at the beginning of the last century, "We are lost because we have been unjust." He was an unlettered man, who did not learn to write until the age of thirty-five. But in the Greece of our day the oral tradition goes back as far as the written tradition, and so does poetry. I find it significant that Sweden wishes to honor not only this poetry, but poetry in general, even when it originates in a small people. For I think that poetry is necessary to this modern world in which we are afflicted by fear and disquiet. Poetry has its roots in human breath—and what would we be if our breath were diminished? Poetry is an act of confidence—and who knows whether our unease is not due to a lack of confidence?

Last year, around this table, it was said that there is an enormous difference between the discoveries of modern science and those of literature, but little difference between modern and Greek dramas. Indeed, the behavior of human beings does not seem to have changed. And I should add that today we need to listen to that human voice which we call poetry, that voice which is constantly in danger of being extinguished through lack of love, but is always reborn. Threatened, it has always found a refuge; denied, it has always instinctively taken root again in unexpected places. It recognizes no small nor large parts of the world; its place is in the hearts of men the world over. It has the charm of escaping from the vicious circle of custom. I owe gratitude to the Swedish Academy for being aware of these facts; for being aware that languages which are said to have restricted circulation should not become barriers which might stifle the beating of the human heart; and for being a true Areopagus, able "to judge with solemn truth life's ill-appointed lot," to quote Shelley, who, it is said, inspired Alfred Nobel, whose grandeur of heart redeems inevitable violence.

In our gradually shrinking world, everyone is in need of all the others. We must look for man wherever we can find him. When on his way to Thebes Oedipus encountered the Sphinx, his answer to its riddle was: "Man." That simple word destroyed the monster. We have many monsters to destroy. Let us think of the answer of Oedipus.

POEMS

By GIORGOS SEFERIS

Translated from the Greek by Rex Warner

I. MYTHISTOREMA

●

'Si j'ai du goût, ce n'est guères
Que pour la terre et les pierres.'

Arthur Rimbaud

I

The messenger,
Three years we waited for him eagerly;
We kept looking very closely at
The shore the pines the stars.
Joining the blade of the plough or the ship's keel
We were searching to find again the first seed
So that the immemorial drama might begin once more.

We came back to our homes broken,
Weak in the limb, mouths ravaged
From taste of the rust and of the brine.
When we awoke we travelled northwards, strangers,
Plunged into mists by immaculate wings of swans
Which wounded us.

In the winter nights the strong wind from the east maddened us.
In the summer we were lost in the agony of the day that would not die.
We brought back
These carvings of a humble art.

II

Again another well inside a cave.
Once it was easy
To bring up from its depth idols and ornaments
To give pleasure to the friends who still remained faithful to us.
The ropes have broken now; only their marks on the well's mouth
Remind us of our departed happiness:
The fingers on the rim, as the poet says.
The fingers feel for a moment the cool of the stone
And the body's fever passes into the stone
And the cave stakes its soul and loses it
Every second, full of silence, without a drop.

III

Remember the baths where you were slain

I awoke with this marble head between my hands
Which tires my elbows out. Where can I put it down?
It was falling into the dream as I rose from the dream
And so our lives grew one, hard now to be separated.

I peer into the eyes, neither shut nor open,
I speak to the mouth which is always trying to speak,
I hold the cheeks which have grown beyond the skin.
I can do no more.

My hands are lost, my hands come back to me,
Maimed.

IV

Argonauts

And for the soul
If it is to know itself
It is into a soul
That it must look.
The stranger and the enemy, we have seen him in the mirror.

They were good lads, the comrades. They did not grumble
Because of weariness or because of thirst or because of frost.
They had the manner of trees and the manner of waves
That accept the wind and the rain,
Accept the night and the sun,
And in the midst of change they do not change.
They were good lads. Day after day with downcast eyes
They used to sweat at the oar,
Breathing rhythmically,
And their blood flushed up to an obedient skin.
There was a time when they sang, with downcast eyes,
When we passed the desert island with the Arabian figs,
Towards the setting of the sun, beyond the cape
Of dogs that howl.
If it is to know itself, they used to say,
It is into a soul it must look, they used to say.
And the oars beat on the gold of the sea
In the middle of sunset.
Many the capes we passed, many the islands, the sea
Which brings the other sea, sea-gulls and seals.
There were times when unfortunate women with lamentations
Cried out for their children gone,
And others with wild faces looked for Great-Alexander
And glories sunken in the depths of Asia.
We anchored by shores steeped in nocturnal perfumes
Among the singing of birds, waters that left on the hands
The recollection of a great good fortune.
But there was never an end to the journeys.

Their souls became one with the oars and the rowlocks,
With the severe figurehead at the prow,
With the wake of the rudder,
With the water that fractured the image of their faces.
One after another the comrades died
With downcast eyes. Their oars
Indicate the places where they sleep on the shore.

There is none to remember them, and the word is Justice.

V

We never knew them.
Deep down within us it was hope that said
We had known them ever since childhood.
We saw them twice perhaps; then they took to their ships;
Cargoes of coal, cargoes of grain, and our friends
Lost on the other side of the ocean for ever.
Dawn finds us by the tired lamp
Drawing clumsily and with difficulty on a piece of paper
Boats, figure-heads and shells.
In the evening we go down to the river
Because it shows us the way to the sea
And we pass the nights in cellars that smell of tar.

Our friends have gone
perhaps we never saw them, perhaps
We only met them at the time sleep still
Was leading us close up to the breathing wave.
Perhaps we look for them because we are looking for
The other life that is beyond the statues.

VI

M.R.

The garden with its fountains in the rain
You will only see it looking through the low window
Behind the blurred pane of glass. Your room
Will have no light but the fire-light on the hearth
And sometimes in flashes of distant lightning will stand out
The wrinkles on your forehead, my old Friend.

The garden with its fountains which were, in your hands,
A rhythm of the other life, beyond the broken
Marbles and the tragic columns
And a dance among the oleanders
Near the new quarries,
A misted glass will have cut it from your hours.
You will not breathe; the earth and the sap of the trees
Will rush from your memory to beat upon
This pane of glass beaten upon by the rain
From the world outside.

VII

South Wind

The sea to westward joins a trail of mountains.
On our left the south wind blows and drives us mad,
This wind that bares bone, stripping off the flesh.
Our house among the pines and the carobs.
Big windows. Big tables
For writing the letters we have been writing to you
For all these months, and drop
Into the parting between us to fill it up.

Star of morning, when you lowered your eyes

Our times and seasons were more sweet than oil
Laid on a wound, more joyful than the coolness
Of water on the palate, calmer than swan's down.
You held our life in the hollow of your hand.
After the bitter bread of exile,
In the night if we stand by the white wall
Your voice comes to us like the hope of a warming fire;
And once again this wind
Stropping its razor's edge upon our nerves.

Each of us writes to you the same things
And each of us in front of another is silent,
Looking, each one of us apart, at the same world,
The light and the shadow on the trail of mountains
And at you.
Who will lift this sorrow from our hearts?
Yesterday evening came a heavy rain. Today
Again the covered sky. Our thoughts
Like the pine needles after yesterday's rain
Against our door heaped up and useless
Attempt to build a tower which collapses.

Among these decimated villages
Upon this headland naked to the south wind
With the trail of mountains before us, hiding you,
Who will reckon up our decision to forget?
Who will accept our offering at this end of autumn?

VIII

But what are they looking for, our souls that travel
On decks of ships out-worn, crowded together with
Sallow-faced women, crying babies,
Unable to distract themselves even with the flying fish
Or with the stars to which the mast heads point;

Rubbed-out by the gramophone records,
Involved unwillingly in aimless pilgrimages,
Murmuring broken thoughts from foreign languages?

What then are they looking for, our souls that travel
On rotting sea-timbers
From one harbour to another harbour?

Shifting broken stones, breathing in
Each day less easily the pine trees' coolness,
Swimming now in the waters of this sea
And now of that one,
Without the sense of touch,
Without men,
In a country that is no longer our own country
And is not yours either.

We knew it, that the islands were beautiful
Somewhere round about here where we are groping,
Maybe a little lower or a little higher,
No distance away at all.

IX

The harbour is old, I cannot wait any longer
Either for the friend who left for the island of pines
Or for the friend who left for the island of planes
Or for the friend who left for the open sea.

I stroke the rusty cannons, I stroke the oars
So that my body may revive and make its decision.
The sails give out only the smell
Of the salt spray of the other storm.

If I wished to stay by myself, I desired to find
Solitude, I did not desire such endless waiting,
The scattering of my soul to the horizon,
These lines, these colours, this silence.

The stars of night bring me back to the expectation
Of Odysseus for the dead among the asphodels.
Among the asphodels when we moored here we wished to find
The mountain glade that saw Adonis wounded.

X

Our country is a shut-in place, all mountains
And the mountains roofed by a low sky, day and night.
We have no rivers, we have no wells, we have no fountains,
Only some cisterns, empty; they ring and are to us
Objects of worship.
A sound stagnant, hollow, like our solitude,
Like our love and like our bodies.
It seems to us strange that once we were able to build
These houses of ours, these huts, these sheep-folds.
And our marriages,—the dewy garlands, the marriage fingers,
Have become insoluble riddles for our souls.
How were they born
Our children? How then did they grow up?

Our country is a shut-in place. It is enclosed
By the two black Clashing Rocks. And when we go
On Sundays down to the harbour for a breath of air,
We see, lit by the sunset,
The broken timbers of unfinished journeys,
Bodies that know no longer how to love.

XI

Your blood froze sometimes like the moon.
In the inexhaustible night your blood
Spread its white wings above
The black rocks, the shapes of trees and the houses
With a gleam of light out of the years of our childhood.

XII

A bottle in the sea

Three rocks, a few burnt pines, a desert chapel,
And higher up
The same landscape, recopied, begins again.
Three rocks in the form of a gate, rusted,
A few burnt pines black and yellow
And a small square building buried in whitewash;
And up the hill again, over and over,
Just the same landscape climbs in tier after tier
Up to the skyline, up to the sunset sky.

Here we moored our ship to mend our broken oars
To drink some water and to get some sleep.
The sea which embittered us is deep and unexplored,
Unfolding boundless calm.
Here among the shingle we found a coin
And threw dice for it.
The youngest of us won it and disappeared.

We embarked again with our broken oars.

XIII

Hydra

Dolphins banners and cannonades.
The sea that was once so bitter to your soul
Carried the many-coloured and shining ships,
It swayed and rocked them, all blue with white wings,
The sea that was once so bitter to your soul
Now bursting out with colours in the sun.

White sails, light, and the wet oars
With drum-beat rhythm on tamed waves.

Your eyes would be beautiful if they were looking,
Your arms would be splendid if you were stretching them out,
Your lips, as once they were, would come alive
At such a miracle;
You were looking for it what were you looking for in front of the ashes
Or in the rain in the fog in the wind,
Even at the hour when the lights were slackening,
When the city was sinking and from the pavements
The Nazarene showed you his heart,
What were you looking for? Why don't you come? What were you looking
for?

XIV

Three red doves in the light
Drawing our fate in the light
With colours and gestures of people
Whom we loved.

XV

Quid πλατανῶν opacissimus?

Sleep wrapped you round, like a tree, with green leaves,
You breathing, like a tree in the peaceful light,
And in the limpid pool I looked at your face:
Shut eyelids and the eyelashes brushed the water.
My fingers in the soft grass found your fingers,
I held your pulse for a moment
And felt in another place the pain of your heart.

Under the plane, by the water, among the laurels
Sleep kept displacing and dispersing you
Around me, near me. I could not touch the whole of you
Together with your silence;
Seeing your shadow growing now larger now smaller,
Losing itself in the other shadows, in the other
World which let go of and kept hold of you.
The life which was given to us to live, we lived it.
Pity those who are waiting with such patience
Lost in the black laurels, under the heavy planes,
And those who, solitary, speak to the cisterns and wells
And are drowned within the circles of their voice.
Pity the comrade who shared in our privation and our sweat
And sunk into the sun, like a crow beyond the ruins,
Without a hope of enjoying our reward.

Grant us, outside of sleep, serenity.

XVI

The name—Orestes

Again, again into the track, once more into the track!
How many turns, how many laps of blood, how many black

Circles of faces watching: the people watching me
Who watched me when, upright in the chariot,
I raised my hand, brilliant, and they roared applause.

The froth of horses beats upon my flesh. When will the horses
Weary? The axle shrieks, the axle glows. When will the axle
Seize up in flame? When will the rein break?
When will the whole hooves tread
Full on the ground, on the soft grass, among
The poppies where in spring you picked a daisy?

They were lovely, your eyes. You did not know where to look with them
Nor did I know where to look, I, without a country,
I who struggle on this spot—how many turns and laps!—
And I feel my knees failing me above the axle,
Above the wheels, above the savage track.
The knees fail easily when the gods will have it so.
No one is able to escape; no strength will do it, you cannot
Escape the sea which cradled you, for which you turn and search
In this moment of contest, among the breathing of horses,
With the reeds that used to sing in autumn to a Lydian mode,
The sea that you cannot find again, run as you may,
Turn as you may, lap after lap, in front of the black
Eumenides who are bored and cannot forgive.

XVII

Astyanax

Now that you are going, take with you the child
Who saw the light under that plane tree
On a day when trumpets sounded and armour gleamed
And sweating horses bowed their heads at the trough
Over the green surface, brushing
The water with their moist nostrils.

The olive trees with the wrinkles of our fathers
The rocks with the wisdom of our fathers
And our brother's blood living upon the earth
Were a robust joy a rich injunction
For the souls who understood their prayer.

Now that you are going, now at the dawn of the day
Of final settlement, now that no one can tell
Whom he will kill and how he will meet his end,
Take with you the child who saw the light
Under the leaves of that plane
And teach him to study the trees.

XVIII

I am sorry to have allowed a broad river to pass between my fingers
Without drinking a single drop.
Now I sink into the stone.
A small pine on the red soil
Is all the companionship I have.
What I loved has disappeared with the houses
Which were new last summer
And fell to pieces before the autumn wind.

XIX

Even if the wind blows it bring us no refreshment
And the shadow remains narrow beneath the cypresses
And all around the slopes go up to the mountains.

They weigh heavily on us
The friends who no longer know the way to die.

XX

Andromeda

In my breast the wound opens again
When the stars are setting and become conjoined with my body
When silence falls after the footsteps of men.

These stones which are sinking into the years, how far will they drag me
with them?
The sea, the sea, who is it that can drain it dry?
I see the hands each dawn beckoning to the hawk and vulture,
I, bound to the rock which suffering has made my own,
I see the trees which breathe the black peace of the dead
And then the smiles, motionless, of the statues.

XXI

We who set out upon this pilgrimage
Looked at the broken statues
We forgot ourselves and said that life
Is not so easily annihilated;
That death has ways that are uncharted
And a justice that is its own;

That while we are dying upright on our feet,
Made one in the brotherhood of stone,
Bound together in hardness and in weakness,
The ancient dead have escaped the circle and risen again
Smiling in a strange silence.

XXII

Because so many things have passed before our eyes
That even our eyes saw nothing but beyond,
And behind us memory like the white screen one night in a walled place
On which we saw strange images, more strange than you,
Passing and fading in the unstirring foliage of a pepper tree;

Because we have known so well this fate of ours,
Wandering among broken stones, three or six thousand years,
Digging in ruined buildings which could have been, perhaps, our homes,
Trying to remember dates and deeds of heroes;
Shall we be able?

Because we have been bound, because we have been scattered,
And have struggled with difficulties described as non-existent,
Lost, then finding again a road full of blind battalions,
Sinking in marshes and in the lake of Marathon,
Shall we be able to die in a normal way?

XXIII

Just a little more
And we shall see the almond trees in blossom
The marbles shining in the sun
The sea, the curling waves.

Just a little more
Let us rise just a little higher.

XXIV

Here end the works of the sea, the works of love.
Those who one day shall live here where we end,
If ever the dark blood should rise to overflow their memory,
Let them not forget us, the strengthless souls among the asphodels.
Let them turn towards Erebus the heads of the victims.
We who had nothing shall teach them peace.

II. GYMNOPAEDIA

•

'Santorin is geologically composed of pumice-stone and china-clay; in her bay islands have appeared and disappeared. This island was once the birthplace of a very ancient religion. The lyrical dance of a strict and heavy rhythm performed here was called: *Gymnopaedia.*'

Guide to Greece

I. SANTORIN

Stoop down, if you can, to the dark sea, forgetting
The sound of a flute played to naked feet
That tread your sleep in the other life, the submerged one.

Write, if you can, upon your last shell
The day, the name, the place
Then throw it into the sea that it may sink.

We found ourselves naked on the pumice stone
Watching the islands rising out of the sea,

Watching the red islands sinking
In their sleep, in our sleep.
Here we stood naked holding
The scales weighted in favour of injustice.

Instep of power, unshadowed will, considered love,
Plans ripening beneath the sun of midday
And course of fate at the clap of a young hand
Upon the shoulder;
In the place that crumbled, that makes no resistance,
In the place that was once our own,
Ashes and rust the islands sink.

Altars in ruins
And friends forgotten
Leaves of palm in mud.
Let your hands, if you can, go travelling
Here on the turn of time with that far ship
Which has touched the horizon.
When the dice struck upon the slab
When the spear struck the breastplate
When the eye recognised the stranger
And love drained out
In pierced souls;
When you look round and you find
All about you swathes of feet
All about you dead hands
All about you darkened eyes;
When there is no longer any choice
Of the death you wanted as your own,
Listening to a great cry,
Even to a wolf that yells——
Your due;
Let your hands, if you can, go travelling;
Tear yourself loose from the unfaithful time
And sink.

Needs must he sink who carries the great stones.

II. MYCENAE

Give me your hands, give me your hands, give me your hands
I saw in the night
The mountain's pointed peak
I saw the plain afar flooded in moonlight
And no moon to be seen;
I saw, turning my head,
Black stones huddled around
And all my life stretched out like a string,
The beginning and the ending,
The final moment
My hands.

Needs must he sink who carries the great stones;
These stones I have carried as long as I was able,
These stones I have loved as long as I was able,
These stones my fate.
Wounded by my own soil
Tortured by my own garment
Condemned by my own gods,
These stones.

I know they do not know; yet I
Who have so often followed
The path that leads from murderer to victim
From victim to the punishment
And from the punishment up to another murder;
Groping my way
Over the purple welling inexhaustible
That night of the return
When the whistling began
Of Furies in the scanty grass——
I have seen snakes crossed with vipers
Knotted about the accursed generation
Our fate.

Voices out of stone, out of sleep,
Voices more deep here where the world grows dark,
Memory of toil that is rooted in the rhythm
Beaten upon the earth by feet forgotten.
Bodies sunk, all naked, in the foundations
Of the other time. Eyes
Staring and staring towards a sign
That you, however you wish it, cannot distinguish.
The soul
That fights to become your soul.

Even the silence is no longer yours
Here where the mill stones have stopped still.

THE LIFE AND WORKS OF GIORGOS SEFERIS

By CONSTANTINE T. DIMARAS

A POET'S LIFE and his works are two facets of the same reality, even when the life is a long one and the poetry relatively small in bulk. Giorgos Seferis, for example, was not a prolific writer; in the original, his collected poems make up a book of about two hundred pages. But Seferis's life is completely expressed in these poems. His lyricism is always autobiographical, for the only source of lyric poetry is the poet's life: such poetry comes into existence only when the outside world has been assimilated by the poet and transmuted into poetry. This outside world is made up of experience and impressions, of sensations and recollections, and of the knowledge gained by reading; the poet's consciousness must often attain sufficient breadth to embrace elements that are more than personal. Anyone who loves poetry should try to understand the process by which this transmutation is brought about.

Seferis was born in Smyrna, or Izmir, on March 13, 1900. He was the eldest son of a well-to-do family—his father, Stelios Sepheriades, was a lawyer of international standing—and he grew up, like all Greek children of his time, passionately devoted to the idea of a free Greece, the symbol and promise of a triumphant Hellenism that was still to come. Few Western European readers can now imagine what it was like for a young Greek to live in the ancient capital of Ionia at the beginning of the 1900s. Step by step, over a period of nearly a century, the nation of Greece had come to full development. But outside the national borders, there were so-called "unredeemed" Greeks, concentrated mainly in the large urban centers of Turkey, where they constituted one of the most mobile and restless components of the population. These townspeople lived in the hope of early union with Greece, the "mother country." In 1912 three small Balkan states, Greece, Serbia, and Bulgaria, were victorious in a war against Turkey, and the optimists among them believed that Greek national claims might soon be satisfied. The young Seferis lived in this feverish atmosphere, with its heady mixture of memory, faith, hope, and impatience, all focused on a mirage of Greece idealized by distance and love.

World War I put an end to this idyllic period. After the outbreak of the war the Greeks of Smyrna could no longer look confidently to the future, and many Greek families left Turkey for Greece. The Sepheriades family settled at first in Athens, where George completed his secondary education. Before the end of the war, they moved to Paris, where Seferis studied law. There he remained until 1924.

The years between 1914 and 1924 were decisive ones for the development of the future poet. The 1920s were marked in France by a tremendous upsurge of activity in literature in general and poetry in particular. Seferis lived in the midst of this movement and turmoil, in circumstances favorable to his literary vocation. He discovered the work of the symbolist poet Jules Laforgue at that time and his reading must have led him on to Guillaume Apollinaire and the dadaists and surrealists. Soon afterward he came into contact with the English poetry of the period which made a profound impression on him.

During these years an event took place that was to be indelibly engraved on the minds of the younger generation of Greeks. A Greek military expedition, attempting to occupy part of Asia Minor, met disastrous defeat in 1922. The flourishing towns of Ionia and thousands of years of Greek traditions were wiped out overnight. A short time later, under a treaty between Greece and Turkey, the remnants of the Greek population of Asia Minor were evacuated to Greece. One and a half million refugees poured into Greece; some of the problems presented by their settlement have not yet been solved. The young "unredeemed" Greek in Paris saw from afar the town where he was born and the familiar, pleasant scenes of his childhood disappear in a catastrophe of unforeseen violence, and at the same time the concrete realities of an age-old tradition were cut short and came to an end. History broke in on Seferis's life—history as something actually experienced, not as something read in a book.

From then on his views of Greece were transformed by a process that is common in lyrical inspiration. Greece, the symbol of a homeland lost forever, also came to represent the poet's nostalgia for an unattainable world. The underlying feelings that are typical of all lyric poetry were intensified by the poet's deeply painful personal experience. Frustration and its psychological effects played an essential part in Seferis's development as a poet. When he subsequently turned his attention to the work of T. S. Eliot and the historical poetry of Constantine Cavafy, these somber and elegiac works touched a familiar chord in him. What may be called a systematic rule of multiple causes must be applied to provide an explanation of the young poet's literary tastes: several different, independent causes all leading by different routes to a single result.

Seferis gave himself time to develop to literary maturity. We have no clue to any discarded poems of his youth; his first published volume of verse, *Strophe* (*Turning Point*), appeared in 1931. One of the poems in this collection bears the date 1924 in later editions, a 1940 volume includes a poem dated 1928. These are the only dates the poet ever indicated prior to the publication of his poems, and this reserve itself is tinged with a classical moderation in keeping with Seferis's gradual development to full maturity. It may be added that his name appeared for the first time in a literary review as the translator of a piece of prose by Paul Valéry, for Seferis has always used the art of translation as a means of perfecting language and style.

Both the slow maturing and the meticulous translating reflect the will to perfect language and style. The titles of some of his volumes of poetry, such as *Tetradio Gymnasmaton* (*Book of Exercises,* 1940) or *Emerologio Katastromatos* (*Logbook*) (I, II, and III; 1940, 1944, and 1955), indicate the importance Seferis attaches to form in poetry. I have also referred to classical moderation. Yet any reader who runs his eye over the pages of Seferis's work will note his constant use of free verse. These free metrics are not due to the loss of rigid form in translation; Seferis's art and spirit are classical in their purity, moderation, and restraint, yet they are as far removed from classicism as it is possible to be. In all his works he implicitly calls for a profound change in the technique of poetry. Seferis did not turn his back on his age or try to set the clock back. He adopted what was alive in the experiments of the surrealists and won a following in Greece through poetry that made free use of symbols and re-invigorated a traditional vocabulary by giving age-old words their original savor.

In the 1940s, once again history took control of the life of the poet, of his generation, and of his country. In 1940 the violence of World War II spread to Greece, first through aggression by Italy and then, a few months later, through a German attack before which Greek military resistance soon crumbled. Seferis, who had entered the diplomatic service in 1926, was working in the Department of Information in Greece at the outbreak of war. He followed his government to Crete and then into exile. Throughout his career as a diplomat, Greece was more than a geographical reality; it became a symbol of absence—of an elusive beloved. He was bound to his land by a love that has nothing abstract about it; in his poems, we always feel the physical presence of Greece. Stones, sand and water arouse a sensual awareness that was heightened and ennobled by distance and nostalgia, and by a craving to be reunited with the land that nurtured him. Everything is pure in this atmosphere, freed of all taint by the spirituality of the poet's desire.

Not long ago, there was much talk among literary critics of "pure poetry"—poetry freed of everything other than itself, everything inherently prosaic in language. Hypothetically, pure poetry is not governed by the rules of logic; it is all music and inner melody, with patterns and combinations of words that are designed solely to please the ear. Pure poetry is seen as poetry devoid of feeling, free from any emotional component, exclusively dedicated to formal perfection. In addition to these concepts, pure poetry is prayer, drawing a natural parallel between two closely related forms of expression. And a final manifestation of purity in poetry is the poet's austerity in stripping his subject bare, in making poetry alive to material things but immaterial in itself.

Pure poetry is Seferis's specific contribution to Greek poetry and to poetry in general. While his lyricism is not restricted to man's rational functions, it does not lie outside their scope but goes beyond it. In its mystical elements, great lyricism represents an advanced stage in man's effort to grasp reality. It is incommensurable with logical analysis and has no common denominator with science or philosophy, but far from being opposed to them, it expresses a disquiet equivalent to the drive which manifests itself in scientific or philosophical research. By his renunciation the poet associates himself with mankind's eternal anxiety.

It is difficult to discuss the language of translated poems, for language is inescapably national or local. But a useful purpose can be served by discussing Seferis's language, for two reasons; first, the reader may be interested in the problems of the Greek language itself, and second, only a series of individual experiences can enable a reader to assess a poet's contribution to language. The Greek people, with their unbroken ancient cultural tradition, are still hesitating today between various stages in the development of their language, unable to choose any one of them. Moreover, there was a time when critics took it for granted that, thanks to a divine gift—the gift of tongues—the poet is the predestined factor in the enrichment and development of language.

The latter assertion seems questionable. The language of lyricism is not an end or result; it comes at the *beginning* of articulate speech and represents a primitive stage in its development. In this view, the final stage of language would lie in the direction of prose, an instrument of absolute precision, fluid and flexible enough to express the subtlest shades of thought. Modern Greece, which has given outward expression to its inner life primarily in the lyric mode, is in urgent need of a strong, precise and flexible tool of this kind.

Seferis has greatly helped the intellectuals and literary men of his country to improve the Greek language and enrich its means of expression. Freer than prose, less fettered by rules, lyricism lends itself better to experiment, innovation, and renovation. It can do more than prose to promote the development of language, while preserving its freshness and vigor. This brief outline sums up the nature of Seferis's poetry in relation to language; his activity in this area alone would have been enough to make him one of the foremost figures in modern Hellenic literature.

But this is only one facet of his art. Poetry is made with words, but words convey a message and in the end this message is of fundamental importance. In Seferis's poetry we are struck by the directness and splendor of his words, by their weight, resonance, symbolism, and power, by their balance, depth, and musicality. But his inspiration—the element in poetry that remains when the magic of the Greek words is removed—is also of incomparable quality. While the effects directly depending on the original language may be blurred in translation, the reader of translated poems can still feel the poetic current streaming violently and forcefully through it.

In all of Seferis's poems there are certain fundamental, simple constants that explain his inner world, and in the last analysis these constants may be reduced to a single one, representing the essence of his life and work. Seferis's inspiration is pre-eminently cyclical in nature. He has the will to strive for perfection, he strives constantly to refine his instrument, but it is always the same instrument. Though he plunges to the depths of consciousness or rises to the highest, most tenuous pinnacle of thought, these changes of level always take place along the same axis. What name can be found for this many-sided, yet unchanging nucleus? Nostalgia—it is in the mood of nostalgia that we must seek the key to Seferis's work, and this key unites his work with his life.

In the need to return lies the innermost meaning of lyricism: the return to God, the return to Paradise Lost, the attraction of the womb, the desire for a life of bliss that has been lost forever. In Seferis's life this mood took on a palpable form and bestowed the gift of poetry on him. The nostalgia that permeates Seferis's works gives both the poet and his poetry their supreme quality. It is the poet's transcending nostalgia for his native soil, the land of Greece that he has lost forever. One line of his poetry, "Wherever my journeying takes me, Greece hurts me," poignantly conveys the source of Seferis's inspiration.

Seferis is associated with both history that he actually experienced and with his historical heritage. But this is not all; in addition, he adopts the great lyrical tradition of his country. More than a century ago, literary critics defined the essence of this lyricism precisely. It is inspired by love for the Greek homeland, and nothing could be closer to the history of the Greek people than this source of inspiration. Modern lyricism was born in Greece at the same time as it was in Western Europe. There are a few exceptions prior to the nineteenth century—folk songs, which cannot easily be fitted into any chronological pattern; and a few isolated, individual, short-lived efforts, usually attempts to graft the fruits of learning onto the sturdy tree of folk poetry. But the true lyrical impetus, along with the vibrant Romantic movement that produced it, came to Greece during the second quarter of the nineteenth century, during the transition period in which modern Hellenic civilization passed from the Eastern to the Western orbit. The nineteenth century, which flooded the world with Romantic poetry and music, had a sense of the sublime.

While Greece was gaining access to European literature, she was also regaining her freedom in a long, hard war after centuries of bondage. The Greek people aspired to independence and fought for it; all energies and minds were bent on the establishment of a free Greek state. The inspiration of Greek poets was fundamentally, almost exclusively, patriotic. Two of the greatest names in modern Hellenic literature, Andrew Calvos (1792–1869) and Dionysios Solomos (1798–1857) answered the call. The impetus had been given; patriotic feeling was to dominate Greek poetry up to the present day. The drive to reclaim the "unredeemed" Greeks, like Seferis himself, lent it topicality and constantly revived it in the national sensibility. The voices of such modern poets as Kostes Palamas (1859–1943), Constantine Cavafy (1863–1933) and Angelos Sikelianos (1884–1951), whose vigorous, oratorical poems inspired the Greece of the underground resistance in World War II, were echoed by the nostalgia of Seferis, contributing from outside to the fight for the liberation of Greece.

This patriotic theme, the constant of all modern Hellenic poetry, is unceasingly developed by Seferis. From volume to volume the same motif is endlessly repeated, constantly growing more piercing, richer, more varied. Seferis is in quest of himself; he plunges to the depths of his consciousness and brings to the surface his Greek self and his love for his homeland. From his first attempts at poetry, in which he masked his feelings with smiles tinged with emotion, to the great successes of his first classical style (to which he has never returned, though he has never repudiated it), and from there to his full, austere maturity, he has worked upon and refined a passionate dream which was ever new because he constantly experienced it anew. It is a dream with a thousand different faces, the dream of Greece, inherited from the work of a series of great predecessors.

A poet's greatness never lies in elements that set him apart from his community; these elements merely enable him to impress, to shock, to scandalize or to create a short-lived fashion. He wins a name for himself and finds a place in the center of intellectual activity—by means very different from these ephemeral triumphs. Clearly, aptly, accurately and expressively, he voices the feelings of his day and the experiences that his fellowmen have been unable to express. He takes up the themes that have been handed down to him, enriching them by his genius, his own experience, and the new facilities for expression provided by his age. He enriches tradition, in effect, by incorporating it in his own works.

Seferis is a perfect example of these general rules. This austere, somewhat unapproachable poet, making no concessions for popular applause, has gained recognition among his own people. He has made them aware of their unformulated desires and of their most intense emotions. In return, they have assigned him a crucial position in the development of Greek poetry. In Greece, people of understanding felt that the Nobel Prize for 1963 fell into the poet's hands like fruit ripening at the proper season—they were delighted, but not surprised. A grace of another kind had bestowed a spokesman on Greece, and the voice of a nation more than two thousand years old was ringing out again, full-toned, melodious, and masterful.

Constantine T. Dimaras, journalist and literary historian, lectures at the University of Athens.
Translated by Annie Jackson.

THE 1963 PRIZE

By KJELL STRÖMBERG

Greece, the source of all Western civilization, had to wait over sixty years before being inscribed on the Nobel Prize roll of honor. But modern Hellas has not lacked brilliant writers able to renew a glorious tradition that had never been completely lost. For thirty or forty years their names appeared on the list of Prize candidates, up to 1963, when the land of Homer at last was honored in the person of Giorgos Seferis. He was the sole survivor of a great generation of poets which included among its leaders Kostes Palamas and Angelos Sikelianos. Both of them had had ardent supporters in the Swedish Academy, and so too had the eminent novelist Nikos Kazantzakis, who died before he could win this supreme award.

Ilias Venezis, the emulator and disciple of Kazantzakis, had written an epic work on the most recent Greek tragedy, the enforced exodus from the shores of Asia Minor to the mother country: he was the only candidate among his compatriots to be proposed in opposition to Seferis.

The number of competitors for the Prize that year beat all the records; there were eighty as opposed to sixty-six the year before.

Giorgos Seferis was proposed as a candidate for the first time in 1955, when a collection of his poems had appeared in a Swedish translation. *The King of Asine,* perhaps his most famous poem, had also been published in a masterly translation by Hjalmar Gullberg, a member of the Swedish Academy. There is a story attached to this poem connecting it with Sweden, and when Seferis was elected he told it during his visit to Stockholm. Some Swedish archeologists under the direction of Professor Axel Persson had unearthed the ruins of the ancient city of Asine, of which Homer speaks in the second book of the *Iliad.* It was during the course of a week spent with the Swedish archeologists on the shore of Argolis, near Mycenae, that Seferis found out about the discovery of the beautiful gold mask around which he built his poem.

This happened a few years before World War II. Afterwards Seferis came in close contact with archeologists and French and English writers whom he met during the course of his peregrinations during and following the occupation of Greece by Germany.

The first selection of his poems to be translated into French, with a very eulogistic preface by Robert Levesque, appeared as early as 1945 in a collection of works published by the French Institute in Athens. Three years later he was introduced for the first time to the English public and was warmly acclaimed by T. S. Eliot, the Nobel Prizewinner for 1948, whose works Seferis had translated into Greek. He was compared to Hesiod and even to Pindar and, after having been appointed by his government as Ambassador in London, Cambridge University gave him an honorary degree in 1960. In 1961, Seferis was the subject of a commemorative publication to which about twenty people, representing the elite of all classes in his country, contributed. In 1962, his work became available in German translations. Thus he was not unknown in the world of letters when, on October 24, 1963, the Swedish Academy awarded him the Nobel Prize for Literature "for his eminent lyrical writing, which is inspired by a deep feeling for the Hellenic cultural heritage."

This Prize seems to have encountered few difficulties: everyone agreed fairly quickly on it.

The report to the Nobel Committee on Seferis was entrusted to the eminent Hellenist Sture Linnér, a personal friend of the laureate-to-be and a former chief lecturer at Uppsala University. He had first met the poet in Athens during the long years he devoted to the organizations for aid to Greece, which had been formed by several countries after the war. He served the United Nations as personal representative of the Secretary-General, Dag Hammarskjöld, in the war-torn Congo. He then returned to Greece to prepare a great work in English on his friend Seferis, of which an abridged edition in Swedish came out just in time for the award. According to this well-informed report, Seferis was well and truly considered to be his country's national poet, since the disappearance from the scene of the two great revivers of Greek literature, Palamas and Sikelianos. Linnér depicted Seferis as a writer with roots deep in his native soil, enamored of Homer and Aeschylus, but equally familiar with writers such as Valéry and Eliot.

When Seferis arrived in Sweden to receive his Prize, accompanied by Sture Linnér and the Swedish Ambassador to Athens, his first unofficial visit was to the grave of Dag Hammarskjöld at Uppsala. After Österling's speech in his honor, Seferis answered with eloquence and dignity. He emphasized that he belonged to a small country, but a country whose tradition had been handed down through the centuries without interruption, a tradition which was immensely strong and still active. Then he spoke in French of the poetry "which Sweden had decided to honor, even though it sprang from the midst of a small people."

To King Gustavus Adolphus the poet was able to talk as though they were two colleagues since the monarch was an archeologist by inclination and almost by profession, and had taken part in the excavation of Asine.

Translated by Camilla Sykes.

Mikhail Sholokhov

1965

"For the artistic power and integrity with which, in his epic of the Don, he has given expression to a historic phase in the life of the Russian people"

Illustrated by *JACQUES PECNARD*

PRESENTATION ADDRESS

By ANDERS ÖSTERLING

MEMBER OF THE SWEDISH ACADEMY

THIS YEAR'S Nobel Prize for Literature, as you all know, has been awarded to the Russian writer Mikhail Sholokhov, born in 1905 and now in his sixty-first year. Sholokhov's childhood was spent in the country of the Don Cossacks; the strong ties that have always bound him to this district grew out of his sympathy for the highly individual temperament of its people and the wildness of its landscape. He saw his native province pass through the various phases of the Revolution and the Russian civil war. After trying his hand at manual work in Moscow, he soon began to concentrate on writing and produced a series of sketches describing the battles along the Don, a subject that was later to bring him fame. It is striking evidence of the precociousness of the war generation that Sholokhov was only twenty-one when he began the first parts of the great epic novel *Tikhi Don* (*And Quiet Flows the Don,* 1928–1940). Its Russian title is simply "The Quiet Don," which acquires an undeniably ironic undertone in view of the extreme violence of the action in Sholokhov's masterpiece.

It took Sholokhov fourteen years to complete the highly exacting project, which covers the period including the First World War, the Revolution, and the civil war, having as its main theme the tragic Cossack revolt. The four parts of the epic appeared at relatively long intervals between 1928 and 1940, and were long viewed with some concern by Soviet critics, whose political affiliation made it difficult for them to accept wholeheartedly Sholokhov's quite natural commitment to his theme, the Cossacks' revolt against the new central authorities; nor could they easily accept his endeavor to explain and defend objectively the defiant spirit of independence that drove these people to resist every attempt at subjection.

In view of the controversial aspects of his theme, there can surely be no doubt that in undertaking the writing of this novel Sholokhov was taking a daring step, a step which at that point in his career also meant the settling of a conflict with his own conscience.

And Quiet Flows the Don is so well known to Swedish readers that an introduction may well seem superfluous. With magnificent realism the book portrays the unique character of the Cossack, the traditional mixture of cavalryman and farmer, whose instincts seem to conflict with one another but nevertheless are welded together to form a firmly coordinated whole. There is no glamorization. The coarse and savage streaks in the Cossack temperament are displayed openly; nothing is hidden or glossed over, but at the same time one is aware of an undercurrent of respect for all that is human. Although a convinced Communist, Sholokhov keeps ideological comment out of his book completely. We are compensated for the amount of bloodshed in the battles he describes by the full-blooded vigor of his narrative.

The Cossack's son, Gregor, who changes allegiance from the Reds to the Whites and is forced against his will to continue the struggle to its hopeless conclusion, is both hero and victim. The conception of honor that he has inherited is put to the sternest of tests, and he is defeated by a necessity of history which here plays the same role as the classical Nemesis. But our sympathy goes out to him and to the two unforgettable women, Natalia, his wife, and Aksinia, his mistress, who both meet disaster for his sake. When he finally returns to his native village after digging Aksinia's grave in the steppe with his saber, he is a gray-haired man who has lost everything in life but his young son.

Stretching away behind the whole gallery of figures, seen either in their personal relationships or playing their parts as military personnel, lies the mighty landscape of the Ukraine: the steppes in all the changing seasons, the villages with their sweet-smelling pastures and grazing horses, the grass billowing in the wind, the banks of the river, and the never-ending murmur of the river itelf. Sholokhov never tires of describing the Russian steppes. Sometimes he interrupts the narrative right in the middle to burst out in exultation: "My beloved steppes under the low sky of the Don country! Ravines winding across the plain with their walls of red earth, a sea of waving feather-grass, marked only by the print of horses' hoofs leaving a trail like a myriad of birds' nests, and by the graves of the Tartars who in wise silence watch over the buried glory of the Cossacks . . . I bow low before you and as a son kiss your fresh earth, unspoiled steppe of the Don Cossacks, watered with blood."

It may well be said that Sholokhov, breaking no new ground, is using a well-tried realistic technique, a technique that may seem naive in its simplicity if compared to many a later model in the art of novel-writing. But his subject surely could not have been presented in any other way, and the powerful, evenly sustained, epic flow of writing makes *And Quiet Flows the Don* a genuine *roman fleuve* in more than one sense.

Sholokhov's more recent work, for example, *Podnyataya tselina* (*Virgin Soil Upturned,* 1932 and 1959)—a novel describing compulsory collectivization and the introduction of *kolkhozy*—has a constant vitality and shows us Sholokhov's fondness for richly comic yet sympathetic characters. But of course, *And Quiet Flows the Don* would, by itself, thoroughly merit the present award, a distinction which has come rather late in the day, but happily not too late to add to the roll of Nobel Prize-winners the name of one of the most outstanding writers of our time.

In support of its choice the Swedish Academy speaks of "the artistic power and integrity with which, in his epic of the Don, Sholokhov has given expression to a historic phase in the life of the Russian people."

Sir—This distinction is intended as a tribute of justice and gratitude to you for your important contribution to modern Russian literature, a contribution as well known in this country as it is all over the world. May I offer you the congratulations of the Swedish Academy, and at the same time ask you to receive from His Majesty the King this year's Nobel Prize for Literature.

ACCEPTANCE SPEECH

By MIKHAIL SHOLOKHOV

On this solemn occasion I find it my pleasant duty to extend my thanks once more to the Swedish Academy, which has awarded me the Nobel Prize.

As I have already had occasion to testify in public, the feeling of satisfaction which this award arouses in me is not solely due to the international recognition of my professional merits and my individual characteristics as a writer. I am proud that this Prize has been awarded to a Russian, a Soviet writer. Here I represent a multitude of writers from my native land.

I have also previously expressed my satisfaction that, indirectly, this Prize is yet another recognition of the novel as a genre. I have not infrequently read and heard recent statements which have quite frankly astonished me, in which the novel has been declared an outdated form that does not correspond to present-day demands. Yet it is just the novel that makes possible the most complete comprehension of the world of reality, that permits the projection of one's attitude to this world, to its burning problems. One might say that the novel is the genre that most predisposes one to a profound insight into the tremendous life around us, instead of putting forward one's own tiny ego as the center of the universe. This genre, by its very nature, affords the very widest scope for a realistic artist.

Many fashionable currents in art reject realism, which they assume has served its time. Without fear of being accused of conservatism, I wish to proclaim that I hold a contrary opinion and am a convinced supporter of realistic art. There is a lot of talk nowadays about literary avant-gardism with reference to the most modern experiments, particularly in the field of form. In my opinion the true pioneers are those artists who make manifest in their works the new content, the determining characteristics of life in our time.

Both realism as a whole and the realistic novel are based upon artistic experiences presented by great masters in the past. During their development, however, they have acquired important new features that are fundamentally modern.

I am speaking of a realism that carries within itself the concept of life's regeneration, its reformation for the benefit of mankind. I refer, of course, to the realism we describe as socialist. Its peculiar quality is that it expresses a philosophy of life that accepts neither a turning away from the world nor a flight from reality, a philosophy that enables one to comprehend goals that are dear to the hearts of millions of people and that lights up their path in the struggle.

Mankind is not divided into a flock of individuals, people floating about in a vacuum, like cosmonauts who have penetrated beyond the pull of Earth's gravity. We live on earth, we are subject to its laws and, as the Gospel puts it, sufficient unto the day is the evil thereof, its troubles and trials, its hopes for a better future. Vast sections of the world's population are inspired by the same desires, and live for common interests that bind them together far more than they separate them. These are the working people, who create everything with their hands and their brains. I am one of those authors who consider it their highest honor and their highest liberty to have a completely untrammeled chance of using their pens to serve the working people.

This is the ultimate foundation. From it are derived the conclusions as to how I, a Soviet writer, view the place of the artist in the world today.

The era we live in is full of uncertainty. Yet there is not one nation on earth that desires a war. There are, however, forces that hurl whole nations into the furnaces of war. Is it not inevitable that the ashes from the indescribable conflagration of the Second World War should move the writer's heart? Is not an honest writer bound to stand up against those who wish to condemn mankind to self-destruction?

What, then, is the vocation and what are the tasks of an artist who sees himself, not as an image of a god who is indifferent to the sufferings of mankind, enthroned far above the heat of battle, but as a son of his people, a tiny particle of humanity?

To be honest with the reader, to tell people the truth—which may sometimes be unpleasant but is always fearless. To strengthen men's hearts in their belief in the future, in the belief in their own ability to build this future. To be a champion of peace throughout the world and with his words breed such champions wherever those words penetrate. To unite people in their natural, noble striving toward progress.

Art possesses a great ability to influence people's intellects and brains. I believe that anyone has the right to call himself an artist, if he channels this ability into creating something beautiful in the minds of men, if he benefits humanity.

My own people have not followed beaten tracks in their historical journey. Their journey has been that of the explorers, the pioneers for a new life. I have regarded and still regard it as my task as an author in all that I have written and in whatever I may come to write, to show my great respect for this nation of workers, this nation of builders, this nation of heroes, which has never attacked anyone but which knows how to put up an honorable defense of what it has created, of its freedom and dignity, of its right to build the future as it chooses.

I should like my books to assist people in becoming better, in becoming purer in their minds; I should like them to arouse love of one's fellow men, a desire to fight actively for the ideal of humanity and the progress of mankind. If I have managed to do this in some measure, then I am happy.

I thank all those of you here tonight, and all those who have sent me greetings and good wishes in connection with the Nobel Prize.

AND QUIET FLOWS THE DON

By MIKHAIL SHOLOKHOV

Translated from the Russian by Stephen Garry

[Part I: Peace]

KEY TO PRINCIPAL CHARACTERS

MELEKHOV, PROKOFFEY. *A Cossack.*
MELEKHOV, PANTALEIMON PROKOFFIEVICH. *Son of Prokoffey.*
MELEKHOVA, ILINICHNA. *Wife of Pantaleimon.*
MELEKHOV, PIOTRA PANTALIEVICH. *Son of Pantaleimon and Ilinichna.*
MELEKHOV, GREGOR (GRISHKA). *Son of Pantaleimon and Ilinichna.*
MELEKHOVA, DUNIA. *Daughter of Pantaleimon and Ilinichna.*
MELEKHOVA, DARIA. *Wife of Piotra.*
KORSHUNOV, GRISHAKA. *A Cossack.*
KORSHUNOV, MIRON GREGORIEVICH. *Son of Grishaka.*
KORSHUNOVA, MARIA LUKINICHNA. *Wife of Miron.*
KORSHUNOV, MITKA MIRONOVICH. *Son of Miron and Maria.*
KORSHUNOVA, NATALIA. *Daughter of Miron and Maria, afterwards Gregor's wife.*
ASTAKHOV, STEPAN. *A Cossack.*
ASTAKHOVA, AKSINIA. *Wife of Stepan.*
BODOVSKOV, FIODOT. *A Cossack.*
KOSHEVOI, MISHKA. *A Cossack.*
KOSHEVOI, MASHUTKA. *Mishka's sister.*
SHAMIL, ALEXEI, MARTIN, and PROKHOR. *Three Cossack brothers.*
TOKIN, CHRISTONIA (CHRISTAN). *A Cossack.*
TOMILIN, IVAN. *A Cossack.*
KOTLIAROV, IVAN ALEXIEVICH. *Engineer at Mokhov's mill. A landless Cossack.*
DAVID. *Worker at Mokhov's mill.*
FILKA. *A shoemaker.*

STOCKMAN, OSIP DAVIDOVICH. *A locksmith and Bolshevik.*
VALET. *Scalesman at Mokhov's mill.*
MOKHOV, SERGEI PLATONOVICH. *Merchant and mill-owner.*
MOKHOVA, ELIZABIETA. *Mokhov's daughter.*
MOKHOV, VLADIMIR. *Mokhov's son.*
LISTNITSKY, NIKHOLAI ALEXIEVICH. *Landowner and retired general.*
LISTNITSKY, EUGENE NIKHOLAEVICH. *Son of Nikholai Listnitsky.*
BUNCHUK, ILIA. *A soldier volunteer, Bolshevik, and machine-gunner.*
GARANZHA. *A Ukrainian conscript.*
GROSHEV, EMELIAN. *A Cossack.*
IVANKOV, MIKHAIL. *A Cossack.*
KRUCHKOV, KOZMA. *A Cossack.*
ZHARKOV, YEGOR. *A Cossack.*
ZYKOV, PROKHOR. *A Cossack.*
SHCHEGOLKOV. *A Cossack.*
URIUPIN, ALEXEI. *Nicknamed "Tufty." A Cossack.*
ANIKUSHKA. *A Cossack.*
BOGATIRIEV. *A Cossack.*
SENILIN, AVDEICH. *Nicknamed "Bragger." A Cossack.*
GRIAZNOV, MAKSIM. *A Cossack.*
KOROLIOV, ZAKHAR. *A Cossack.*
KRIVOSHLIKOV, MIKHAIL. *Secretary of Don Revolutionary Committee.*
LAGUTIN, IVAN. *A Cossack. Member of Don Revolutionary Committee.*
PODTIELKOV, FIODOR. *Chairman of Don Revolutionary Committee.*
POGOODKO, ANNA. *Jewish student and Bolshevik.*
BOGOVOI, GIEVORKIANTZ, KHVILICHKO, KRUTOGOROV, MIKHALIDZE, REBINDER, STEPANOV: *Members of Bunchuk's revolutionary machine-gun detachment.*
ABRAMSON. *A Bolshevik organizer.*
GOLUBOV. *A captain and commander of Don revolutionary forces.*
ALEXIEV. *Czarist general.*
KORNILOV. *Czarist general.*
ATARSHCHIKOV. *Lieutenant in Cossack regiment.*
IZVARIN. *Captain in Cossack regiment.*
KALMIKOV. *Captain in Cossack regiment.*
MERKULOV. *Lieutenant in Cossack regiment.*
CHUBOV. *Lieutenant in Cossack regiment.*

AND QUIET FLOWS THE DON

CHAPTER 1

The Melekhov farm was right at the end of Tatarsk village. The gate of the cattle-yard opened northward towards the Don. A steep, sixty-foot slope between chalky, grass-grown banks, and there was the shore. A pearly drift of mussel-shells, a grey, broken edging of shingle, and then —the steely-blue, rippling surface of the Don, seething beneath the wind. To the east, beyond the willow-wattle fence of the threshing-floor, was the Hetman's highway, greyish wormwood scrub, vivid brown, hoof-trodden knotgrass, a shrine standing at the fork of the road, and then the steppe, enveloped in a shifting mirage. To the south a chalky range of hills. On the west the street, crossing the square and running towards the leas.

The Cossack Prokoffey Melekhov returned to the village during the last war with Turkey. He brought back a wife—a little woman wrapped from head to foot in a shawl. She kept her face covered and rarely revealed her yearning eyes. The silken shawl was redolent of strange, aromatic perfumes; its rainbow-hued patterns aroused the jealousy of the peasant women. The captive Turkish woman did not get on well with Prokoffey's relations, and before long old Melekhov gave his son his portion. The old man never got over the disgrace of the separation, and all his life he refused to set foot inside his son's hut.

Prokoffey speedily made shift for himself; carpenters built him a hut, he himself fenced in the cattle-yard, and in the early autumn he took his bowed, foreign wife to her new home. He walked with her through the village, behind the cart laden with their worldly goods. Everybody from the oldest to the youngest rushed into the street. The Cossacks laughed discreetly into their beards, the women passed vociferous remarks to one another, a swarm of unwashed Cossack lads called after Prokoffey. But, with overcoat unbuttoned, he walked slowly along as though over newly ploughed furrows, squeezing his wife's fragile wrist in his own enormous swarthy palm, defiantly bearing his lint-white, unkempt head. Only the wens below his cheekbones swelled and quivered, and the sweat stood out between his stony brows.

Thenceforth he went but rarely into the village and was never to be seen even at the market. He lived a secluded life in his solitary hut by the Don. Strange stories began to be told of him in the village. The boys who pastured the calves beyond the meadow road declared that of an evening, as the light was dying, they had seen Prokoffey carrying his wife in his arms as far as the Tatar mound. He would seat her, with her back to an ancient, weather-beaten, porous rock, on the crest of the mound; he would sit down at her side, and they would gaze fixedly across the steppe. They would gaze until the sunset had faded, and then Prokoffey would wrap his wife in his coat and carry her back home. The village was lost in conjecture, seeking an explanation for such astonishing behaviour. The women gossiped so much that they had no time to hunt for their fleas. Rumour was rife about Prokoffey's wife also; some declared that she was of entrancing beauty; others maintained the contrary. The matter was set at rest when one of the most venturesome of the women, the soldier's wife Maura, ran to Prokoffey on the pretext of getting some leaven; Prokoffey crawled into the cellar for the leaven, and Maura had time to notice that Prokoffey's Turkish conquest was a perfect fright.

A few minutes later Maura, her face flushed and her kerchief awry, was entertaining a crowd of women in a by-lane:

"And what could he have seen in her, my dears? If she'd only been a woman, now, but she's got no bottom or belly; it's a disgrace. We've got better-looking girls going begging for a husband. You could cut through her waist, she's just like a wasp. Little eyes, black and strong, she flashes with them like Satan, God forgive me. She must be near her time, God's truth."

"Near her time?" the women marvelled.

"I'm no babe! I've reared three myself."

"But what's her face like?"

"Her face? Yellow. Unhappy eyes—it's no easy life for a woman in a strange land. And what is more, women, she wears—Prokoffey's trousers!"

"No!" The women drew their breath in abrupt alarm.

"I saw them myself; she wears trousers, only without stripes. It must be his everyday trousers she has. She wears a long shift, and below it you see the trousers, stuffed into socks. When I saw them my blood ran cold."

The whisper went round the village that Prokoffey's wife was a witch. Astakhov's daughter-in-law (the Astakhovs lived in the hut next to Prokoffey's) swore that on the second day of Trinity, before dawn, she saw Prokoffey's wife, straight-haired and barefoot, milking the Astakhovs' cow. From that day the cow's udder withered to the size of a child's fist; she gave no more milk and died soon after.

That year there was unusual mortality among the cattle. By the shallows of the Don the carcasses of cows and young bulls littered the sandy shore every day. Then the horses were affected. The droves grazing on the village pasture-lands melted away. And through the lanes and streets of the village crept an evil rumour.

The Cossacks held a village meeting and went to Prokoffey. He came out on the steps of his hut and bowed.

"What good does your visit bring, worthy elders?" he asked.

Dumbly silent, the crowd drew nearer to the steps. One drunken old man was the first to cry:

"Drag your witch out here! We're going to try her. . . ."

Prokoffey flung himself back into the hut, but they caught him in the porch. A sturdy Cossack nicknamed Lushnia knocked Prokoffey's head against the wall and exhorted him:

"Don't make a sound, not a sound, you're all right. We shan't touch you, but we're going to trample your wife into the ground. Better to destroy her than have all the village die for want of cattle. But don't you make a sound, or I'll smash your head against the wall!"

"Drag the bitch into the yard!" came a roar from the steps. A regimental comrade of Prokoffey's wound the Turkish woman's hair around one hand, pressed his other hand over her screaming mouth, dragged her at a run through the porch, and flung her beneath the feet of the crowd. A thin shriek rose above the howl of voices. Prokoffey sent half a dozen Cossacks flying, burst into the hut, and snatched a sabre from the wall. Jostling against one another, the Cossacks rushed out of the porch. Swinging the gleaming, whistling sabre around his head, Prokoffey ran down the steps. The crowd shuddered and scattered over the yard.

Lushnia was heavy of gait, and by the threshing-floor Prokoffey caught up with him; with a diagonal sweep down across the left shoulder from behind he clave the Cossack's body to the belt. Tearing out the stakes of the wattle fence, the crowd poured across the threshing-floor into the steppe.

Some half-hour later the crowd ventured to approach Prokoffey's farm again.

Two of them crept cautiously into the porch. On the kitchen threshold, in a pool of blood, her head flung back awkwardly, lay Prokoffey's wife; her lips writhed tormentedly back from her teeth, her gnawed tongue protruded. Prokoffey, with shaking head and glassy stare, was wrapping a squealing, crimson, slippery little ball—the prematurely-born infant—in a sheepskin.

Prokoffey's wife died the same evening. His old mother had pity on the child and took charge of it. They plastered it with bran mash, fed it with mare's milk, and after a month, assured that the swarthy, Turkish-looking boy would survive, they carried him to church and christened him. They named him Pantaleimon after his grandfather. Prokoffey came back from penal servitude twelve years later. With his clipped, ruddy beard streaked with grey and his Russian clothing he did not look like a Cossack. He took his son and returned to his farm.

Pantaleimon grew up darkly swarthy and ungovernable. In face and figure he was like his mother. Prokoffey married him to the daughter of a Cossack neighbour.

Thenceforth Turkish blood began to mingle with that of the Cossacks. That was how the hook-nosed, savagely handsome Cossack family of Melekhovs, nicknamed "Turks," came into the village.

When his father died, Pantaleimon took over the farm; he had the hut rethatched, added an acre of common land to the farmyard, built new barns, and a granary with a sheet-iron roof. He ordered the tinsmith to cut a couple of cocks from the odd remnants and had them fastened to the roof. They brightened the Melekhov farmyard with their carefree air, giving it a self-satisfied and prosperous appearance.

Under the weight of the passing years Pantaleimon Prokoffievich grew stouter; he broadened and stooped somewhat, but still looked a well-built old man. He was dry of bone, and lame (in his youth he had broken his leg while hurdling at an Imperial review of troops), he wore a silver half-moon ear-ring in his left ear, and retained the vivid raven hue of his beard and hair until old age. When angry he completely lost control of himself, and undoubtedly this had prematurely aged his corpulent wife, Ilinichna, whose face, once beautiful, was now a perfect spider-web of furrows.

Piotra, his elder, married son, took after his mother: stocky and snub-nosed, a luxuriant shock of corn-coloured hair, hazel eyes. But the younger, Gregor, was like his father: half a head taller than Piotra, some six years younger, the same hanging hook-nose as his father's, bluish almonds of burning irises in slightly oblique slits, brown, ruddy skin drawn over angular cheekbones. Gregor stooped slightly, just like his father; even in their smile there was a common, rather savage quality.

Dunia—her father's favourite—a long-boned, large-eyed lass, and Piotra's wife, Daria, with her small child, completed the Melekhov household.

CHAPTER 2

Here and there stars were still piercing through the ashen, early-morning sky. A wind was blowing from under a bank of cloud. Over the Don a mist was rolling high, piling against the slope of a chalky hill, and crawling into the cliff like a grey, headless serpent. The left bank of the river, the sands, the backwaters, stony shoals, the dewy weeds, quivered with the ecstatic, chilly dawn. Beyond the horizon the sun yawned and rose not.

In the Melekhov hut Pantaleimon Prokoffievich was the first to awake. Buttoning the collar of his cross-stitched shirt as he went, he walked out on the steps. The grass-grown yard was coated with a dewy silver. He let the cattle out into the street. Daria ran past in her undergarments to milk the cows. The dew sprinkled over the calves of her bare, white legs, and she left a smoking, beaten trail behind her over the grass of the yard. Pantaleimon Prokoffievich stood for a moment watching the grass rising from the pressure of Daria's feet, then turned back into the kitchen.

On the sill of the wide-open window lay the dead-rose petals of the cherry blossoming in the front garden. Gregor was asleep face-downward, his hand flung out back uppermost.

"Gregor, coming fishing?" his father called him.

"What?" he asked in a whisper, dropping one leg off the bed.

"We'll row out and fish till sunrise," Pantaleimon proposed.

Breathing heavily through his nose, Gregor pulled his everyday trousers down from a peg, drew them on, tucked the legs into his white woollen socks, and slowly drew on his shoes, turning out the infolded flaps.

"But has Mother boiled the bait?" he hoarsely asked, as he followed his father into the porch.

"Yes. Go to the boat. I'll be after you in a minute."

The old man poured the strong-smelling, boiled rye into a jug, carefully swept up the fallen grains into his palm, and limped down to the beach. He found his son sitting restively in the boat.

"Where shall we go?" Gregor asked.

"To the black cliff. We'll try around the log where they were lying the other day."

Its stern scraping the ground, the boat settled into the water and broke away from the shore. The current carried it off, rocking it and trying to turn it broadside on. Gregor steered with the oar, but did not row.

"Why aren't you rowing?" his father demanded.

"We'll get into the middle first."

Cutting across the swift main-stream current, the boat moved towards the left bank. Muffled by the water, the crowing of cocks reached them from the village. Its side scraping the black, gravelly cliff rising high above the river, the boat hove to in the pool below. Some forty feet from the bank the peeled branches of a sunken elm emerged from the water. Around it turbulent flecks of foam eddied and swirled.

"Pay out the line while I'm tying her fast," Pantaleimon whispered. He thrust his hand into the steaming mouth of the jug. The rye scattered audibly over the water, just as though someone had whispered in an undertone: "Shick." Gregor strung some swollen grains on the hook and smiled.

"Fish, fish! There are fish both large and small here," the old man ordered.

The line fell in spirals into the water and tautened, then slackened again. Gregor set his foot on the end of the rod and fumbled cautiously for his pouch.

"We'll have no luck today, Father. The moon is on the wane," he remarked.

"Did you bring the tinder?"

"Aha!"

"Give me a light."

The old man began to smoke and glanced at the sun, stranded on the farther side of the elm.

"You can't tell when a carp will bite," he replied. "Sometimes he will when the moon is waning."

The water lapped noisily around the sides of the boat, and a four-foot carp, gleaming as though cast from ruddy copper, leaped upward, doubling his broad, curving tail above the water. Granular sprinkles scattered over the boat.

"Wait now!" Pantaleimon wiped his wet beard with his sleeve.

At the side of the sunken tree, among

the branching, naked boughs, two carp leaped simultaneously; a third, smaller, writhed in the air and struggled stubbornly close to the cliff.

Gregor impatiently chewed the wet end of the twine. The misty sun was half up. Pantaleimon scattered the rest of the bait and, glumly pursing his lips, stolidly watched the motionless end of the rod.

Gregor spat out the end of his cigarette, wrathfully watching its rapid flight. He inwardly cursed his father for awakening him so early. Through smoking on an empty stomach his mouth reeked like burnt bristles. He was about to bend and scoop up some water in his palm, but at that moment the end of the line feebly swayed and slowly sank.

"Play him!" the old man breathed.

Starting up, Gregor seized the rod, but it bent in an arc from his hand, and the end disappeared violently into the water.

"Hold him!" Pantaleimon muttered as he pushed the boat off from the bank.

Gregor attempted to lift the rod, but the fish was too strong, and the stout line snapped with a dry crack. Gregor staggered and almost fell.

"Now you can drink!" his father cursed, just failing to catch the line as it slipped across the gunwale.

Smiling agitatedly, Gregor fastened a new line to the rod and threw out the end. Hardly had the lead touched bottom when the end of the rod bent.

"There he is, the devil," Gregor grumbled, with difficulty holding in the fish, which was making for the middle current.

The line cut the water with a loud swish, raising a sloping, greenish rampart behind it. Pantaleimon picked up the bailer-handle in his stumpy fingers.

A great red and yellow carp rose to the surface, lashed the water into foam, and dived back into the depths.

"Strike till it stings your hand! No, wait!" Gregor exclaimed.

"Hold him!" his father cried.

"I am holding him!"

"Don't let him get under the boat!"

Taking breath, Gregor drew the carp towards the side of the boat. The old man thrust out the bailer, but with its last strength the carp again disappeared into the depths.

"Raise his head! Make him swallow some air and he'll be quieter!" Pantaleimon ordered.

Once more Gregor drew the exhausted fish towards the boat. Its nose struck against the rough side, and it lay there with gaping mouth, its orange-golden fins flickering.

"We've won!" Pantaleimon croaked, lifting the fish in the bailer.

They sat on for another half-hour. But they had no more battles with carp.

"Wind in the line. They won't leap again today!" the old man said at last.

Gregor pushed off from the bank. As he rowed he saw from his father's face that he wished to say something, but Pantaleimon sat silently gazing at the huts of the village scattered under the hill.

"Look here, Gregor—" he began uncertainly, pulling at the knot of the sack beneath his feet. "I've noticed that you and Aksinia Astakhova . . ."

Gregor flushed violently and turned his head away. His shirt collar cut into his muscular, sunburnt neck, pressing out a white band in the flesh.

"You watch out, young man," the old man continued, now roughly and angrily. "Stepan's our neighbour, and I won't allow any playing about with his wife. That kind of thing can lead to mischief, and I warn you beforehand. If I see you at it I'll whip you!"

Pantaleimon twisted his fingers into his gnarled hand and watched the blood ebbing from his son's face.

"It's all lies!" Gregor snarled, and gazed straight into his father's eyes.

"Silence!"

"What if people do talk—"

"Hold your tongue, you son of a bitch!"

Gregor bent to the oars. The boat leaped forward. The water rocking behind the stern danced away in little scrolls.

They remained silent until, as they were approaching the shore, his father reminded Gregor:

"You look out, don't forget what I've said, or from today I'll stop your little game. Not a step will you stir outside the yard!"

Gregor made no answer. As he beached the boat he asked:

"Shall I hand the fish to the women?"

"Take and sell it to Mokhov the merchant," the old man said more gently. "You can have the money for tobacco."

Biting his lips, Gregor followed his father, his eyes wrathfully gnawing the back of the old man's head. "Try it, Father! I'm going out tonight even if you hobble me!" he was thinking.

At the farm gate he ran into his old friend Mitka Korshunov. Mitka was playing with the end of his silver-studded belt as he walked along. His round, yellow eyes gleamed greasily in their narrow slits. His irises were long like a cat's, giving him a shifty and evasive look.

"Where are you off to with the fish?" Mitka asked.

"We caught it today. I'm going to sell it to Mokhov."

With a glance Mitka estimated the weight of the fish.

"Fifteen pounds?" he guessed.

"And a half. We weighed it on the steelyard."

"Take me with you. I'll do the selling for you," Mitka proposed.

"Come on, then."

"And what do I get?"

"You needn't fear. We shan't quarrel over that," Gregor laughed.

Mass was just ended, and the villagers were scattering through the streets. The three brothers nicknamed Shamil came striding down the road side by side. The eldest, one-armed Alexei, was in the middle. The tight collar of his army tunic held his veiny neck erect, his thin, curly, pointed little beard twisted provokingly sideways, his left eye winked nervously. His carbine had exploded in his hands at the shooting-range many years previously, and a piece of the flying iron had ploughed into his cheek. Thenceforth his left eye had winked in season and out of season, and a blue scar furrowed across his cheek to bury itself in his tow of hair. The left arm had been torn off at the elbow, but Alexei was past master at rolling a cigarette with one hand. He could press his pouch against his chest, tear off the right quantity of paper with his teeth, would bend it into a trough-shape, rake up the tobacco, and roll the cigarette almost before you realized what he was doing.

Although he had only one arm he was the finest fighter in the village. His fist was not particularly large as fists go—the size of a calabash—but if he happened to get annoyed with his bullock when ploughing and had mislaid his whip, he would give it a blow with his fist and the bullock would be stretched out over the furrows, blood streaming from its ears. And there it would lie. The other brothers, Martin and Prokhor, resembled Alexei down to the last detail. They were just as stocky and broad-shouldered, only each had two arms.

As he came up with Mitka and Gregor, Alexei winked five times in succession.

"Selling your load?" he asked.

"Want to buy it?" Gregor replied.

"How much do you want for it?"

"A couple of bullocks, and a wife thrown in."

Winking violently, Alexei waved the stump of his arm.

"You're a funny lad! He-he-he! A wife

thrown in! And you'll take the offspring, too?"

"Clear off, or there will be some Shamils missing!" Gregor snarled.

In the square the villagers were gathered around the church palings.

In the middle of a ring of people a grizzled old man, his chest covered with crosses and medals, was waving his arms about.

"My old grandfather Grishka is telling one of his tales about the Turkish war," Mitka directed Gregor's attention with a glance. "Let's go and listen."

"While we're listening to him the carp will start stinking and swell," Gregor objected.

In the square behind the fire-cart shed rose the green roof of Mokhov's house. Striding past the shed the two lads approached the steps. The balustrade was ornamented with wild vine entwined in the railings. On the steps lay a speckled, lazy shade.

"See how some folk live, Mitka!" Gregor said.

"A handle, and gilt, too!" Mitka sniffed as he opened the door leading to the veranda.

"Who is there?" someone called from the other side of the door.

Suddenly smitten with shyness, Gregor went in. The tail of the carp dragged over the painted floorboards.

"Whom do you want?"

A girl was sitting in a wicker rocking-chair, a dish of strawberries in her hand. Gregor stared silently at the full, rosy, heart-shaped lips embracing a berry. Raising her head, the girl looked the lads up and down. The berry rested patiently in the warm lips.

Mitka came to Gregor's help. He coughed and asked:

"Want to buy some fish?"

Her lips opened to admit the berry and then smiled swiftly, almost imperceptibly.

"Fish? I'll tell you in a moment."

She rocked the chair upright and, rising, shuffled off in her embroidered slippers. The sun shone through her white dress, and Mitka saw the dim outline of full legs and the broad, billowing lace of her underskirt. He was astonished at the satiny whiteness of her bare calves; only on the cushioned little heels was the skin milkily yellow.

"Look, Grishka, what a dress! Like glass! You can see everything through it," he said, nudging the carp instead of Gregor.

The girl came back through the door leading to the corridor and sat down gently on the chair.

"Go into the kitchen!" she ordered.

Gregor tiptoed into the house. When he had gone Mitka stood blinking at the white thread of the parting dividing the girl's hair into two golden half-circles. She studied him with saucy, restless eyes.

"Are you from the village?" she asked.

"Yes."

"Whose son are you?"

"Korshunov's."

"And what is your name?"

"Mitka!"

She attentively examined her rosy nails and with a swift movement tucked up her legs.

"Which of you caught the fish?" she continued her cross-examination.

"My friend, Gregor."

"And do you fish, too?"

"When I feel like it."

"With fish-hooks?"

"Yes."

"I'd like to go fishing some time," she said after a silence.

"All right, I'll take you if you want to."

"How is it to be done? Really, are you serious?"

"You must get up very early," Mitka declared.

"I'll get up, only you'll have to waken me."

"I can do that. But how about your father?"

"What about my father?"

Mitka smiled. "He might take me for a thief. The dogs will have to be baited!"

"That's simple! I sleep alone in the corner room. That's the window," she pointed with her finger. "If you come for me knock at the window and I'll get up."

The sound of Gregor's timid voice and the thick, oily tones of the cook came brokenly from the kitchen. Mitka was silent, fingering the tarnished silver of his belt.

"Are you married?" she asked, warming with a secretive smile.

"Why?"

"Oh, I'm just curious."

"No, I'm single."

Mitka suddenly blushed, and she, playing with a smile and a little twig from the hothouse strawberries scattered over the floor, queried:

"And are the girls fond of you, Mitka?"

"Some are, some aren't."

"You don't say. . . . And why have you got eyes like a cat?"

"A cat?" Mitka was now completely abashed.

"Yes, that's just it, they're cat's eyes."

"I must have got them from my mother. I can't help it."

"And why don't they marry you, Mitka?"

Mitka recovered from his momentary confusion and, sensing the hidden sneer in her words, twinkled the yellows of his eyes.

"My wife hasn't grown up yet."

She raised her eyebrows in astonishment, bridled up, and rose from her seat. Her fleeting smile lashed Mitka like a nettle.

There was the sound of feet ascending the steps from the street. Shuffling softly along in his capacious kid boots, the master of the house, Sergei Platonovich Mokhov, carried his corpulent body with dignity past Mitka.

"Want me?" he asked as he passed, without turning his head.

"He's brought some fish, Papa," the girl replied.

Gregor came out with empty hands.

CHAPTER 3

The first cock had crowed when Gregor returned from his evening out. From the porch came the scent of over-sour hops and the spicy perfume of chickweed.

He tiptoed into the hut, undressed, carefully hung up his Sunday striped trousers, crossed himself, and lay down. A golden, crisscrossed pool of moonlight lay on the floor. In the corner under embroidered towels was the tarnished lustre of silvered ikons, from the shelf over the bed came the droning hum of agitated flies.

He would have fallen asleep, but in the kitchen his brother's infant started to cry. The cradle began to creak like an ungreased cartwheel. He heard his brother's wife, Daria, mutter in a sleepy voice:

"Sleep, little brat! Neither rest nor peace do I get with you!" She quietly crooned a lullaby to the child.

As he dozed off under the measured, soothing creak, Gregor remembered: "Why, tomorrow Piotra goes off to the camp. Daria will be left with the baby. . . . We'll have to do the mowing without him."

He was aroused from sleep by a prolonged neighing. By its tone he recognized Piotra's army horse. Helpless with sleep, his fingers were slow in buttoning up his shirt, and he almost dropped off again under the flowing rhythm of Daria's song:

> "And where are the geese?
> They've gone into the reeds.
> And where are the reeds?
> The girls have pulled them up.

And where are the girls?
The girls have taken husbands.
And where are the Cossacks?
They've gone to the war."

Rubbing his eyes, Gregor made his way to the stable and led Piotra's horse out into the street. A flying cobweb tickled his face, and his drowsiness unexpectedly left him.

Along the Don lay a slantingly undulating, never trodden track of moonlight. Over the Don hung a mist, and above it a starry grain. The horse set its hind hoofs down cautiously. The drop to the water was bad going. From the farther side of the river came the quacking of ducks. A sheat-fish turned and darted over the water above the mud by the bank, hunting at random for smaller fry.

Gregor stood a long time by the river. The bank exuded a dank and sickly rottenness. A tiny drop of water fell from the horse's lips. A light, pleasant void was in Gregor's heart, life was good and free from care. The red-tailed dawn was pecking up the starry grain from the dove-coloured floor of heaven.

Close to the stable he ran into his mother.

"That you, Grishka?" she asked.

"And who else should it be?"

"Watered the horse?"

"Yes," he answered shortly.

Carrying some dried dung for fuel, his mother ran back to the hut, her withered bare feet slapping on the ground.

"You might go and wake up the Astakhovs. Stepan said he would go with our Piotra," she called.

The morning rawness set a spring stiffly quivering in Gregor. His body tingled with prickles. He ran up the three echoing steps leading to the Astakhovs' hut. The door was on the latch. Stepan was asleep on an outspread rug in the kitchen, his wife's head on his breast.

In the greying twilight Gregor saw Aksinia's shift wrinkled above her knees, and her birch-white, unashamedly parted legs. For a moment he stood gazing, feeling his mouth going dry and his head bursting with an iron clangour.

His eyes wandered. In a strange, hoarse voice he called:

"Hey! Anyone here? Get up."

Aksinia started out of her sleep.

"Oh, who's that?" She hurriedly began to fumble with her shift, and in drawing it down, her bare arm was entangled in her legs. A little drop of spittle was left on her pillow; a woman's sleep is heavy at dawn.

"It's me. Mother sent me to wake you up."

"We'll be up in a minute. We're sleeping on the floor because of the fleas. Stepan, get up, do you hear?" By her voice Gregor guessed that she felt awkward, and he hastened to go out.

Thirty Cossacks were going from the village to the May training camp. Just before seven o'clock wagons with tarpaulin covers, Cossacks on foot and on horseback, in sailcloth shirts and carrying their equipment, began to stream towards the square.

Gregor found Piotra standing on the steps, hurriedly stitching a broken rein.

His father, Pantaleimon, was attending to Piotra's horse, pouring oats into a trough.

"Not finished eating yet?" Piotra asked, nodding towards the horse.

"He's hungry," his father replied deliberately, testing the saddle-cloth with his rough palm. "Let even a crumb stick to the cloth and it will chafe the animal's back into a sore in one march."

"When he's finished eating, he must have a drink, Father."

"Gregor will take him down to the Don," Pantaleimon answered.

Gregor took the high, raw-boned Don horse with a white star on its forehead, led it outside the gate, and resting his left hand lightly on its withers, vaulted on to its back and went off at a swinging trot. He tried to rein the horse in at the descent to the river, but the animal stumbled, quickened its pace, and flew down the slope. As he flung himself back and almost lay along the animal's spine, Gregor saw a woman with pails going down the hill. He turned sharply off the path and dashed into the water, leaving a cloud of dust behind him.

Aksinia Astakhova came swinging down the slope. When still some little distance away, she shouted to him:

"You mad devil! You almost rode me down. You wait, I'll tell your father how you ride."

"Now, neighbour, don't get angry. When you've seen your husband off to camp maybe I'll be useful on your farm," he replied.

"How the devil would you be useful to me?"

"When mowing-time comes you may yet be asking me," Gregor smiled.

Aksinia dextrously drew a full pail of water from the river and pressed her skirt between her knees away from the wind.

"So they're taking your Stepan?" Gregor asked.

"What's that to do with you?"

"What a spitfire! Can't I ask?"

"Well, they are taking him, and what of it?"

"So you'll be left a grass-widow?"

"Yes!"

The horse raised its lips from the water and stood gazing across the Don, its forefeet treading the stream. Aksinia filled her second pail, hoisted the yoke across her shoulders, and set off up the slope. Gregor turned the horse and followed her. The wind fluttered her skirt and played with the fine fluffy curls on her swarthy neck. Her flat embroidered cap flamed on her heavy knot of hair, her rose-coloured shirt, gathered into her skirt at the waist, tightly embraced her back and shoulders. As she climbed the slope she bent forward, and the hollow between her shoulders showed clearly beneath her shirt. Gregor watched her every movement. He badly wanted to renew the talk with her.

"You'll be missing your husband, won't you?" he asked.

Aksinia turned her head and smiled without halting.

"And how else? You get married!" She spoke pantingly. "Marry and you'll know whether you miss your friend or not."

Gregor brought the horse level with her and gazed into her eyes.

"But other wives are glad when their husbands go. Our Daria will grow fat without her Piotra," he remarked.

"A husband's not a leech, but he sucks your blood all the same. Shall we be seeing you married soon?" she asked.

"I don't know, it depends on Father. After my army service, I suppose."

"You're still young; don't get married."

"Why not?"

"It's nothing but sorrow." She looked up under her brows and smiled grimly without parting her lips. For the first time Gregor noticed that her lips were shamelessly greedy and swollen. Combing his horse's mane with his fingers, he replied:

"I've no desire to get married. Someone loves me already as I am."

"Have you noticed anyone, then?"

"What should I notice? Now you're seeing your Stepan off . . . ?"

"Don't try to play about with me. I'll tell Stepan."

"I'll show your Stepan. . . ."

"Mind you don't cry first, my brave one!"

"Don't alarm me, Aksinia!"

"I'm not alarming you. Let other girls hem your tear-wipers, but keep your eyes off me."

"I'll look at you all the more now."

"Well, look then."

Aksinia smiled pacifically and left the

track, seeking to pass round the horse. Gregor turned the animal sideways and blocked the road.

"Let me pass, Grishka."

"I won't."

"Don't be a fool. I must see to my husband."

Gregor smilingly teased the horse, and it edged Aksinia towards the cliff.

"Let me pass, you devil! There are people over there. If they see us what will they think?" she muttered. She swept a frightened glance around and passed by, frowning and without a backward look.

Piotra was saying good-bye to his family on the steps. Gregor saddled the horse. His brother hurried down the steps and took the reins. Scenting the road, the horse fretted and chewed the bit. With one foot in the stirrup, Piotra said to his father:

"Don't overwork the baldheads, Father. Come autumn, we'll sell them. Gregor will need an army horse, you know. And don't sell the steppe grass; you know yourself what hay there'll be in the meadow this year."

"Well, God be with you. It's time you were off," the old man replied, crossing himself.

Piotra flung his bulky body into the saddle and adjusted the folds of his shirt in his belt at the back. The horse moved towards the gate. The sabre swung to the rhythm of the motion, and its pommel glittered dully in the sun.

Daria followed with the child on her arm. Wiping her eyes with her sleeve, his mother, Ilinichna, stood in the middle of the yard.

"Brother! The pasties! You've forgotten the pasties! The potato pasties!" Dunia ran to the gate. "He's left his pasties behind," she groaned, leaning against the gate-post, and tears ran down her greasy, burning cheeks on to her jacket.

Daria stood gazing under her hand after her husband's white, dusty shirt.

Shaking the rotting gate-post, old Pantaleimon looked at Gregor. "Take and mend the gate, and put a new post in." He stood in thought a moment, then communicated the news: "Piotra's gone."

Through the wattle fence Gregor saw Stepan getting ready. Aksinia, bedecked in a green woollen skirt, led out his horse. Stepan smilingly said something to her. Unhurriedly, in lordly fashion, he kissed his wife, and his arm lingered long around her shoulder. His sunburnt and work-stained hand showed coal-black against her white jacket. He stood with his back to Gregor; his stiff, clean-shaven neck, his broad, somewhat heavy shoulders, and, whenever he bent towards his wife, the twisted end of his light-brown moustache were visible across the fence.

Aksinia laughed at something and shook her head. Sitting as though rooted in the saddle, Stepan rode his black horse at a hurried walk through the gate, and Aksinia walked at his side, holding the stirrup and looking up lovingly and thirstily into his eyes.

With a long, unwinking stare Gregor watched them to the turn of the road.

Towards evening a thunder-storm gathered. A mass of heavy clouds lay over the village. Lashed into fury by the wind, the Don sent great foaming breakers against its banks. The sky flamed with dry lightning, occasional peals of thunder shook the earth. A vulture circled with outspread wings below the clouds, and ravens croakingly pursued him. Breathing out coolness, the clouds passed down the Don from the east. Beyond the water-meadows the heaven blackened menacingly, the steppe lay in an expectant silence. In the village the closed shutters rattled, the old people hurried home, crossing themselves. A grey pillar of dust whirled over the square, and the heat-burdened earth was already beginning to be sown with the first grains of rain.

Shaking her braided tresses, Dunia ran across the yard, clapped fast the door of the chicken-house, and stood in the middle of the yard with nostrils distended like a horse scenting danger. In the street the children were kicking up their heels. Eight-year-old Mishka, his father's absurdly large peaked cap drawn over his eyes, was spinning round and piercingly chirruping:

"Rain, rain, go away,
We're going off for the day,
To pay God our vow
And to Christ to bow."

Dunia enviously watched Mishka's scarred bare feet brutally trampling the ground. She, too, wanted to dance in the rain and to get her head wet, so that her hair might grow thick and curly; she, too, wanted to stand on her hands like Mishka's friend in the roadside dust, at the risk of falling into the nettles. But her mother was watching and angrily moving her lips at the window. With a sigh she ran into the house. The rain was now falling heavily. A peal of thunder broke right over the roof and went rolling away across the Don.

In the porch Pantaleimon and perspiring Gregor were hauling a folded drag-net out of the side room.

"Raw thread and a pack-needle, quick!" Gregor called to Dunia. Daria sat down to mend the net. Her mother-in-law grumbled as she rocked the baby:

"You're beyond belief, old man! We could go to bed. Light costs more and more, and yet you go on burning it. What are you up to now? Where the plague are you going? And you'll get drowned into the bargain, the terror of the Lord is in the yard. Hark how it shakes the house! Lord Jesus Christ, Queen of Heaven! . . ."

For a moment it became dazzlingly blue and silent in the kitchen; the rain could be heard drumming on the shutters. A clap of thunder followed. Dunia whimpered and buried her face in the net. Daria signed the cross towards the windows and door. The old woman stared with terrible eyes down at the cat rubbing itself against her legs.

"Dunia, chase this cat away," she exclaimed. "Queen of Heaven, forgive me my sins. . . . Dunia, turn the cat out into the yard! Stop it, unclean power! May you . . ."

Dropping the net, Gregor shook with silent laughter.

"Well, what are you grinning at? Enough of that!" his father shouted at him. "Hurry with your mending, women. I told you the other day to see to the net."

"And what fish do you expect to catch?" his wife stammered.

"If you don't understand, hold your tongue! The fish will make for the bank now, they're afraid of storms. I fear the water will be turned muddy already. Run, Dunia, and see whether you can hear the watercourses running."

Dunia edged unwillingly towards the door.

Old Ilinichna would not be repressed. "Who's going to wade with you? Daria mustn't, she may catch cold in her breast," she persisted.

"Me and Gregor, and for the other net—we'll call Aksinia and another of the women."

Dunia ran in, out of breath. Drops of rain hung trembling on her lashes. She smelt of the dank, black earth.

"The courses are roaring like anything," she panted.

"Put on your coat and run to Aksinia," her father told her. "If she'll go, ask her to fetch Malashka Frolova, too."

Dunia quickly returned with the women. Aksinia, in a blue skirt and a ragged jacket belted with rope, looked shorter and thinner. Exchanging laughs with Daria, she took off her kerchief, wound her hair into a tighter knot, and throwing back her head, stared coldly at

Gregor. As corpulent Malashka tied up her stocking, she said hoarsely:

"Have you got sacks? True God, we'll stir up the fish today."

They all went into the yard. The rain was still falling heavily, the puddles frothed and crawled in streams down towards the Don.

Gregor led the way down to the river.

"Aren't we near the landing-place yet, Gregor?" his father asked after a while.

"Here we are."

"Begin from here," Pantaleimon shouted, attempting to drown out the howling wind.

"Can't hear you, grand-dad," Malashka called throatily.

"Start wading, for God's sake," he replied. "I'll take the deep side. . . . The deep—I say. Malashka, you deaf devil, where are you dragging to? I'll go out into the deeps. . . . Gregor! Let Aksinia take the bank!"

A groaning roar from the Don. The wind was tearing the slanting sheet of rain to shreds. Feeling the bottom with his feet, Gregor waded up to his waist into the water. A clammy cold crept into his chest, drawing tightly in a ring round his heart. The waves lashed his face and tightly screwed-up eyes like a knout. The net bellied out and was carried off into the deeps. Gregor's feet, shod in woollen socks, slipped over the sandy bottom. The net was dragged out of his hand. Deeper, deeper. A sudden drop. His legs were carried away. The current snatched him up and bore him towards the middle of the stream. With his right hand he vigorously paddled back to the bank. The black, swirling depths frightened him as never before. His feet joyously found the muddy bottom. A fish knocked against his knee.

Again the net heeled over and slipped out into the depths. Again the current carried the ground away from under his feet, and Gregor swam, spitting out water.

"Aksinia, you all right?" he called.

"All right so far," he heard her answer.

"Isn't the rain stopping?"

"The fine rain's stopping and a heavy rain beginning."

"Talk quietly. If my father hears he'll go for me."

"Afraid of your father, too?" she sneered.

For a moment they hauled in silence.

"Grishka, there's a sunken tree by the bank, I think. We must get the net round it."

A terrible buffet flung Gregor far away from her.

"Ah—ah!" Aksinia screamed somewhere near the bank. Terrified, he swam in the direction of her call.

"Aksinia!"

Wind and the flowing roar of the water.

"Aksinia!" Gregor shouted again, going cold with fear. He struck out at random. He felt something slipping beneath his feet and caught it with his hand—it was the net.

"Grishka, where are you?" he heard Aksinia's tearful voice.

"Why didn't you answer my shout?" he bawled angrily, crawling on hands and knees up the bank.

Squatting down on his heels, he tremblingly disentangled the net. The moon peeled out of a slash of broken cloud. There was a restrained mutter of thunder beyond the water-meadows. The earth gleamed with moisture. Washed clean by the rain, the sky was stern and clear.

As he disentangled the net Gregor stared at Aksinia. Her face was a chalky white, but her red, slightly upturned lips were smiling.

"As I was knocked against the bank," she said, "I went out of my mind. I was frightened to death. I thought you were drowned."

Their hands touched. Aksinia attempted to thrust hers into the sleeve of his shirt.

"How warm it is up your arm," she said mournfully, "and I'm frozen."

Someone came running along the bank. Gregor guessed it to be Dunia. He shouted to her:

"Got the thread?"

"Yes. What are you sitting here for? Father sent me for you to come at once to the point. We've caught a sackful of sterlet." Unconcealed triumph sounded in her voice.

With teeth chattering, Aksinia sewed up the holes in the net. Then, to get warm, they ran at full speed to the point.

Pantaleimon was rolling a cigarette with scarred fingers swollen by the water; he danced and boasted:

"The first time, eight fish; and the second time—" he paused and silently pointed with his foot to the sack. Aksinia stared inquisitively: from it came the swishing sound of stirring fish.

"Well, we'll wade in once more up to our knees, and then home. In you go, Grishka; what are you waiting for?" his father asked.

Gregor stepped out with numbed legs. Aksinia was trembling so much that he felt her movement at the other end of the net.

"Don't shake!"

"I'd be glad not to, but I can't get my breath."

"Listen! Let's crawl out, and damn the fish!"

At that moment a great carp bored through the net like a golden corkscrew. Gregor hurried and folded the net over it. Aksinia ran out on to the bank. The water splashed on the sands and ran back. A fish lay quivering in the net.

"Back through the meadow?" she asked.

"The wood is nearer," Gregor replied.

Frowning, Aksinia wrung out her skirt, flung the sack over her shoulder, and set off almost at a trot. Gregor picked up the net. They had covered some two hundred yards when Aksinia began to groan:

"I've no strength left."

"Look, there's a last year's haystack. You might get warm inside it," he suggested.

"Good! While I'm getting home I might die."

Gregor turned back the top of the stack and dug out a hole. The long-lying hay smelt warm and rotten.

"Crawl into the middle. It's like a stove here," he told her.

She threw down the sack and buried herself up to the neck in the hay. Shivering with cold, Gregor lay down at her side. A tender, agitating scent came from her damp hair. She lay with head thrown back, breathing regularly through her half-open mouth.

"Your hair smells like henbane—you know, the white flower," Gregor whispered, bending towards her. She was silent. Her gaze was misty and distant, fixed on the waning, crescent moon.

Taking his hand out of his pocket, Gregor suddenly drew her head towards him. She tore herself away fiercely and raised herself from the hay.

"Let me go!" she demanded.

"Keep quiet!"

"Let me go, or I'll shout."

"Wait, Aksinia!"

"Daddy Pantaleimon!"

"Have you lost yourselves?" Pantaleimon's voice sounded quite close, from beyond a clump of hawthorn bush. Grinding his teeth, Gregor jumped out of the haystack.

"What are you shouting for? Are you lost?" the old man questioned as he approached.

Aksinia stood by the haystack adjusting her kerchief, steam rising from her.

"We're not lost, but I'm all but frozen," she answered.

"Look, woman, there's a haystack, warm yourself," the old man told her.

Aksinia smiled as she stooped to pick up the sack.

From Tatarsk to Sietrakov—the training-camp centre—it was some forty miles. Piotra Melekhov and Stepan Astakhov rode in the same covered wagon. With them were three others from their village: Fiodot Bodovskov, a young Kalmyk-faced and pock-marked Cossack, Christonia Tokin, a second reservist in the ataman's regiment of Life Guards, and the artilleryman Ivan Tomilin. After the first halt for food they harnessed Christonia's and Astakhov's horses to the wagon, and the other horses were tethered behind. Christonia, strong and crack-brained like all the men of the ataman's regiment, took the reins. He sat in front with bowed back, shading the light from the interior of the wagon, urging on the horses with his deep, rumbling bass voice. Piotra, Stepan, and Tomilin lay smoking under the tightly stretched tarpaulin cover. Bodovskov walked behind.

Christonia's wagon led the way. Behind trailed seven or eight others, leading saddled and unsaddled horses behind them. The road was noisy with laughter, shouts, songs, the snorting of horses, and the jingling of empty stirrups.

Under Piotra's head was his bag of biscuit. He lay twirling his tawny whiskers.

"Stepan!" he said.

"Eh?"

"Let's have a song."

"It's too hot. My mouth's all dried out."

"There are no taverns anywhere near, so don't wait for that!"

"Well, sing up. Only you're no good at it. Your Grishka now, he can sing. His isn't a voice, it's a pure silver thread."

Stepan threw back his head, coughed, and began in a low, tuneful voice:

"Hey, the ruddy, flushing sunrise
Early came up in the sky."

Tomilin put his palm against his cheek and caught up the refrain in a thin, wailing undertone. Smiling, Piotra watched the little knots of veins on his temples going blue with his efforts.

"Young was she, the little woman
Went for water to the stream."

Stepan, who was lying with his head towards Christonia, turned round on his elbow:

"Christonia, join in!" he ordered.

"And the lad, he guessed her purpose,
Saddled he his chestnut mare."

Stepan turned his smiling glance towards Piotra, and Piotra added his voice. Opening wide his heavily bearded jaws, Christonia roared in a voice that shook the tarpaulin cover.

"Saddled he his chestnut mare,
Overtook the little woman."

Christonia set his bare foot against the singletree and waited for Piotra to begin again. Closing his eyes, his perspiring face in shadow, Stepan affably sang on, now dropping his voice to a whisper, then causing it to ring out metallically.

"Let me, let me, little woman,
Water my mare in the stream."

And again Christonia joined in with his alarming howl. Voices from the neighbouring wagons took up the song. The wheels clashed on their iron frames, the horses snorted with the dust. A white-winged peewit flew up from the parching steppe. It flew with a cry into a hollow, watching the chain of wagons, the horses kicking up clouds of white dust with their hoofs, the men, in white, dusty shirts, walking at the edge of the road.

Stepan stood up in the wagon, holding the tarpaulin with one hand, beating a rough time with the other, and sang on;

Fiodot Bodovskov whistled; the horses strained at the traces; leaning out of the wagon, Piotra laughed and waved his cap; Stepan, gleaming with a dazzling smile, impudently swung his shoulders; along the road the dust rolled in a cloud. Christonia jumped out of the wagon in his unbelted, over-long shirt, his hair matted, and, wet with sweat, did the Cossack dance, whirling in a swinging circle, frowning and groaning and leaving the monstrous, spreading marks of his bare feet in the silky grey dust.

They stopped for the night by a barrow with a sandy summit. Clouds gathered from the west. Rain dripped out of their black wings. The horses were watered at a pond. Above the dike dismal willows bowed before the wind. In the water, covered with stagnant duckweed and scaled with miserable little ripples, the lightning was distortedly reflected. The wind scattered the raindrops as though showering largesse into the earth's swarthy palms.

The fettered horses were turned out to graze, three men being appointed as guards. The other men lit fires and hung pots on the singletrees of the wagons.

Christonia was cooking millet. As he stirred it with a spoon, he told a story to the Cossacks sitting around:

"The barrow was high, like this one. And I says to my dead father: 'Won't the ataman stop us for digging up the barrow without his being asked?' "

"What is he lying about?" asked Stepan, as he came back from the horses.

"I'm telling how me and my dead father looked for treasure. It was the Merkulov barrow. Well, and Father says: 'Come on, Christonia, we'll dig up the Merkulov barrow.' He'd heard from his father that treasure was buried in it. Father promised God: 'Give me the treasure and I'll build a fine church.' So we agreed and off we went. It was on common land, so only the ataman could stop us. We arrived late in the afternoon. We waited until nightfall and then set to work with shovels at the summit. We began to dig straight down from the top. We'd dug a hole six feet deep; the earth was like stone. I was wet through. Father kept on muttering prayers, but believe me, brothers, my belly was grumbling so much. . . . You know what we eat in summer: sour milk and kvass. My dead father, he says: 'Pfooh!' he says, 'Christan, you're a heathen. Here am I praying, and you can't keep your food down. I can't breathe for the stink. Crawl out of the barrow, you ——, or I'll split your head open with the shovel. Through you the treasure may sink into the ground.' I lay outside the barrow and suffer with my belly, and my dead father—a strong man he was—goes on digging alone. And he digs down to a stone plate. He calls me. I push a crowbar under it and lift it up. Believe me, brothers, it was a moonlight night, and under this plate was such a shine—"

"Now you are lying, Christonia," Piotra broke in, smiling and tugging at his whispers.

"How am I lying? Go to the devil, and to the devil's dam!" Christonia gave a hitch to his broad-bottomed trousers and glanced around his hearers. "No, I'm not lying. It's God's truth! There it shone. I look, and it's charcoal. Some forty bushels of it. Father says: 'Crawl in, Christan, and dig it up.' I dig out this rubbish. I went on digging till daylight. In the morning I look, and he—there he is."

"Who?" asked Tomilin.

"Why, the ataman, who else? He happens to come driving by. 'Who gave you permission?' and all the rest of it. He lays hold of us and hauls us off to the village. We were called before the court at Kaminskaya the year before last, but Father, he guessed what was coming and managed to die beforehand. We wrote back saying he was not among the living."

Christonia took his pot with the boiling millet and went to the wagon for spoons.

"Well, what of your father? He promised to build a church; didn't he do it?" Stepan asked when he returned.

"You're a fool, Stepan. What could he build with coal?"

"Once he promised, he ought to have done it."

"There was no agreement whatever about coal, and the treasure . . ." The flames of the fire shook with the laughter that arose. Christonia raised his head from the pot, and not understanding what the laughter was about, drowned all the rest with his heavy roar.

Aksinia was seventeen when she was given in marriage to Stepan Astakhov. She came from the village of Dubrovka, from the sands on the other side of the Don.

About a year before her marriage she was ploughing in the steppe some five miles from the village. In the night her father, a man of some fifty years, tied her hands and raped her.

"I'll kill you if you breathe a word, but if you keep quiet I'll buy you a plush jacket and gaiters with galoshes. Remember, I'll kill you if you . . ." he promised her.

Aksinia ran back through the night in her torn petticoat to the village. She flung herself at her mother's feet and sobbed out the whole story. Her mother and elder brother harnessed horses to the wagon, made Aksinia get in with them, and drove to the father. Her brother almost drove the horses to death in the five miles. They found the old man close to the field camp. He was lying in a drunken sleep on his overcoat, with an empty vodka bottle by his side. Before Aksinia's eyes her brother unhooked the singletree from the wagon, picked up his father by the feet, curtly asked him a question or two, and struck him a blow with the iron-shod singletree between the eyes. He and his mother went on beating steadily for an hour and a half. The ageing and always meek mother frenziedly tore at her senseless husband's hair, the brother used his feet. Aksinia lay under the wagon, her head covered, silently shaking. They carried her father home just before dawn. He lay bellowing mournfully, his eyes wandering around the room, seeking for Aksinia, who had hidden herself away. Blood and matter ran from his torn ear on to the pillow. Towards evening he died. They told the neighbours he had fallen from the wagon.

Within a year the matchmakers came in a gaily bedecked wagonette to ask for Aksinia's hand. The tall, stiff-necked, well-proportioned Stepan approved of his future bride, and the wedding was fixed for the autumn.

The day was frosty and ringingly icy. Aksinia was installed as young mistress of the Astakhov household. The morning after the festivities her mother-in-law, a tall old woman doubled up with some female complaint, woke Aksinia up, led her into the kitchen, and, aimlessly shifting things about, said to her:

"Now, dear little daughter, we've taken you not for love, nor for you to lie abed. Go and milk the cows, and then get some food ready. I'm old and feeble. You must take over the household, it will all fall on you."

The same day Stepan took his young wife into the barn and beat her deliberately and terribly. He beat her on the belly, the breast, and the back, taking care that the marks should not be visible to others. After that he neglected her, kept company with flighty grass-widows, and went out almost every night, first locking Aksinia into the barn or the room.

For eighteen months, so long as there was no child, he would not forgive her his disgrace. Then he was quieter, but was niggardly with caresses and rarely spent the night at home.

The large farm with its numerous cattle burdened Aksinia with work; Stepan was lazy and went off to smoke, to play cards, to learn the latest news, and Aksinia had to do everything. Her mother-in-law was a poor help. After bustling around a little, she would drop on the bed and, with lips tight-drawn and eyes gazing agonizedly at the ceiling, would lie groaning, rolled into a bundle. Throwing down her work, Aksinia would hide in a corner and stare at her mother-in-law's face in fear and pity.

The old woman died some eighteen months after the marriage. In the morning Aksinia was taken in travail, and about noon, an hour or so before the child's entry into the world, the grandmother dropped dead by the stable door. The midwife ran out to warn tipsy Stepan not to go into the bedroom and saw the old woman lying with her legs tucked up beneath her. After the birth of the child Aksinia devoted herself to her husband, but she had no feeling for him, only bitter womanly pity and force of habit. The child died within the year. The old life was resumed. And when Gregor Melekhov crossed Aksinia's path she realized with terror that she was attracted to the swarthy youngster. He waited on her stubbornly, with bulldog insistence. She saw that he was not afraid of Stepan, she felt that he would not hold back because of him, and without consciously desiring it, resisting the feeling with all her might, she noticed that on Sundays and weekdays she was attiring herself more carefully. Making pretexts to herself, she sought to place herself more frequently in his path. She was happy to find Gregor's black eyes caressing her heavily and rapturously. When she awoke of a morning and went to milk the cows she smiled and, without realizing why, recalled: "Today's a happy day. But why? . . . Oh, Gregor—Grishka." She was frightened by the new feeling which filled her, and in her thoughts she went gropingly, cautiously, as though crossing the Don over the broken ice of March.

After seeing Stepan off to camp she decided to see Gregor as little as possible. After the fishing expedition her decision was still further strengthened.

CHAPTER 4

Some two days before Trinity the distribution of the village meadowland took place. Pantaleimon attended the allotment. He came back at dinner-time, threw off his boots with a groan, and noisily scratching his weary legs, announced:

"Our portion lies close to the Red Cliff. Not over-good grass as grass goes. The upper part runs up to the forest, it's just scrub in places. And speargrass coming through."

"When shall we do the mowing?" Gregor asked.

"After the holidays."

The old wife opened the oven door with a clatter and drew out the warmed-up cabbage soup. Pantaleimon sat over the meal a long time, telling of the day's events, and of the knavish ataman, who had all but swindled the whole assembly of Cossacks.

"But who's going to do the raking and stacking, Dad?" Dunia asked timidly. "I can't do it all by myself."

"We'll ask Aksinia Astakhov. Stepan asked us to mow for him."

Two mornings later Mitka Korshunov rode on his white-legged stallion up to the Melekhov yard. A fine rain was falling. A heavy mist hung over the village. Mitka leaned out of his saddle, opened the wicket, and rode in. The old wife called to him from the steps.

"Hey, you rapscallion, what do you want?" she asked with evident dissatisfaction in her voice. The old lady had no love for the desperate and quarrelsome Mitka.

"And what do you want, Ilinichna?" Mitka said in surprise, as he tied his horse to the balustrade of the steps. "I want Gregor. Where is he?"

"He's asleep under the shed. But have you had a stroke? Have you lost the use of your legs that you must ride?"

"You're always sticking in your spoke, old lady!" Mitka took umbrage. Smacking an elegant whip against the legs of his polished boots, he went to look for Gregor and found him asleep in a cart. Screwing up his left eye as though taking aim, Mitka tugged at Gregor's hair.

"Get up, peasant!"

"Peasant" was the most abusive word Mitka could think of using. Gregor jumped up as though on springs.

"What do you want?" he demanded.

Mitka sat down on the side of the cart, and scraping the dried mud off his boots with a stick, he said:

"I've been insulted, Grishka."

"Well?"

"You see, it's . . ." Mitka cursed heavily. "He's a troop commander, he says." He threw out the words angrily, not opening his mouth, his legs trembling. Gregor got up.

"What troop commander?"

Seizing him by the sleeve, Mitka said more quietly:

"Saddle your horse at once and come to the meadows. I'll show him! I said to him: 'Come on, Your Excellency, and we'll see.' 'Bring all your friends and comrades,' he said, 'I'll beat the lot of you. The mother of my mare took prizes at the officers' hurdle-races at Petersburg.' What are his mare and mother to me? Curse them! I won't let them outrace my stallion!"

Gregor hastily dressed. Choking with wrath, Mitka hurried him up.

"He has come on a visit to the Mokhovs. Wait, what is his name? Listnitsky, I think. He's stout and serious-looking and wears glasses. Well, let him! His glasses won't help him; I won't let him catch my stallion!"

With a laugh, Gregor saddled the old mare and, to avoid meeting his father, rode out to the steppe through the threshing-floor gate. They rode to the field at the top of the hill. Close to a withered ash horsemen were awaiting them: the officer Listnitsky on a clean-limbed, handsome mare, and seven of the village lads mounted bareback.

"Where shall we start from?" The officer turned to Mitka, adjusting his pince-nez and admiring the stallion's powerful chest muscles.

"From the ash to the Czar's Lake."

"Where is the Czar's Lake?" Listnitsky screwed up his eyes short-sightedly.

"There, Your Excellency, close to the forest."

They lined up the horses. The officer raised his whip above his head.

"When I say three. All right? One—two—three."

Listnitsky got away first, pressing close to the saddle-bow, holding his cap on with his hand. For a second he led all the rest. Mitka, with face desperately pale, rose in his stirrups—to Gregor he seemed insufferably slow in bringing the whip down on the croup of his stallion.

It was some two miles to the Czar's Lake. Stretched into an arrow, Mitka's stallion caught up with Listnitsky's mare when half the course had been covered. Left behind from the very beginning, Gregor trotted along, watching the straggling chain of riders.

By the Czar's Lake was a sandy hillock, washed up through the ages. Its yellow camel-hump was overgrown with sandwort. Gregor saw the officer and Mitka gallop up the hillock and disappear over the brow together, the others following. When he reached the lake the horses were already standing in a group around Listnitsky. Mitka was sleek with restrained delight, his every movement expressive of triumph. Contrary to his expectation, the officer seemed not at all disconcerted. He stood with his back against a tree, smoking a cigarette, and said, pointing to his foam-flecked horse:

"I've raced her a hundred and twenty miles. I rode over from the station only yesterday. If she were fresh, you'd never overtake me, Korshunov."

"Maybe," Mitka said magnanimously.

Gregor and Mitka left the others and rode home around the hill. Listnitsky took a chilly leave of them, thrust two fingers under the visor of his cap, and turned away.

As he was approaching the hut, Gregor saw Aksinia coming towards him. She was stripping a twig as she walked. When she noticed him she bent her head lower.

Gazing straight before him, Gregor almost rode her down, then suddenly touched up the peacefully ambling mare with his whip. She sat back on her hind legs and sent a shower of mud over Aksinia.

"Oh, you stupid devil!" she exclaimed.

Turning sharply and riding his excited horse at her, Gregor asked:

"Why don't you pass the time of day?"

"You're not worth it!"

"And that's why I sent the mud over you. Don't hold your head so high!"

"Let me pass!" Aksinia shouted, waving her arms in front of the horse's nose. "What are you trampling me with your horse for?"

"She's a mare, not a horse."

"I don't care; let me pass."

"What are you getting angry for, Aksinia? Surely not for the other day, in the meadow?"

Gregor gazed into her eyes. Aksinia tried to say something, but abruptly a little tear hung in the corner of her black eye, her lips quivered pitifully. Shudderingly choking, she whispered:

"Go away, Gregor. I'm not angry—I—" and she went.

The astonished Gregor overtook Mitka at the gate.

"Coming out for the evening?" Mitka asked.

"No."

"Why, what's on? Or did she invite you to spend the night with her?"

Gregor wiped his brow with his palm and made no reply.

All that was left of Trinity in the village farms was the dry thyme scattered over the floors, the dust of crumpled leaves, and the shrivelled, withered green of broken oak and ash branches fastened to the gates and stairs.

The haymaking began immediately after Trinity. From early morning the meadow blossomed with women's holiday skirts, the bright embroidery of aprons, and coloured kerchiefs. The whole village turned out for the mowing. The mowers and rakers attired themselves as though for an annual holiday. So it had been from of old. From the Don to the distant alder clumps the ravaged meadowland stirred and pulsed.

The Melekhovs were late in starting. They set out when all but half the village were already in the meadow.

"You sleep late, Pantaleimon Prokoffievich," the perspiring haymakers clamoured.

"Not my fault—the women again!" the old man laughed, and urged on the bullocks with his knout of rawhide.

At the back of the cart sat Aksinia, her face completely wrapped up to protect it from the sun. From the narrow slits left for her eyes she calmly and severely stared at Gregor, seated opposite her.

Daria, also wrapped up and dressed in her Sunday best, her legs hanging between the rungs of the wagon-side, was giving her breast to the child dozing in her arms. Dunia danced alongside, her happy eyes scanning the meadow and the people met along the road.

Drawing the sleeve of his cotton shirt over his fists, Pantaleimon wiped away the sweat running down from under the visor of his cap. His bent back, with the shirt stretched tightly across it, darkened with moist patches. The sun pierced slantingly through a grey scrawl of cloud and dropped a fan of misty, refracted rays over the meadow, the village, and the distant, silvery hills of the Don.

The day was sultry. The little clouds crept along drowsily, not even overtaking Pantaleimon's bullocks dragging along the road. The old man himself lifted and waved the knout heavily, as though in doubt whether to strike their bony flanks or not. Evidently realizing this, the bullocks did not hasten their pace and slowly, gropingly set forward their cloven hoofs. A dusty-gold and orange-tinged horsefly circled above them.

"There's our strip." Pantaleimon waved his knout.

Gregor unharnessed the weary bullocks. His ear-ring glittering, the old man went to look for the mark he had made at the end of the strip.

"Bring the scythes," he called out after a moment, waving his hand.

Gregor went to him, treading down the grass and leaving an undulating track behind him. Pantaleimon faced towards the distant bell-tower and crossed himself. His hook-nose shone as though freshly varnished, the sweat lingered in the hollows of his swarthy cheeks. He smiled, baring his white, gleaming teeth in his raven beard, and, with his wrinkled neck bent to the right, swept the scythe through the grass. A seven-foot half-circle of mown grass lay at his feet.

Gregor followed in his steps, laying the grass low with the scythe. The women's aprons blossomed in an outstretched rainbow before him, but his eyes sought only one, white with an embroidered border; he glanced at Aksinia and renewed his mowing, adjusting his own to his father's pace.

Aksinia was continually in Gregor's thoughts. Half-closing his eyes, in imagination he kissed her shamelessly and tenderly, spoke to her in burning and speechless words that came to his tongue he knew not whence. Then he dropped this line of thought, stepped out again methodically, one—two—three; his memory urged up fragments of the past . . . sitting under the damp hayrick . . . the moon over the meadow . . . rare drops falling from the bush into the puddle . . . one—two—three. . . . Good! Ah, that had been good!

He heard laughter behind him. He looked back: Daria was lying under the cart, and Aksinia was bent over her, telling her something. Daria waved her arms, and again they both laughed.

"I'll get to that bush and then I'll drop my scythe," Gregor thought. At that moment he felt the scythe pass through something soft and yielding. He bent down: a little wild duckling went scurrying into the grass with a squawk. By the hole where the nest had been, another was huddled, cut in two by the scythe. He laid the dead bird on his palm. It had evidently only come from the egg a few days previously; a living warmth was still to be felt in the down. With a sudden feeling of keen compassion he stared at the inert little ball lying in his hand.

"What have you found, Grishka?"

Dunia came dancing along the mown alley, her pigtails tossing on her breast. Frowning, Gregor threw away the duckling and angrily renewed his mowing.

After dinner the women began to rake the hay. The cut grass sunned and dried, giving off a heavy, stupefying scent. Dinner was eaten in haste. Fat meat and the Cossacks' stand-by, sour milk: such was the entire repast.

"No point in going home!" Pantaleimon said after dinner; "we'll turn the bullocks to graze in the forest, and tomorrow as soon as the dew is off the grass we'll finish the mowing."

Dusk had fallen when they stopped for the day. Aksinia raked the last rows together and went to the cart to cook some millet mash. All day she had laughed evilly at Gregor, gazing at him with eyes full of hatred, as though in revenge for some great unforgettable injury. Gregor, gloomy and brooding, drove the bullocks down to the Don for water. His father had watched him and Aksinia all day. Staring unpleasantly after Gregor, he said:

"Have your supper and then guard the bullocks. See they don't get into the grass! Take my coat."

Daria laid the child under the cart and went into the forest with Dunia for brushwood.

Over the meadow the waning moon mounted the dark, inaccessible heaven. Moths sprinkled around the fire like early snow. The millet boiled in the smoky field-pot. Wiping a spoon with the edge of her underskirt, Daria called to Gregor:

"Come and have your supper."

His father's coat flung around his shoulders, Gregor emerged from the darkness and approached the fire.

"What has made you so bad-tempered?" Daria smiled.

"He doesn't want to watch the bullocks," Dunia laughed, and sitting down by her brother, she tried to start a conversation. But somehow her efforts were unsuccessful. Pantaleimon sipped his soup and crunched the under-cooked millet between his teeth. Aksinia ate without lifting her eyes, smiling half-heartedly at Daria's jokes. Her burning cheeks were flushed troubledly.

Gregor was the first to rise; he went off to the bullocks.

The fire burned low. The smouldering brushwood wrapped the little group in the honey scent of burning leaves.

At midnight Gregor stole up to the camp and halted some ten paces away. His father was snoring tunefully in the cart. The unquenched embers stared out from the ash with golden peacock's eyes.

A grey, shrouded figure broke away from the cart and came slowly towards Gregor. When just two or three paces away, it halted. Aksinia! Gregor's heart thumped fast and heavily; he stepped forward crouchingly, flinging back the edge of his coat, and pressed the compliant, fervently burning woman to himself. Her legs bowed at the knees; she trembled, her teeth chattering. Gregor suddenly flung her over his arm as a wolf throws a slaughtered sheep across its back and, stumbling over the trailing edges of his open coat, ran pantingly off.

"Oh, Grishka, Grishka! Your father . . ."

"Quiet!"

Tearing herself away, gasping for breath in the sour sheep's wool of the coat, abandoning herself to the bitterness of regret, Aksinia almost shouted:

"Put me down. What matter now? . . . I'll go of my own accord."

Not like an azure and blood-red blossom, but like wayside henbane is a woman's belated love.

After the mowing Aksinia was a changed woman: as though someone had set a mark, burned a brand on her face. When other women met her they snarled spitefully and nodded their heads after her. The maidens were envious, but she carried her happy, shameful head proudly and high.

Soon everybody knew of her liaison with Gregor Melekhov. At first it was talked about in whispers—only half-believed—but after the village shepherd had seen them in the early dawn close to the windmill, lying under the moon in the low-growing rye, the rumour spread like a turbid tidal wave.

It reached Pantaleimon's ears also. One Sunday he happened to go along to the Mokhovs' shop. The throng was so great that no more could have crowded through the door. He entered, and everybody seemed to be making way for him. He pushed towards the counter where the textiles were sold. The master, Mokhov, took it upon himself to attend to the old man.

"Where have you been all this long while, Prokoffich?" he asked.

"Too much to do. Troubles with the farm."

"What? Sons like yours, and troubles?"

"What of my sons? I've seen Piotra off to camp, and Grishka and I do everything."

Mokhov divided his stiff, ruddy beard in two with his fingers and significantly glanced out of the corners of his eyes at the crowd of Cossacks.

"Oh, yes, old lad, and why haven't you told us anything about it?" he asked.

"About what?"

"How do you mean, what? Thinking of marrying your son, and not one word to anybody!"

"Which son?"

"Why, your son Gregor isn't married."

"And at present he doesn't show any sign of marrying."

"But I've heard that your daughter-in-law's going to be—Stepan Astakhov's Aksinia."

"What? With her husband alive. . . . Why, Platonich, surely you're joking? Aren't you?" Pantaleimon stuttered.

"Joking? But I've had it from others."

Pantaleimon smoothed out the piece of material spread over the counter, then, turning sharply, limped towards the door. He made straight for home. He walked with his head bowed as usual, pressing his fingers into his fist, hobbling more obviously on his lame leg. As he passed the Astakhovs' hut he glanced through the wattle fence: Aksinia, swaying from the hips, spruce and looking younger than ever, was going into the hut with an empty bucket.

"Hey, wait!" he called, and pushed through the wicket gate. Aksinia halted and waited for him. They went into the hut. The cleanly swept earthen floor was sprinkled with red sand; on the bench in the corner were pastries fresh from the oven. From the kitchen came the smell of fusty clothes and sweet apples.

A large-headed tabby cat came up to make a fuss of Pantaleimon's legs. It arched its back and rubbed itself against his boots. He sent it flying against the bench and shouted:

"What's all this I hear? Eh? Your husband's traces not yet cold, and you already setting your cap at other men! I'll make Grishka's blood flow for this, and I'll write to your Stepan! Let him hear of it! . . . You whore, your bitch of a mother didn't beat you enough. Don't set your foot inside my yard from this day on. Carrying on with a young man, and when Stepan comes, and me, too . . ."

Aksinia listened with eyes contracted. And suddenly she shamelessly swept up the edge of her skirt, enveloped Pantaleimon in the smell of women's clothes, and came breasting at him with writhing lips and bared teeth.

"What are you to me, old man? Eh? Who are you, to teach me? Go and teach your own fat-bottomed woman! Keep order in your own yard! You limping, stump-footed devil! Clear out of here, don't foam at me like a wild boar, you won't frighten me!"

"Wait, you fool!"

"There's nothing to wait for! Get back where you came from! And if I want your Grishka, I'll eat him, bones and all! Chew that over! What if Grishka does love me? You'll punish him? . . . You'll write to my husband? Write to the ataman if you like, but Grishka belongs to me! He's mine! Mine! I have him and I shall keep him. . . ."

Aksinia pressed against the quailing Pantaleimon with her breast (it beat against her thin jacket like a bustard in a noose), burned him with the flame of her black eyes, overwhelmed him with more and more terrible shameless words. His eyebrows quivering, the old man retreated to the door, groped for the stick he had left in the corner, and waving his hand, pushed open the door with his bottom. Aksinia pressed him out of the porch, pantingly, frenziedly shouting:

"All my life I'll love him! Kill him if you like! He's my Grishka! Mine!"

Gurgling something into his beard, Pantaleimon limped off to his hut.

He found Gregor in the kitchen. Without saying a word, he brought his stick down over his son's back. Doubling up, Gregor hung on his father's arm.

"What's that for, Father?" he demanded.

"For your goings-on, you son of a bitch!"

"What goings-on?"

"Don't soil your neighbour! Don't disgrace your father! Don't run after women, you hound!" Pantaleimon snorted, dragging Gregor around the kitchen as his son tried to snatch away the stick.

"I'm not going to let you beat me!" Gregor cried hoarsely, and setting his teeth, he tore the stick out of his father's hand. Across his knee it went and—snap!

"I'll whip you publicly. You accursed son of the devil! I'll wed you to the village idiot! I'll geld you!" his father roared.

At the sound of fighting the old mother came running. "Pantaleimon, Pantaleimon! Cool down a little! Wait!" she exclaimed.

But the old man had lost his temper in earnest. He sent his wife flying, overthrew the table with the sewing-machine on it, and victoriously flew out into the yard. Gregor, whose shirt had been torn in the struggle, had not had time to fling it off when the door banged open and his father appeared once more like a stormcloud on the threshold.

"I'll marry him off, the son of a bitch!" He stamped his foot like a horse and fixed his gaze on Gregor's muscular back. "I'll drive tomorrow to arrange the match. To think that I should live to see my son laugh in my face!"

"Let me get my shirt on, and get me married after," Gregor retorted.

"I'll marry you! I'll marry you to the village idiot!" The door slammed, the old man's steps clattered down the stairs and died away.

Beyond the village of Sietrakov the carts with tarpaulin covers stretched in rows across the steppe. At unbelievable speed a white-roofed and neat little town grew up, with straight streets and a small square in the centre where sentries kept guard.

The men lived the usual monotonous life of a training camp. In the morning the detachment of Cossacks guarding the grazing horses drove them into the camp. Then followed cleaning, grooming, saddling, the roll-call, and muster. The staff officer in command of the camp bawled stentoriously; the military commissary bustled around; the sergeants training the young Cossacks shouted their orders. They were assembled behind a hill for the attack, they cunningly encircled the "enemy." They fired at targets. The younger Cossacks eagerly vied with one another in the sabre exercises, the old hands dodged the fatigues.

About a week before the break-up of

the camp Ivan Tomilin's wife came to visit him. She brought him some home-made cracknel, an assortment of dainties, and a sheaf of village news.

She left again very early in the morning, taking the Cossacks' greetings and instructions to their families and relations in the village. Only Stepan Astakhov sent no message back by her. He had fallen ill the evening before, had taken vodka to cure himself, and was incapable of seeing anything in the whole wide world, including Tomilin's wife. He did not turn up on parade; at his request the doctor's assistant let his blood, setting a dozen leeches on his chest. Stepan sat in his undershirt against one wheel of his cart (making the white linen casing of his cap oily with cart grease) and with gaping mouth watched the leeches sucking at his swollen breasts and distending with dark blood.

Tomilin approached. He winked.

"Stepan, I'd like a word with you," he said.

"Well, get on with it."

"My wife's been here on a visit. She left this morning."

"Ah. . . ."

"There's a lot of talk about your wife in the village."

"What?"

"Not pleasant talk, either."

"Well?"

"She's playing about with Gregor Melekhov. Quite openly."

Turning pale, Stepan tore the leeches from his chest and crushed them underfoot. He crushed them to the very last one, buttoned up his shirt, and then, as though suddenly afraid, unbuttoned it again. His blenched lips moved incessantly. They trembled, slipped into an awkward smile, shrivelled and gathered into a livid pucker, Tomilin thought Stepan must be chewing something hard and solid. Gradually the colour returned to his face, the lips, caught by his teeth, froze into immobility. He took off his cap, smeared the grease over the white casing with his sleeve, and said aloud:

"Thank you for telling me."

"I just wanted to warn you. . . . You won't mind. . . ."

Tomilin commiseratingly clapped his hands against his trousers and went off to his horse. Stepan stood for a moment staring fixedly and sternly at the black smear on his cap. A half-crushed, dying leech crawled up his boots.

In ten more days the Cossacks would be returning from camp.

Aksinia lived in a frenzy of belated, bitter love. Despite his father's threats, Gregor slipped off and went to her at night, coming home at dawn.

For two weeks he had strained like a horse striving beyond its powers. With lack of sleep his brown face was suffused with a blue tinge, his tired eyes gazed wearily out of their sunken sockets. Aksinia went about with her face completely uncovered, the deep pits under her eyes darkened funereally, her swollen, slightly pouting, avid lips smiled troubledly and challengingly.

So extraordinary and open was their mad association, so ecstatically did they burn with a single, shameless flame, neither conscience-stricken nor hiding their love from the world, that people began to be ashamed to meet them in the street. Gregor's comrades, who previously had chaffed him about Aksinia, now silently avoided him or felt awkward and constrained in his company. In their hearts the women envied Aksinia, yet they condemned her, malevolently exulting at the prospect of Stepan's return and pining with bestial curiosity.

If Gregor had made some show of hiding the liaison from the world, and if Aksinia had kept her relations with Gregor comparatively secret, the world would have seen nothing unusual in it. The village would have gossiped a little and then forgotten all about it. But they lived together almost openly, they were bound by a mighty feeling which had no likeness to any temporary association, and the villagers held their breath in filthy expectation. Stepan would return and cut the knot.

Over the bed in the Astakhovs' bedroom ran a string threaded with decorative empty white and black spools. The flies spent their nights on the spools, and spiders' webs stretched from them to the ceiling. Gregor was lying on Aksinia's bare, cold arm and gazing up at the chain of spools. Aksinia's other hand was playing with the thick strands of hair on his head. Her fingers smelt of warm milk; when Gregor turned his head, pressing his nose into Aksinia's armpit, the pungent, sweetish scent of woman's sweat flooded his nostrils.

In addition to the wooden, painted bedstead with pointed pine-cones at the corners, the room contained, close to the door, an iron-bound, capacious chest holding Aksinia's dowry and finery. In the corner was a table, an oleograph with General Skoboliov riding at a flapping banner dipped before him, two chairs, and above them ikons in miserable paper aureoles. Along the side wall were hung fly-blown photographs. One was of a group of Cossacks, with tousled heads, swelling chests decorated with watch-chains, and drawn sabres: Stepan with his comrades in army service. On a hook hung Stepan's uniform. The moon stared through the window and uncertainly fingered the two ornamental white knots on the shoulder-straps.

With a sigh Aksinia kissed Gregor on his brow between the eyes.

"Grishka, my love," she said.

"What is it?" he asked.

"Only nine days left. . . ."

"That's not so soon."

"What am I to do, Grishka?"

"How am I to know?"

Aksinia restrained a sigh and again smoothed and parted Gregor's matted hair.

"Stepan will kill me," she half-asked, half-declared.

Gregor was silent. He wanted to sleep. With difficulty he forced open his clinging eyelids and saw right above him the bluish depths of Aksinia's eyes.

"When my husband returns, I suppose you will give me up. Are you afraid?" she asked.

"Why should I be afraid of him? You're his wife, it's for you to be afraid."

"When I'm with you I'm not afraid, but when I think about it in the daytime I'm frightened."

Gregor yawned and said:

"It isn't Stepan's return that matters. My father is talking of getting me married off."

He smiled and was going to add something, but beneath his head he felt Aksinia's hand suddenly wilt and soften, bury itself in the pillow, and after a moment harden again.

"Who has he spoken to?" she asked in a stifled voice.

"He's only talking about it. Mother said he's thinking of Korshunov's Natalia."

"Natalia—she's a beautiful girl. Too beautiful. . . . Well, and you'll marry her. I saw her in church the other day. Dressed up she was. . . ."

"Don't talk to me about her beauty. I want to marry you."

Aksinia sharply pulled her arm away from under Gregor's head and stared with dry eyes at the window. A frosty, yellow mist was in the yard. The shed cast a heavy shadow. The crickets were chirruping. Down by the Don the bitterns boomed; their deep bass tones came through the window.

"Grishka!" she said.

"Thought of something?"

Aksinia seized Gregor's rough, unyielding hands, pressed them to her breast, to her cold, deathly cheeks, and cried:

"What did you take up with me for, curse you! What shall I do? Grishka! . . . I am lost. . . . Stepan is coming, and what answer shall I give him? . . . Who is there to look after me?"

Gregor was silent. Aksinia gazed mournfully at his handsome eagle nose, his shadowed eyes, his dumb lips. . . . And suddenly a flood of feeling swept away the dam of restraint. She madly kissed his face, his neck, his arms, the rough, curly black hair on his chest, and while gathering her breath, whispered (and Gregor felt her body trembling):

"Grishka—my dearest—beloved—let us go away. My dear! We'll throw up everything and go. I'll leave my husband and all else, so long as you are with me. . . . We'll go far away to the mines. I shall love you and care for you. I have an uncle who is a watchman at the Paromonov mines; he'll help me. . . . Grishka! Say just one little word!"

Gregor lay thinking, then unexpectedly opened his burning Asiatic eyes. They were laughing, blinding with derision.

"You're a fool, Aksinia, a fool! You talk away, but you say nothing worth listening to. Where shall I go to away from the farm? I've got to do my military service next year. . . . I'll never stir anywhere away from the land. Here there is the steppe, and something to breathe—but there? Last summer I went with Father to the station. I almost died. Engines roaring, the air heavy with burning coal. How the people live I don't know; perhaps they're used to it!" Gregor spat out and said again: "I'll never leave the village."

The night grew darker outside the window, a cloud passed over the moon. The frosty yellow mist vanished from the yard, the shadows were washed away, and it was no longer possible to tell whether it was last year's brushwood or some old bush that loomed darkly beyond the fence outside the window.

In the room also the shadows gathered. The knots on Stepan's uniform faded, and in the grey, stagnant impenetrability Gregor failed to see the fine shiver that shook Aksinia's shoulders, nor her head pressed between her hands and silently shaking on the pillow.

After the visit of Tomilin's wife Stepan's features noticeably darkened. His brows hung over his eyes, a deep and harsh frown puckered his forehead. In his sullen, seething rage Stepan carried his burden of sorrow like a horse bearing a rider. He talked but little with his comrades, began to quarrel over trifles, and would hardly look at Piotra Melekhov. The threads of friendship which had previously united them were snapped. They returned home enemies.

They set out for their village in the same group as before. Piotra's and Stepan's horses were harnessed to the wagon. Christonia rode behind on his own horse. Tomilin was suffering with a fever and lay covered with his coat in the wagon. Fiodot Bodovskov was too lazy to drive, so Piotra took the reins. Stepan walked along at the side of the wagon, lashing off the purple heads of the roadside thistles with his whip. Rain was falling. The rich black earth stuck to the wheels like grease. The sky was an autumnal blue, ashy with cloud. Night fell. No lights of any village were to be seen. Piotra belaboured the horses liberally with the knout. And suddenly Stepan shouted in the darkness:

"You, what the—you—! You spare your own horse and keep the knout on mine all the time."

"Watch more carefully! The one that doesn't pull is the one I whip up."

Stepan did not reply. They rode on for another half-hour in silence. The mud squelched beneath the wheels. The rain pattered noisily against the tarpaulin. Piotra dropped the reins and smoked, mentally reviewing all the insulting words he would use in the next quarrel with Stepan.

The wagon suddenly jolted and stopped. Slipping in the mud, the horses pawed the earth.

"What's the matter?" Stepan took alarm.

"Give us a light," Piotra demanded.

In front the horses struggled and snorted. Someone struck a match. A tiny orange ring of light, then darkness again. With trembling hands Piotra held the fallen horse down by the bridle.

The horse sighed and rolled over, the centre shaft groaned. Stepan struck a bundle of matches. His own horse lay with one foreleg thrust to the knee in a marmot's hole.

Christonia unfastened the traces.

"Unharness Piotra's horse, quickly," he ordered.

At last Stepan's horse was lifted with difficulty to its feet. While Piotra held it by the bridle, Christonia crawled on his knees in the mud, feeling the helplessly hanging leg.

"Seems to be broken," he boomed. "But see if he can walk."

Piotra pulled at the bridle. The horse hopped a step or two, not putting its left foreleg to the ground, and whinnied. Drawing on his greatcoat, Tomilin stamped about bitterly.

"Broken, is it? A horse lost!" he fumed.

Stepan, who all this while had not spoken a word, almost seemed to have been awaiting such a remark. Thrusting Christonia aside, he flung himself on Piotra. He aimed at his head, but missed and struck his shoulder. They grappled together and fell into the mud. There was the sound of a tearing shirt. Stepan got Piotra beneath him and, holding his head down with one knee, pounded away with his fists. Christonia dragged him off.

"What's that for?" Piotra shouted, spitting out blood.

"Don't drive off the road, you serpent!"

Piotra tore himself out of Christonia's hands.

"Now, now! You try fighting me!" Christonia roared, with one hand holding Piotra against the wagon.

They harnessed Bodovskov's small but sturdy horse with Piotra's. Christonia ordered Stepan to ride his horse, and himself crawled into the cart with Piotra. It was midnight when they arrived at a village. They stopped at the first hut, and Christonia begged a night's shelter.

Bodovskov led the horses in. He stumbled over a pig's trough thrown down in the middle of the yard, and cursed vigorously. They led the horses under the roof of the shed. Tomilin, his teeth chattering, went into the hut. Piotra and Christonia remained in the cart.

At dawn they made ready to set out again. Stepan came out of the hut, an ancient, bowed woman hobbling after him. She followed him under the shed.

"Which one is it?" she asked.

"The black," sighed Stepan.

The woman lay her stick on the ground and with an unusually strong, masculine movement raised the horse's damaged leg. She felt the knee-cap carefully with her fine, crooked fingers. The horse set back its ears and reared on its hind legs with the pain.

"No, there's no break there, Cossack. Leave him and I'll heal him."

Stepan waved his hand and went to the cart.

"Leave him or not?" the old woman blinked after him.

"Let him stay," he replied.

"I yearn after him, old woman! I'm

pining away in my own eyes. I can't put tucks into my skirt fast enough. When he goes past the yard my heart burns. I'd fall to the ground and kiss his footprints. Help me! They're going to wed him off. . . . Help me, dear. . . . Whatever it costs, I'll give you. . . . My last shirt I'll give you, only help me!"

With luminous eyes set in a lacework of furrows the old crone Drozdikha looked at Aksinia, shaking her head at the girl's bitter story.

"Whose is the young man?"

"Pantaleimon Melekhov's."

"That's the Turk, isn't it?"

"Yes."

The old woman chewed away with her withered mouth and dallied with her answer.

"Come to me very early tomorrow, child, as soon as it is getting light. We'll go down to the Don, to the water. We'll wash away your yearning. Bring a pinch of salt with you."

Aksinia wrapped her face in her yellow shawl and crept cautiously out through the gate. Her dark figure was swallowed up in the night. Her steps died away. From somewhere at the end of the village came the sound of singing.

At dawn Aksinia, who had not slept a wink all night, was at Drozdikha's window.

"Old woman!" she called.

"Who's there?"

"It's me, Aksinia! Get up!"

They made their way by side-turnings down to the river. By the waterside the sand stung icily. A damp, chilly mist crept up from the Don.

Drozdikha took Aksinia's hand in her own bony hand and drew her towards the river.

"Give me the salt. Cross yourself to the sunrise," she told her.

Aksinia crossed herself, staring spitefully at the happy rosiness of the east.

"Take up some water in your palm and drink. Hurry!"

Aksinia drank. Like a black spider the old woman straddled over a lazily rolling wave, squatted down, and whispered:

"Prickly chilliness, flowing from the bottom. . . . Burning flesh. . . . A beast in the heart. . . . Yearning and fever. . . . By the holy cross, most holy, most immaculate Mother. . . . The slave of God, Gregor . . ." reached Aksinia's ears.

Drozdikha sprinkled some salt over the damp sand at her feet and some more into the water, then gave the rest to Aksinia.

"Sprinkle some water over your shoulder. Quickly!"

Aksinia did so. She stared sadly and spitefully at Drozdikha's russet cheeks.

"That's all, surely?" she asked.

"Yes, that's all."

Aksinia ran breathlessly home. The cows were lowing in the yard. Daria, sleepy-eyed and flushed, was driving her cows off to join the village herd. She smiled as she saw Aksinia run past.

"Slept well, neighbour?" she asked.

"Praise be!"

"And where have you been so early?"

"I had a call to make in the village."

The church bells were ringing for matins. The copper-tongued clanging rang out brokenly. The village herdsman cracked his stock-whip in the side street. Aksinia hurriedly drove out the cows, then carried the milk into the porch to strain it. She wiped her hands on her apron and, lost in thought, poured the milk into the strainer.

A heavy rattle of wheels and snorting of horses in the street. Aksinia set down the pail and went to look out of the front window. Holding the pommel of his sabre, Stepan was coming through the wicket gate. Aksinia crumpled her apron in her fingers and sat down on the bench. Steps up the stairs. . . . Steps in the porch. . . . Steps at the very door. . . .

Stepan stood on the threshold, gaunt and estranged.

"Well—" he said.

Aksinia, all her full, buxom body reeling, went to meet him.

"Beat me," she said slowly, and stood sideways to him.

"Well, Aksinia—"

"I shan't hide. Beat me, Stepan!"

Her head sunk on her breast, huddled into a heap, protecting only her belly with her arms, she faced him. Her eyes stared unwinkingly from their dark rings, out of her dumb, fear-distorted face. Stepan swayed and passed by her. The scent of male sweat and the bitter pungency of road travel came from his unwashed shirt. He dropped on the bed without removing his cap. He lay shrugging his shoulders, throwing off his sword-belt. His blond moustaches hung limply down. Not turning her head, Aksinia glanced sidelong at him. Stepan put his feet on the foot of the bed. The mud slowly slipped from his boots. He stared at the ceiling and played with the leather tassel of his sword.

"Had breakfast?" he asked.

"No. . . ."

"Get me something to eat."

He sipped some milk, wetting his moustache. He chewed slowly at the bread. Aksinia stood by the stove. In a burning terror she watched her husband's little gristly ears rising and falling as he ate.

Stepan slipped away from the table and crossed himself.

"Tell me all, dear," he curtly demanded.

With bowed head Aksinia cleared the table. She was silent.

"Tell me how you waited for your husband, how you defended a man's honour. Well?"

A terrible blow on the head tore the ground from Aksinia's feet and flung her towards the door. Her back struck against the door-post, and she groaned heavily.

Not only a limp and feeble woman, but lusty and sturdy men could Stepan send flying with a well-aimed blow on the head. Whether fear lifted Aksinia or whether she was moved by a woman's vital nature—she lay a moment, rested, then scrambled on to all fours.

Stepan had lit a cigarette and was standing in the middle of the room yawning as she rose to her feet. He threw his tobacco-pouch on to the table, but Aksinia was already slamming the door behind her. He chased after her.

Streaming with blood, Aksinia ran towards the fence separating their yard from the Melekhovs'. Stepan overtook her at the fence. His black hand fell like a hawk on her head. The hair slipped between his fingers. He tore at it and threw her to the ground.

What if a husband does trample his own wife with his boots? One-armed Alexei Shamil walked past the gate, looked in, winked, and split his bushy little beard with a smile; after all, it was very understandable that Stepan should be punishing his lawfully wedded wife. Shamil wanted to stop to see whether he would beat her to death or not, but his conscience would not allow him. After all, he wasn't a woman.

Watching Stepan from afar, you would have thought someone was doing the Cossack dance. And so Gregor thought, as through the kitchen window he saw Stepan jumping up and down. But he looked again and flew out of the hut. Pressing his fists against his chest, he ran on his toes to the fence. Piotra followed him.

Over the high fence Gregor flew like a bird. He ran at full speed into Stepan from behind. Stepan staggered, and turning round, came at Gregor like a bear.

The Melekhov brothers fought desperately. They pecked at Stepan like carrion-crows at a carcass. Gregor went several times to earth, sent down by Stepan's knuckles. Sturdy Piotra was stout by comparison with the stiffer-jointed Stepan, but he bent under the blows like a reed before the wind, yet remained on his feet.

Stepan, one eye flashing (the other was going the colour of an under-ripe plum), retreated to the steps.

Christonia happened to come along to borrow some harness from Stepan, and he separated them.

"Stop that!" He waved his arms. "Break away or I'll report it to the ataman."

Piotra cautiously spat blood and half a tooth into his palm and said hoarsely:

"Come on, Gregor. We'll catch him some other time."

"Don't you try lying in wait for me!" Stepan threatened from the steps.

"All right, all right!"

"And no 'all right' about it or I'll pull your guts out, soul and all."

"Is that serious or joking?"

Stepan came swiftly down the steps. Gregor broke forward to meet him, but pushing him towards the gate, Christonia promised him: "Only dare and I'll give you a good hiding."

CHAPTER 5

"Tell Piotra to harness the mare and his own horse," Pantaleimon ordered Gregor as, solemn as a churchwarden at Mass, and sweating like a bull, he sat finishing his soup. Dunia was vigilantly watching Gregor's every movement. Ilinichna, bobtailed, and looking important in her lemon-yellow Sunday shawl, a motherly anxiety lurking in the corners of her lips, said to the old man:

"Get some more down your neck, Prokoffich. You're starving yourself."

"No time to eat," he replied.

Piotra's long, wheaten-yellow moustaches appeared at the door.

"Your carriage is ready, if you please!" he announced.

Dunia burst into a laugh and hid her face in her sleeve.

Ilinichna's shrewd widow cousin, Aunty Vasilisa, was to go with them as matchmaker. She was the first to nestle herself into the wagonette, twisting and turning her head, laughing, and displaying her crooked black teeth beneath the pucker of her lips.

"Don't show your teeth, Vasilisa," Pantaleimon warned her. "You'll ruin everything with your gap. Your teeth are set all drunk in your mouth; one one way and one the other. . . ."

"Ah, Dad, I'm not the bridegroom to be. . . ."

"Maybe you're not, but don't laugh, all the same."

Vasilisa took umbrage, but meantime Piotra had opened the gate. Gregor sorted out the smelly leather reins and jumped into the driver's seat. Pantaleimon and Ilinichna sat side by side at the back like two youngsters, with no room to give or take.

Gregor bit his lips and whipped up the horses. They pulled at the traces and started off without warning.

"Look out! You'll catch your wheel!" Daria shrilled, but the wagonette swerved sharply and, bouncing over the roadside hummocks, rattled down the street.

Leaning to one side, Gregor touched up Piotra's lagging horse with the whip. His father held his beard in his hand, afraid that the wind would catch and carry it away.

"Whip up the mare!" he cried hoarsely, bending towards Gregor's back. With the lace sleeve of her jacket Ilinichna wiped away the tear that the wind had brought to her eye and winkingly watched Gregor's blue satin shirt fluttering and billowing on his back. The Cossacks along the road stepped aside and stood staring after them. The dogs came running out of the yards and yelped under the horses' feet.

Gregor spared neither whip nor horses, and within ten minutes the village was left behind. Korshunov's large hut with its plank-fence enclosure was quickly reached. Gregor pulled on the reins, and the wagonette suddenly stopped at the painted, finely fretted gates.

Gregor remained with the horses; Pantaleimon limped towards the steps. Ilinichna and Vasilisa sailed after him with rustling skirts. The old man hurried, afraid of losing the courage he had summoned up during the ride. He stumbled over the high step, knocked his lame leg, and frowning with pain, clattered up the well-swept stairs.

He and Ilinichna entered the kitchen almost together. He disliked standing at his wife's side, as she was taller by a good six inches; so he stepped a pace forward and, removing his cap, crossed himself to the black ikon.

"Good health to you!" he said.

"Praise be!" the master of the house, a stocky, tow-haired old man replied, rising from the bench.

"Some guests for you, Miron Gregorievich," Pantaleimon continued.

"Guests are always welcome. Maria, give the visitors something to sit on."

His elderly, flat-chested wife wiped non-existent dust from three stools and pushed them towards the guests. Pantaleimon sat down on the very edge of one and mopped his perspiring brow with his handkerchief.

"We've come on business," he began without beating about the bush. At this point Ilinichna and Vasilisa, pulling up their skirts, also sat down.

"By all means; on what business?" The master smiled.

Gregor entered, stared around him and greeted the Korshunovs. Across Miron's freckled face spread a vivid russet. Only now did he guess the object of the visit. "Have the horses brought into the yard. Get some hay put down for them," he ordered his wife.

"We've just a little matter to talk over," Pantaleimon went on, twisting his curly beard and tugging at his ear-ring in his agitation. "You have a girl unmarried, we have a son. Couldn't we come to some arrangement? We'd like to know. Will you give her away now, or not? And we might become relations?"

"Who knows?" Miron scratched his bald spot. "I must say, we weren't thinking of giving her in marriage this autumn. We've our hands full with work here, and she's not so very old. She's only just past her eighteenth spring. That's right, isn't it, Maria?"

"That will be it."

"She's the very age for marriage," Vasilisa joined in. "A girl soon gets too old!" She fidgeted on her stool, prickled by the besom she had stolen from the porch and thrust under her jacket. Tradition had it that matchmakers who stole the girl's besom were never refused.

"Proposals came for our girl away back in early spring. Our girl won't be left on the shelf. We can't grumble to the good God. . . . She can do everything, in the field or at home . . ." Korshunov's wife replied.

"If a good man were to come along, you wouldn't say no," Pantaleimon broke into the women's cackle.

"It isn't a question of saying no." The master scratched his head. "We can give her away at any time."

The negotiations were on the point of breaking down. Pantaleimon began to get agitated, and his face flooded with beet juice, while the girl's mother clucked like a sitting hen shadowed by a kite. But Vasilisa intervened in the nick of time. She poured out a flood of quiet, hurrying words, like salt on a fire, and healed the breach.

"Now, now, my dears! Once a matter like this is raised, it needs to be settled decently and for the happiness of your child. Even Natalia—and you might search far in broad daylight and not find another like her!—work burns in her hands! What a capable woman! What a housewife! And for her, as you see for yourselves, good folk"—she opened her arms in a generous sweep, turning to Pantaleimon and bridling Ilinichna. "He's a husband worthy of any. As I look at him my heart beats with yearning, he's so like my late husband, and his family are great workers. Ask anyone in these parts about Prokoffich. In all the world he's known as an honest man and a good. . . . In good faith, do we wish evil to our children?"

Her chiding little voice flowed into Pantaleimon's ears like syrup. He listened, pulling the little tufts of black hair from his nostrils with his middle and index fingers, and thinking rapturously: "Ah, the smooth-tongued devil, how she talks! You can get what she's driving at! Another woman would stun a Cossack with her many words. . . . And this from a petticoat!" He was lost in admiration of Vasilisa, who was fulsomely praising the girl and her family as far back as the fifth generation.

"Of course, we don't wish evil to our child," Maria declared.

"The point is it's early to give her in marriage," the master said pacifically, beaming with a smile.

"It's not early, true God! Not early," Pantaleimon rejoined.

"Sooner or later we have to part with her," the mistress sobbed, half-hypocritically, half in earnest.

"Call your daughter, Miron Gregorievich, and let's look at her."

"Natalia!"

A girl appeared timidly at the door, her swarthy fingers fiddling with the gathering of her apron.

"Come in! Come in! She's shy," the mother encouraged her, smiling through her tears.

Gregor looked at her.

Bold grey eyes under a dusty black scarf. A shallow, rosy dimple in the elastic cheek. Gregor turned his eyes to her hands; they were large and marred with hard work. Beneath the short green jacket embracing the strong body, the small, maidenly, firm breasts rose and fell, outlined naïvely and pitifully; their sharp little nipples showed like buttons.

In a moment Gregor's eyes had run over all of her, from the head to the arched, beautiful feet. He looked her over as a horse-dealer surveys a mare before purchase, thought: "She'll do," and met her eyes, directed stubbornly at him. The simple, sincere, slightly embarrassed gaze seemed to be saying: "Here am I all, as I am. As you wish, judge of me." "Splendid!" Gregor replied with his eyes and a smile.

"Well, that's all." Her father waved her out.

As she closed the door behind her, Natalia looked at Gregor without attempting to conceal her smile and her curiosity.

"Listen, Pantaleimon Prokoffievich," Korshunov began, after exchanging glances with his wife, "you talk it over, and we'll talk it over among the family. And then we'll decide whether we'll call it a match or not."

As he went down the steps, Pantaleimon slipped in a last word:

"We'll call again next Sunday."

Korshunov remained deliberately silent, pretending he had not heard.

Only after he learned of Aksinia's conduct from Tomilin did Stepan, nursing his pain and hatred in his soul, realize that, despite his poor sort of life with her, he loved her with a dreary, hateful love. He had lain in the wagon at night, covered with his coat, his arms flung above his head, and thought of how his wife would greet him on his return home. His eyes veiled with their black lids, he had lain thinking over a thousand details of his revenge.

From the day of his homecoming an unseen spectre dwelt in the Astakhovs' hut. Aksinia went about on tiptoe and spoke in whispers, but in her eyes, sprinkled with the ash of fear, lurked a little spark left from the flame Gregor had kindled.

As he watched her, Stepan felt rather than saw this. He tormented himself. Nights, when the drove of flies had fallen asleep on the crossbeam, and Aksinia had made the bed, he beat her, his hairy hand pressed over her mouth. He demanded shameless details of her relations with Gregor. Aksinia tossed about on the hard bed and could hardly breathe. Tired of torturing her soft body, he passed his hand over her face, seeking for tears. But her cheeks were burningly dry.

"Will you tell?" he demanded.

"No!"

"I'll kill you!"

"Kill me, kill me, for the love of Christ! This isn't life. . . ."

Grinding his teeth, Stepan twisted the fine skin, all damp with sweat, on her womanly breast. Aksinia shuddered and groaned.

"Hurts, does it?" Stepan said jocularly.

"Yes, it hurts."

"And do you think it didn't hurt me?"

It would be late before he fell asleep. In his sleep he clenched his fists. Rising on her elbow, Aksinia gazed at her husband's face, handsome and changed in slumber. Throwing her head back on the pillow, she whispered to herself.

She hardly saw Gregor now. She happened to meet him once down by the Don. Gregor had driven the bullocks down to drink and was coming up the slope, waving a switch and watching his steps. Aksinia was going down to the Don. She saw him and felt the yoke of the buckets turn cold in her hands and the blood boil in her veins.

Afterwards, when she recalled the meeting, she found it difficult to convince herself that it had really happened. Gregor noticed her when she was all but passing him. At the insistent scrape of the buckets he raised his head, his eyebrows quivered, and he smiled stupidly. Aksinia gazed right through his head at the green waves of the Don and beyond to the ridge of sandy headland.

"Aksinia!" he called.

She walked on several paces and stood with her head bent as though before a blow. Angrily whipping a lagging bullock, he said without turning his head:

"When is Stepan going out to cut the rye?"

"He's getting ready now."

"See him off, then go to our sunflower patch and I'll come along after."

Her pails scraping, Aksinia went down to the Don. The foam serpentined along the shore in an intricate yellow lacework on the green hem of the wave. White seagulls were hovering and mewing above the river. Tiny fish sprinkled in a silver rain over the surface of the water. On the other side, beyond the white of the sandy headland, the grey tops of ancient poplars rose haughtily and sternly. As Aksinia was drawing water she dropped her pail. Raising her skirt, she waded in up to her knees. The water swirled and tickled her calves, and for the first time since Stepan's return she laughed quietly and uncertainly.

She glanced back at Gregor. Still waving his switch, he was slowly climbing the slope. With eyes misty with tears Aksinia caressed his strong legs as they confidently trod the ground. His broad-legged trousers, gathered into white woollen stockings, were gay with crimson stripes. On his back, by one shoulder-blade, fluttered a strip of freshly torn dusty shirt, and through the hole showed a triangle of swarthy flesh. With her eyes Aksinia kissed this tiny scrap of the beloved body which once had been hers; the tears fell over her pallid, smiling lips.

She set her pails down on the sand to hook them on to the yoke and noticed the traces of Gregor's boots. She looked stealthily around: no one in sight except some boys bathing from the distant strand. She squatted down and covered the footprint with her palm, then rose, swung the yoke across her shoulders, and hastened home, smiling at herself.

Caught in a muslin mistiness, the sun was passing over the village. Beyond the curly flock of little white clouds spread a deep, cool, azure pasture. Over the burning iron roofs, over the deserted dusty streets, over the farmyards with their parched, yellow grass, hung a deathly sultriness.

As Aksinia approached the steps, Stepan, in a broad-brimmed straw hat, was harnessing the horses to the reaping machine. He flung his sailcloth coat over the front seat and took up the reins.

"Open the gate," he told her.

As she did so, she ventured to ask:

"When will you be back?"

"Towards evening. I've agreed to reap with Anikushka. Take the food along to him. He'll be coming out to the fields when he's finished at the smith's."

The wheels of the reaping machine squeaked, and carved into the grey plush of the dust. Aksinia went into the hut and stood a moment with her hand pressed to her head, then, flinging a kerchief over her hair, ran down to the river.

"But supposing he returns? What then?" the thought suddenly burned into her mind. She stopped as though she saw a deep pit at her feet, glanced back, and sped almost at a run along the river-bank to the meadows.

Fences. Gardens. A yellow sea of sunflowers outstaring the sun. The pale green of potato plants. There were the Shamil women hoeing their potato-patch, their bowed backs in rose-coloured shirts. Reaching the Melekhovs' garden, Aksinia glanced around, then lifted the wattle hasp and opened the gate. She followed the path along to the green thicket of sunflower stems. Stooping, she pressed into the midst of them, smothering her face with golden pollen, and lifting her skirt, sat down on the ground.

She listened: the silence rang in her ears. Somewhere above her was the lonely drone of a bee. For perhaps half an hour she sat thus, torturing herself with doubt. Would he come? She was about to go and was adjusting her kerchief when the gate scraped heavily.

"Aksinia!"

"This way," she called.

"Aha; so you've come, then!" Rustling the leaves, Gregor approached and sat down at her side.

Their eyes met. And in reply to Gregor's mute inquiry she broke into weeping.

"I've no strength. . . . I'm lost, Grishka."

"What does he do?"

Wrathfully she tore open the collar of her jacket. On the rosy, girlishly swelling breasts were numerous cherry-blue bruises.

"Don't you know? He beats me every day. He is sucking my blood. . . . And you're a fine one. Soiled me liked a dog, and off you go. . . . You're all . . ." She buttoned her jacket with trembling fingers, and, frightened lest he was offended, glanced at Gregor, who had turned away.

"So you're trying to put the blame on me?" he said slowly, biting a blade of grass.

"And aren't you to blame?" she cried fiercely.

"A dog doesn't worry an unwilling bitch."

Aksinia hid her face in her hands. The strong, calculated insult came like a blow.

Frowning, Gregor glanced sidelong at her. A tear was trickling between her first and middle fingers. A broken, dusty sun-ray gleamed on the transparent drop and dried its damp trace on her skin.

Gregor could not endure tears. He fidgeted in disquiet, ruthlessly brushed a brown ant from his trousers, and glanced again at Aksinia. She sat without changing her position, but three runnels of tears were now chasing down the back of her hand.

"What's the matter? Have I offended you? . . . Aksinia! Now, wait! Stop, I want to say something."

She tore her hands from her face. "I came here to get advice. What did you come for? It's bitter enough as it is. And you—I didn't come to fasten myself on you. Don't be afraid," she panted.

At that moment she really believed that she had not come to fasten herself on Gregor, but as she had run along by the Don she had vaguely thought: "I'll talk him over! Who else am I to live with?" Then she had remembered Stepan and had obstinately shaken her head, driving away the troublesome thought.

"So our love is done with?" Gregor asked, and turned on to his stomach, supporting himself on one elbow and spitting out the rosy petals of the flower he had been chewing.

"How, done with?" Aksinia took alarm. "How?" she insisted, trying to look into his eyes.

He turned his eyes away.

The dry, exhausted earth smelt of moisture and sun. The wind rustled among the sunflower leaves. For a moment the sun was darkened, overcast by a fleeting cloud; and over the steppe, over the village, over Aksinia's moody head, fell a smoky shadow.

Gregor sighed—his sigh was like that of a horse with a sore throat—and lay on his back, warming his shoulders against the hot soil.

"Listen, Aksinia," he began slowly, "I've—got—an idea. I've been thinking . . ."

Through the garden came the creaking sound of a cart, and a woman's voice: "Gee up, baldhead!"

To Aksinia the call seemed so close that she dropped full length to the ground. Raising his head, Gregor whispered:

"Take your kerchief off. It shows up. . . . They mayn't have seen us."

She removed her kerchief. The burning breeze wandering among the sunflowers played with the wisps of golden down on her neck. The noise of the cart slowly died away.

"And this is what I've been thinking," Gregor began again. Then, more animatedly: "What's done can't be undone. Why try to fix the blame? Somehow we've got to go on living. . . ."

Aksinia listened anxiously, breaking a stalk in her hand as she waited. She looked into Gregor's face and caught the dry and sober glitter of his eyes.

"I've been thinking, let us put an end to . . ."

Aksinia swayed. Her fingers contorted and her nostrils distended as she awaited the end of the sentence. A fire of terror and impatience avidly licked her face, her mouth went dry. She thought he was about to say: "put an end to Stepan," but he vexatiously licked his writhing lips and said:

". . . put an end to the story. Eh?"

Aksinia stood up and, pressing through the swaying, yellow heads of the sunflowers, went towards the gate.

"Aksinia!" Gregor called in a strangled voice. The gate scraped.

He threw off his cap so that the crimson band should not be seen, and stared after Aksinia. It was not she that he saw—it was not her usual virile, swinging walk—but another, an unknown and a stranger.

Immediately after the rye was cut, and

before it could be carried to the barns, the wheat ripened. In the clayey fields and on the slopes the parching leaves turned yellow and wilted into tubes, and the stalks withered.

The harvest was good, everybody joyfully remarked. The ears were full, the grain heavy and large. But since the spring the grain had been affected by a drought coming from the east, so the stalks were short and the straw worthless.

After talking the matter over with Ilinichna, Pantaleimon decided that if the Korshunovs agreed to the match, the wedding would have to be postponed until the 1st of August. He had not yet called on the Korshunovs for an answer; first the harvesting had to be done, and then he had waited for a convenient holiday.

The Melekhovs set out to begin reaping on a Friday. Pantaleimon stripped a wagon and prepared the under-frame for carrying the sheaves. Piotra and Gregor went to the fields to reap. Piotra rode and Gregor walked alongside. Gregor was moody, and knobs of flesh went quivering up from the lower jaw to his cheekbones. Piotra knew this to be a sure sign that his brother was seething and ready for a quarrel, but, smiling behind his wheaten moustache, he set to work to tease Gregor.

"God's truth, she told me herself!" he declared.

"Well, what if she did?" Gregor muttered, chewing the down of his moustache.

" 'As I'm on my way back from town,' she says, 'I hear voices in the Melekhovs' sunflower patch.' "

"Piotra, stop it!"

" 'Yes, voices. And I glance through the fence. . . .' "

Gregor blinked, and he went grey. "Will you stop it, or won't you?" he demanded.

"You're a queer lad! Let me finish!"

"I warn you, Piotra, we shall come to blows," Gregor threatened, falling behind.

Piotra raised his eyebrows and turned round in his seat to face Gregor.

" '. . . I glance through the fence, and there I see them, the two lovers, lying in each other's arms!' she says. 'Who?' I asked, and she answers: 'Why, Aksinia and your brother.' I say . . ."

Seizing the handle of a pitchfork lying at the back of the reaping machine, Gregor flung himself at his brother. Piotra dropped the reins, leaped from his seat, and sprang in front of the horses.

"Pah, the devil!" he exclaimed. "He's gone crazy! Pah! Just look at him. . . ."

Baring his teeth like a wolf, Gregor threw the pitchfork at his brother. Piotra dropped to his hands and knees, and flying over him, the pitchfork buried its points a couple of inches into the earth and stuck upright, whanging and quivering.

Scowling, Piotra caught at the bridles of the startled horses and swore lustily. "You might have killed me, you swine!"

"Yes, and I would have killed you!"

"You're a fool, a mad devil. You're your father's son all right, you true Turk."

Gregor pulled the pitchfork out of the ground and followed after the reaping machine. Piotra beckoned to him with his finger.

"Come here! Give me that pitchfork," he ordered.

He passed the reins into his left hand and took the pitchfork by the prongs. Then with the handle he struck Gregor across the spine.

"A strap would have been better," he grumbled, keeping his eyes on Gregor, who had leaped away. After a moment or two they lit cigarettes, stared into each other's eyes, and burst into peals of laughter.

Christonia's wife, who was driving home along another road, had seen Gregor attack his brother. She stood up in her wagon, balancing precariously on the rye sheaves; but she could not see what happened, as the Melekhovs' reaping machine and horses were between her and the brothers. Hardly had she reached the village street when she cried to a neighbour:

"Klimovna! Run and tell Prokoffievich the Turk that his boys have been fighting with pitchforks close to the Tatar mound. Gregor jabbed Piotra in the side with the fork, and then Piotra gave him— The blood poured out. It was horrible!"

Meantime the brothers had begun reaping. Piotra was growing hoarse with bawling at the tired horses, and Gregor, his dusty foot resting on the crossbar, was pitchforking the swathes off the reaper. Reaping was in progress all over the steppe. The blades of the machines rattled and groaned, the steppe was spotted with swathes of corn. Mimicking the drivers, the marmots whistled in the hollows.

"Two more lengths and we'll stop for a smoke!" Piotra shouted above the noise of the machine. Gregor nodded. He could hardly open his parched lips. He gripped his pitchfork closer to the prongs in order to get a better leverage on the heavy swathes and breathed spasmodically. A bitter perspiration poured down his face and stung in his eyes like soap. Halting the horses, they had a drink and a smoke.

"There's someone riding a horse pretty hard along the road," Piotra remarked, shading his eyes with his palm.

Gregor stared, and raised his eyebrows in astonishment.

"It's Father, surely?"

"You're mad! What could he be riding? We've got both horses here."

"It's him! God's truth, it's Father."

The rider drew nearer, and after a moment he could be seen clearly. "Yes, it's Father!" Piotra began to dance in anxious surprise.

"Something happened at home," Gregor gave expression to the thought troubling them both.

When still a hundred yards away, Pantaleimon reined his horse in. "I'll thrash you, you sons of a bitch!" he yelled, waving his leather whip above his head.

"What on earth—!" Piotra was completely flabbergasted, and thrust half his moustache into his mouth.

"Get the other side of the reaper! By God, he'll lash us with that knout; while we're getting to the bottom of it he'll whip our guts out." Gregor smiled, putting the machine between himself and his father.

The foaming horse came over the swathes of grain at a trot. His feet knocking against the horse's sides (for he was riding bareback), Pantaleimon shook his whip. "What have you been up to out here, you children of the devil?" he demanded.

"We've been reaping, as you can see." Piotra swept his arms around, nervously eyeing the whip.

"Who's been sticking which with the fork? What have you been fighting about?"

Turning his back on his father, Gregor began in a loud whisper to count the clouds.

"What fork? Who's been fighting?" Piotra looked his father up and down.

"Why, she came running, the daughter of a hen, and shrieking: 'Your boys have stuck each other with pitchforks.' Eh? What do you say to that?" Pantaleimon shook his head ecstatically and, dropping the reins, jumped off his horse. "I borrowed a horse and came out at a gallop. Eh?"

"Who told you all this?" Piotra asked.

"A woman!"

"She was lying, Father. She must have been asleep in her wagon and dreamt it."

"A petticoat again!" Pantaleimon half-shouted, half-whistled, slobbering down his beard. "That hen, Klimovna! My God! Eh? I'll whip the bitch!" He danced with rage.

Shaking with silent laughter, Gregor kept his eyes fixed on the ground. Piotra did not remove his eyes from his father, who was stroking his perspiring brow.

Pantaleimon danced to his heart's content and then calmed down. He took the seat of the reaping machine and reaped a couple of lengths, then mounted his horse and rode back to the village. He left his forgotten whip lying on the ground. Piotra picked it up and swung it appraisingly, remarking to his brother:

"We'd have had a bad time, young man. This isn't a whip! It would have maimed you, brother. It could cut your head clean off."

The Korshunovs had the reputation of being the richest family in the village of Tatarsk. They had fourteen pairs of bullocks, horses, mares from stud farms, fifteen cows, innumerable other cattle, a flock of several hundred sheep. Their iron-roofed house was as good as that of Mokhov the merchant: it had six panelled rooms. The yard was paved with new and handsome tiles. The garden covered a good three acres. What more could man want?

So it was rather timidly and with secret reluctance that Pantaleimon had paid his first visit to the Korshunovs to propose the match. The Korshunovs could find a much richer husband than Gregor for their daughter. Pantaleimon knew this and was afraid of a refusal. He did not like to go begging to Korshunov, but Ilinichna ate into him like rust into iron, and at last she overcame the old man's obstinacy. So he drove one day to the Korshunovs' for an answer, heartily cursing Gregor and Ilinichna and the whole wide world.

Meantime, beneath the painted iron roof of the Korshunovs' hut a burning dissension had arisen. After the Melekhovs' departure Natalia declared to her father and mother:

"If Gregor loves me, I'll never wed another."

"She's found herself a bridegroom, the idiot," her father replied. "Only he's as black as a gypsy. My little berry, I didn't want you to have a husband like that."

"I want no other, Father." The girl flushed and began to weep. "You can take me to the convent otherwise."

"He's too fond of walking the streets, he's a woman-chaser, he runs after grass-widows," her father played his last card.

"Well, let him!"

Natalia, the eldest daughter, was her father's favourite, and he had not pressed her into a marriage. Proposals for her hand had been plentiful, some coming from distant villages, from rich, Old Believer Cossacks. But Natalia had not taken to any of the prospective bridegrooms, and nothing had come of them.

In his heart Miron liked Gregor for his Cossack skill, his love of farming and hard work. He had picked him out among the crowd of village youths when Gregor had won the first prize in the horse-races, but he thought it a little humiliating to give his daughter to a poor man, one, moreover, who had gained a bad notoriety.

"A hard-working lad and a good-looking," his wife whispered to him at night, stroking his freckled, hairy hand. "And Natalia has quite lost her heart to him. . . ."

Miron turned his back to his wife's cold, withered breast and snorted angrily:

"Dry up, you turnip! God has taken away your reason. Good-looking!" he stuttered. "Will you reap a harvest off his mug? It's a come-down for me to give my daughter to the Turks!"

"They're a hard-working family and comfortably off," his wife whispered, and moving closer to her husband's back, pacifyingly stroked his hand.

"Hey, the devil! Get away, can't you? Leave me a little room! What are you stroking me for as if I was a cow with calf? And you know what Natalia is! She'd fall for anything in trousers."

"You should have some feeling for your child," she murmured right into his hairy ear. But Miron pressed himself against the wall and began to snore as though falling off to sleep.

The Melekhovs' arrival for an answer caught the Korshunovs in confusion. They came just after matins. As Ilinichna set her foot on the step of the wagonette she nearly overturned it, but Pantaleimon jumped down from the seat like a young cockerel.

"There they are! What the devil brought them here today?" Miron groaned, as he looked out of the window.

"Good health!" Pantaleimon crowed, stumbling over the doorstep. He was at once abashed by the loudness of his own voice and attempted to amend matters by stuffing a good half-pound of his black beard into his mouth and crossing himself unnecessarily before the ikon.

"Good day," Miron replied, staring at them askance.

"God is giving us good weather."

"Praise be, and it's lasting."

"The people will be a little better off for it."

"That's so."

"Ye-e-es."

"Ahem."

"And so we've come, Miron Gregorievich, to find out what you have come to among yourselves—whether we are to make a match of it or not."

"Come in, please; sit down, please," Maria welcomed them, bowing and sweeping the floor with the edge of her long, pleated skirt.

Ilinichna sat down, her poplin coat rustling. Miron Gregorievich rested his elbows on the new French cloth of the table, and was silent. The French cloth was adorned with pictures of the late Czar and Czarina in the corners, while in the centre were the august Imperial Princesses in white hats, and the fly-blown Czar Nicholas Alexandrovich.

Miron broke the silence.

"Well . . . we've decided to give our daughter. So we shall be kinsmen if we can agree on the dowry."

At this point, from somewhere in the mysterious depths of her glossy, puff-sleeved jacket, and apparently from behind her back, Ilinichna drew out a great loaf of white bread and smacked it down on the table. For some unknown reason Pantaleimon wanted to cross himself, but his withered talon fingers, set to the appropriate sign and raised half the requisite distance, suddenly changed their form. Against its master's will the great black thumb slipped unexpectedly between the index and middle fingers, and this shameless bunch of fingers stealthily slipped behind the open edge of his blue overcoat and drew out a red-headed bottle.

Blinking excitedly, Pantaleimon glanced at Miron's freckled face and caressingly slapped the bottle's broad bottom.

"And now, dear friends, we'll offer up a prayer to God and drink and talk of our children and the marriage agreement," he proposed.

Within an hour the two men were sitting so close together that the greasy rings of Melekhov's beard were groping among the straight red strands of Korshunov's. Pantaleimon's breath smelt sweetly of pickled cucumbers as he argued over the amount of the marriage settlement.

"My dear kinsman," he began in a hoarse whisper.

"My dearest kinsman," he repeated, raising his voice to a shout.

"Kinsman," he roared, baring his great, blunt teeth. "Your demands are far too heavy for me to stand. Think, dear kinsman, think of how you are trying to shame me. Gaiters with galoshes, one; a fur coat, two; two woollen dresses, three; a silk kerchief, four. That means ruin to me."

Pantaleimon opened his arms wide. Miron drooped his head and stared at the French cloth, flooded with spilt vodka and pickled cucumber water. He read the inscription written in a sportive scroll at the top: "The Russian Autocrats." He brought his eyes lower. "His Imperial Majesty and Sire Emperor Nicholas. . . ." A potato-skin lay over the rest. He stared at the picture. The Emperor's features were not visible, an empty vodka bottle stood on them. Blinking reverently, Miron attempted to make out the style of the rich uniform with its white belt, but it was thickly covered with slippery cucumber seeds. The Empress stared self-satisfiedly out of a broad-brimmed hat, surrounded by the circle of insipid daughters. Miron felt so affronted that tears almost came to his eyes. "You look very proud now, like a goose staring out of a basket, but wait till you have to give your daughters away to husbands, then I shall stare, and you'll flutter," he thought.

Pantaleimon droned on into his ear like a great black bumble-bee. He raised his tearfully misty eyes and listened.

"In order to make such a gift in exchange for your, and now we can say our, daughter—these gaiters and galoshes and fur coats—we shall have to drive a cow to the market and sell it."

"And do you begrudge it?" Miron struck the table with his fist.

"It isn't that I begrudge it—"

"Do you begrudge it?"

"Wait, kinsman!"

"And if you do begrudge it—the devil take you!" Miron swept his perspiring hand over the table and sent the glasses to the floor.

"A cow sold from the yard!" Pantaleimon shook his head.

"There has to be a gift. She has a dowry chest of her own, and you take heed of what I say if you've taken to her. That's our Cossack custom. That's how it was of old, and we stick to the old ways."

"I do take heed!"

"Take heed!"

"I do take heed!"

"And let the youngsters fend for themselves. We've fended for ourselves, and we live as well as anybody. Let them do the same!"

The two men's beards mingled in a vari-coloured weave. Pantaleimon began to eat a juiceless, shrivelled cucumber and wept with mixed, conflicting feelings.

The kinswomen were sitting locked in an embrace on a chest, deafening each other with the cackle of their voices. Ilinichna burned with a cherry-coloured flush; Maria was green with vodka, like a winter pear caught by the frost.

"Two such children you won't find anywhere else in the world. She'll be dutiful and obedient and will never say a word to contradict you," said Maria.

"My dear," Ilinichna interrupted her, supporting her cheek with her left hand and holding her left elbow in her right hand, "so I've told him, I don't know how many times, the son of a swine. He was getting ready to go out the other Sunday evening and I said to him: 'When will you throw her over, you accursed heathen? How long have I got to go on standing this shame in my old age? That Stepan will stop your little game one fine day!' "

Mitka stared into the room through the door crack, and below him Natalia's two younger sisters whispered to each other. Natalia herself was sitting in the farther room, wiping her tears on the tight sleeve of her jacket. She was afraid of the new life opening before her, oppressed by the unknown.

In the front room the third bottle of vodka was finished; it was decided to bring the bridegroom and the bride together on the 1st of August.

The Korshunovs' hut hummed like a

beehive with the bustle of preparations for the wedding. Underclothes were hurriedly sewn for the bride. Natalia sat every evening knitting her bridegroom the traditional gloves and scarf of goat's wool. Her mother sat till dusk bent over a sewing-machine, assisted by a hired sempstress. When Mitka returned with his father and the hands from the fields, he did not stop to wash or pull off his heavy farming boots, but went to keep Natalia company. He found great satisfaction in tormenting his sister.

"Knitting?" he would ask briefly, nodding at the scarf.

"Yes; what of it?"

"Knit away, you idiot; but instead of being grateful to you, he'll break your nose."

"What for?"

"Oh, I know Gregor; he's a friend of mine. He's that sort, he'll bite and not say what it's for."

"Don't tell lies. You think I don't know him."

"But I know him better. We went to school together."

Natalia grew angry, choked down her tears, and bent a miserable face over the scarf.

"But the worst of all is he's got consumption. You're a fool, Natalia! Throw him over! I'll saddle the horse and ride over and tell them. . . ."

Natalia was rescued from Mitka by Grandfather Grishaka, who came into the room, groping over the floor with his knobbly stick and stroking his hempen-yellow beard. Poking his stick into Mitka's side, he asked:

"What are you doing here, eh?"

"I came to pay a visit, Grand-dad," Mitka said apologetically.

"To pay a visit? Well, I tell you to get out of here. Quick march!"

Grand-dad Grishaka had walked the earth for sixty-nine years. He had taken part in the Turkish campaign of 1877, had been orderly to General Gurko, but had fallen into disfavour and been sent back to his regiment. He had been awarded the Cross of St. George and two medals for distinction under fire at Plevna and Rossitz. And now, living with his son, enjoying the universal respect of the village for the clarity of his mind, his incorruptible honesty, and his hospitable ways, he was spending his few remaining years turning over memories.

In the summer he sat from dawn till dusk on the ledge in front of the hut, drawing his stick over the ground, his head bowed. The broken visor of his cap threw a dark shade over his closed eyes. The black blood flowed sluggishly through the fingers curved over his stick, through the swollen veins on his hands.

"Are you afraid to die, Grand-dad?" Natalia would ask.

The old man twisted his withered neck as though working it free of the stiff collar of his uniform coat and shook his greenish-grey whiskers.

"I wait for death as I would for a dear guest. It's time—I've lived my days, I've served my Czars and drunk vodka enough in my day," he replied with a smile.

Natalia would stroke her grandfather's hand and leave him still bowed, scraping in the earth with his stick. He took the news of Natalia's approaching marriage with outward calm, but inwardly he grieved and was furious. At table Natalia always gave him the choicest pieces; she washed his linen, mended and knitted his stockings, his trousers and shirts. And so when the old man heard the news, he gave her harsh, stern looks for a couple of days.

"The Melekhovs are famous Cossacks. I served in the same regiment as Prokoffey. But what are his grandsons like? Eh?" he asked Miron.

"They're not too bad," Miron replied evasively.

"That Gregor's a disrespectful lad. I

was coming from church the other day and he passed me without a word of greeting. The old men don't get much respect these days. . . . Well, so long as Natalia likes him . . ."

He took almost no part in the negotiations; he came out of the kitchen and sat down at the table for a moment or two, drank a glass of vodka, and then, feeling himself getting drunk, went off again. For two days he silently watched the happy Natalia, then evidently softened in his attitude.

"Natalia!" he called to her. "Well, my little granddaughter, so you're very happy, eh?"

"I don't rightly know, myself, Granddad," Natalia confided.

"Well, well! Christ be with you. God grant . . ." and he bitterly and spitefully upbraided her. "I didn't think you'd be going off while I was alive . . . my life will be bitter without you."

Mitka was listening to their talk, and he remarked:

"You're likely to live another hundred years, Grandfather. And is she to wait all that time? You're a fine one!"

The old man turned almost purple with anger. He rapped with his stick and feet. "Clear off, you son of a bitch! Clear off, I say! You devil's demon! Who told you to listen?"

The wedding was fixed to take place on the first day after the feast. On the Day of the Assumption Gregor came to visit his future bride. He sat at the round table in the best room, shelled sunflower seeds and nuts with the bride's girl friends, then drove away again. Natalia saw him off. Under the roof of the shed, where his horse was standing saddled with a smart new saddle, she slipped her hand into her breast, and flushing, gazing at him with eyes expressive of her love, she thrust a soft little bundle, warm from her breast, into his hand. As he took the gift, Gregor dazzled her with the whiteness of his wolfish teeth, and asked:

"What is it?"

"You'll see. I've sewn you a tobacco-pouch."

Gregor irresolutely drew her towards himself, wanting to kiss her; but she held him off forcefully with her hands against his chest, bent herself back, and turned her eyes fearfully towards the window of the hut.

"They'll see us!" she whispered.

"Let them!"

"I'm ashamed to!"

Natalia held the reins while he mounted. Frowning, Gregor caught the stirrup with his foot, seated himself comfortably in the saddle, and rode out of the yard. She opened the gate and stood gazing after him. Gregor sat his horse with a slight list to the left, dashingly waving his whip.

Eleven more days, Natalia mentally calculated, and sighed and smiled.

CHAPTER 6

The green, spike-leafed wheat breaks through the ground and grows; within a few weeks a rook can fly into its midst and not be seen. The grain sucks the juices from the earth and comes to ear, it swells with the sweet and scented milk; then it flowers and a golden dust covers the ear. The farmer goes out into the steppe and stands gazing, but cannot rejoice. Wherever he looks, a herd of cattle has strayed into the corn; they have trodden the laden grain into the glebe. Wherever they have thronged is a circle of crushed wheat; the farmer grows bitter and savage at the sight.

So with Aksinia. Over her feelings, ripened to golden flower, Gregor had trodden with his heavy, rawhide boots. He had sullied them, burnt them to ash—and that was all.

As she came back from the Melekhovs' sunflower garden Aksinia's spirit grew empty and wild, like a forgotten farmyard overgrown with goose-grass and scrub. She walked along chewing the ends of her kerchief, and a cry swelled her throat. She entered the hut and fell to the floor, choking with tears, with torment, with the dreary emptiness that lashed through her head. But then it passed. The piercing pain was drawn down and exhausted at the bottom of her heart.

The grain trampled by the cattle stands again. With the dew and the sun the trodden stalks rise; at first bowed like a man under a too heavy burden, then erect, lifting their heads; and the days shine on them and the winds set them swinging.

At night, as she passionately caressed her husband, Aksinia thought of another, and hatred was mingled with a great love in her heart. The woman mentally planned a new dishonour—yet the old infamy; she was resolved to take Gregor from the happy Natalia, who had known neither the bitterness nor the joy of love. She lay thinking over her plans at night, with Stepan's heavy head resting on her right arm. Aksinia lay thinking, but only one thing could she resolve firmly: she would take Gregor from everybody else, she would flood him with love, she would possess him as before she had possessed him.

During the day Aksinia drowned her thoughts in cares and household duties. She met Gregor occasionally and would turn pale, proudly carrying her beautiful body that yearned so after him, gazing shamelessly, challengingly into the black depths of his eyes.

After each meeting Gregor was seized with yearning for her. He grew angry without cause, and poured out his wrath on Dunia and his mother, but most frequently he took his cap, went out into the back yard, and chopped away at the stout brushwood until he was bathed in perspiration. It made Pantaleimon curse:

"The lousy devil, he's chopped up enough for a couple of fences. You wait, my lad! When you're married you can chop away at that! That'll soon take it out of you!"

Four gaily-decorated pair-horsed wagonettes were to drive to fetch the bride. A crowd of village folk in holiday attire thronged around them as they stood in the Melekhovs' yard.

Piotra was the best man. He was dressed in a black frock-coat and blue-striped trousers, his left arm was bound with two white kerchiefs, and he wore a permanent, unchanging smile under his wheaten whiskers.

"Don't be shy, Gregor," he said to his brother. "Hold your head up like a young cock!"

Daria, as slender and supple as a willow switch, attired in a woollen, raspberry-coloured skirt, gave Piotra a nudge.

"Time you were off," she reminded him.

"Take your places," Piotra ordered. "On my wagon five and the bridegroom." They climbed into the wagonettes. Red and triumphant, Ilinichna opened the gates. The four wagonettes chased after one another along the street.

Piotra sat at Gregor's side. Opposite them Daria waved a lace handkerchief. The ruts and bumps interrupted their voices raised in a song. The crimson bands of the Cossack caps, the blue and black uniforms and frock-coats, the sleeves bound with white kerchiefs, the scattered rainbow of the women's kerchiefs, the gay skirts, and muslin trains of dust behind each wagonette made a colourful picture.

Gregor's second cousin, Anikhy, drove the bridegroom's wagonette. Bowed over the tails of the horses, almost falling off his seat, he cracked his whip and whistled, and the perspiring horses pulled harder at the tautened traces.

"Get a move on!" Ilia Ozhogin, the bridegroom's uncle on his mother's side, roared as he tried to overtake them with the second wagonette. Gregor recognized Dunia's happy face behind his uncle's back.

"No you don't!" Anikhy shouted, jumping to his feet and emitting a piercing whistle. He whipped up the horses into a frenzied gallop. "You'll fall!" Daria exclaimed, embracing Anikhy's polished top-boots with her arms. "Hold on!" Uncle Ilia called at their side, but his voice was lost in the continual groan and rattle of the wheels.

The two other wagonettes, tightly packed with men and women, drove along side by side. The horses were decorated with red, blue, and pale rose pompons, paper flowers, and ribbons woven into their manes and forelocks. The wagonettes rumbled over the bumpy road, the horses threw off flakes of soapy foam, and the pompons on their wet, foaming backs danced and ruffled in the wind.

At the Korshunovs' gate a horde of urchins was on the look-out for the cavalcade. They saw the dust rising from the road and ran into the yard bawling:

"They're coming!"

The wagonettes came rattling up to the gate. Piotra led Gregor to the steps, the others followed behind.

The door from the porch to the kitchen was shut fast. Piotra knocked.

"Lord Jesus Christ, have mercy on us!" he intoned.

"Amen!" came from the other side of the door.

Piotra repeated the words and the knock three times, each time receiving the same answer.

"May we come in?" he then asked.

"By all means."

The door was thrown open. The parents' representative, Natalia's godmother, greeted Piotra with a curtsy and a fine, raspberry-lipped smile. "Take this for your health's sake, best man!" she said, handing him a glass of bitter, overfresh kvass. Piotra smoothed his whiskers, drank it down, and spluttered amid a general restrained laugh:

"Well, you've made me welcome! You wait, my blackberry, I'll not treat you like that. I'll make you pay for it!"

While the best man and Natalia's godmother were competing in a duel of wits, the relatives of the bridegroom were brought three glasses of vodka each, in accordance with the marriage agreement.

Natalia, already attired in her wedding dress and veil, was behind the table, guarded by her two sisters. Maria held a rolling-pin in her outstretched hand, and Aggripina, a challenging fervour in her eyes, shook a poker. Sweating, and slightly intoxicated with vodka, Piotra bowed and offered them a fifty-kopek piece in his glass. But Maria struck the table with her rolling-pin.

"Not enough! We shan't sell the bride!" she declared.

Once more Piotra offered them a pinch of small silver in the glass.

"We won't let you have her!" the sisters said firmly, elbowing aside the downcast Natalia.

"Here, what's all this? We've already paid and overpaid," Piotra protested.

"Back you get, girls!" Miron ordered, and smilingly pressed towards the table. At this signal the bride's relatives and friends seated around the table stood up and made room for the newcomers.

Piotra thrust the end of a shawl into Gregor's hand, jumped on to a bench, and led him to the bride, who had seated herself beneath the ikons. Natalia took the other end of the shawl in her moist and agitated hand. Gregor sat down beside her.

There was a champing of teeth around the table; the guests tore the boiled chicken into pieces with their hands, afterwards wiping them on their hair. As Anikhy chewed at a handful of chicken the yellow grease ran down his bare chin on to his collar.

With a feeling of self-pity Gregor stared first at his own and Natalia's spoons tied together by a handkerchief, then at the vermicelli smoking in a bowl. He badly wanted to eat, his stomach was rolling over with hunger. But the marriage custom forbade.

The guests ate long and heartily. The smell of resinous masculine sweat mingled with the more caustic and spicy scent of the women. From the skirts, frock-coats and shawls, long packed in chests, came the odour of naphthaline.

Gregor glanced sidelong at Natalia. And for the first time he noticed that her upper lip was swollen and hung like the peak of a cap over her under lip. He also noticed that on the right cheek, below the upper jaw-bone, was a brown mole, and that two golden hairs were growing out of the mole; and for some reason this irritated him. He recalled Aksinia's slender neck with its curly, fluffy locks, and he had the feeling that someone had dropped a handful of prickly hay down his back. He bristled and with a suppressed feeling of wretchedness watched the others munching, chewing, and smacking their lips.

When he got up from the table someone, breathing the sour scent of wheaten bread over him, poured a handful of grain down the leg of his boot in order to protect him against the evil eye. All the way back to his own hut the grain hurt his feet; moreover, the tight collar-band of his shirt choked him, and in a cold, deperate fury Gregor muttered curses to himself.

On its return the procession was met by the old Melekhovs. Pantaleimon, his silver-streaked black beard glistening, held the ikon, and his wife stood at his side, her thin lips set stonily.

Beneath a shower of hops and wheat grain Gregor and Natalia approached them to receive their blessing. As he blessed them tears ran down Pantaleimon's face, and he frowned and fidgeted, annoyed that anyone should be witness of his weakness.

The bride and bridegroom went into the hut. Daria went to the steps to look for Piotra and ran into Dunia.

"Where's Piotra?" she demanded.

"I haven't seen him."

"He ought to go for the priest, and he's nowhere to be found, curse him!"

She found Piotra, who had drunk more vodka than was good for him, lying in a cart, groaning. She seized him like a kite a lamb. "You've overeaten, you image! Get up and run for the priest!" she raged.

"Clear off! Who are you ordering about?" Piotra protested.

With tears in her eyes Daria thrust two fingers into his mouth, gripped his tongue, and helped him to ease himself. Then she poured a pitcher of cold well-water over him, wiped him as dry as she could, and took him to the priest.

Less than an hour later Gregor was standing at Natalia's side in the church, clutching a wax candle in his hand, his eyes wandering over the wall of whispering people around him, and mentally repeating the importunate words: "I'm done now. I'm done now!" Behind him Piotra coughed. Somewhere in the crowd he saw Dunia's eyes twinkling; he thought he recognized other faces. He caught the dissonant chorus of voices and the droning responses of the deacon. He was fettered with apathy. He walked round the lecturn, treading on the down-at-heel shoes of Father Vissarion; he halted when Piotra gave a gentle tug at his frock-coat. He stared at the flickering little tongues of

candle-flame, and struggled with the sleepy torpor which had taken possession of him.

"Exchange rings!" he heard Father Vissarion say.

They obeyed. "Will it be over soon?" Gregor mutely asked, as he caught Piotra's gaze. And the corners of Piotra's lips twitched, stifling a smile. "Soon now." Then Gregor kissed his wife's moist, insipid lips, the church began to smell foully of extinguished candles, and the crowd pressed towards the door.

Holding Natalia's large, rough hand in his, Gregor went out into the porch. Someone clapped his hat on his head. A warm breeze from the east brought the scent of wormwood to his nostrils. The cool of evening came from the steppe. Lightning flickered beyond the Don, rain was coming; outside the white church fence, above the hum of voices he heard the inviting and tender tinkle of the bells on the restive horses.

The Korshunovs did not arrive at the Melekhovs' hut until after the bridegroom and bride had gone to the church. Pantaleimon went several times to the gate to see whether they were coming, but the grey road, lined with a growth of prickly thorns, was completely deserted. He turned his eyes towards the Don. The forest was turning a golden yellow. The ripened reeds bent wearily over the Donside marshes. Blending with the dusk, an early autumnal, drowsy, azure haze enwrapped the village. He gazed at the Don, the chalky ridge of hills, the forest lurking in a lilac haze beyond the river, and the steppe. At the turn beyond the crossroads the fine outline of the wayside shrine was silhouetted against the sky.

Pantaleimon's ears caught the hardly audible sound of wheels and the yapping of dogs. Two wagonettes turned out of the square into the street. In the first sat Miron with his wife at his side; opposite them was Grand-dad Grishaka in a new uniform, wearing his Cross of St. George and his medals. Mitka drove, sitting carelessly on the box and not troubling to show the foaming horses his whip.

Pantaleimon threw open the gate, and the two wagonettes drove into the yard. Ilinichna sailed down from the porch, the hem of her dress trailing in the dust.

"Of your kindness, dear friends! Do our poor hut the honour of entering." She bent her corpulent waist in a bow.

His head on one side, Pantaleimon flung open his arms and welcomed them: "We humbly invite you to come in!"

He called for the horses to be unharnessed and went towards the newcomers. After exchanging greetings they followed their host and hostess into the best room, where a crowd of already half-intoxicated guests was sitting around the table. Soon after their arrival the newly married couple returned from the church. As they entered, Pantaleimon poured out a glass of vodka, tears standing in his eyes.

"Well, Miron Gregorievich, here's to our children! May their life be filled with good, as ours has been. May they live happily, and enjoy the best of health."

They poured Grandfather Grishaka out a large glass of vodka and succeeded in sending half of it into his mouth and half behind the stiff collar of his uniform. Glasses were clinked together. The company drank and drank. The hubbub was like the noise of a market. A distant relation of the Korshunovs, Koloveidin, who was sitting at the end of the table, raised his glass and roared:

"It's bitter!"

"Bitter! Bitter!" the guests seated around the table clamoured after him.

"Oh, bitter!" came the response from the crowded kitchen.

Scowling, Gregor kissed his wife's insipid lips and sent a venomous glance around the room. A crimson fever of faces. Coarse, drunkenly muddy glances and smiles. Mouths chewing greedily, slobbering on the embroidered tablecloth. A howl of voices.

Koloveidin opened wide his gap-toothed mouth, and raised his glass:

"It's bitter!"

"Bitter!" the cry was taken up once more.

Gregor stared hatefully into Koloveidin's mouth and noticed the livid tongue between the teeth as he cried the word: "Bitter!"

"Kiss, little chicks!" Piotra spluttered.

In the kitchen Daria, flushed and intoxicated, began a song. It was taken up by the others and passed into the best room. The voices blended, but above all the rest rose Christonia's rumble, shaking the window-panes.

The song ended, eating was resumed.

"Try this mutton!"

"Take your hand away, my husband's looking."

"Bitter! Bitter!"

In the kitchen the groaning floor shook, heels clattered, and a glass fell to the floor; its jangle was lost in the general hubbub. Across the heads of those sitting at the table Gregor glanced into the kitchen. The women were dancing now, to the accompaniment of shouts and whistles. They shook their ample bottoms (there was not a thin one there, for each was wearing five or six skirts), waved lace handkerchiefs, and worked their elbows in the dance.

The music of the three-tiered accordion sounded imperatively. The player began the tune of the Cossack dance. A shout went up:

"A circle! Form a circle!"

"Squeeze up a bit!" Piotra demanded, pushing the women aside.

Gregor roused himself and winked at Natalia. "Piotra's going to dance the 'Cossack'! You watch him!"

"Who with?" she asked.

"Don't you see? With your mother."

Maria Lukinichna set her arms akimbo, her handkerchief in her left hand. Piotra went up to her with mincing steps, dropped to his haunches and rose again, and returned backward to his place. Lukinichna picked up her skirt as though about to trip across a damp meadow, picked out the tempo with her toe, and danced amid a howl of approbation, kicking out her legs like a man.

The accordion-player accelerated the tempo. But Piotra kept pace with the music, dancing with incredibly small steps, then with a shout dropped to a squatting position and danced around, smacking the palms of his hands against the legs of his boots, biting the ends of his moustache in the corner of his mouth. He swung his knees in and out at great speed; his forelock tossed on his head.

Gregor's view was blocked by the crowd at the door. He heard only the shouts of the drunken guests and the continual rattle of the iron-shod heels, like the crackle of a burning pine board.

Then Miron danced with Ilinichna; they stepped out seriously and with their accustomed businesslike air. Pantaleimon stood on a stool watching them, dangling his lame leg and clicking his tongue. Instead of his legs his lips and ear-ring danced.

Others not so expert tried to dance the Cossack and other difficult dances. But the crowd shouted at them:

"Don't spoil it!"

"Smaller steps! Oh, you—!"

"His legs are light enough, but his bottom gets in his way."

"Oh, get on with it!"

Long ere this Grandfather Grishaka was completely drunk. He embraced the bony back of his neighbour on the bench and buzzed like a gnat in his ear:

"What year did you first see service?"

His neighbour, an old man stunted like an ancient oak, replied:

"1839, my son!"

"When?" Grishaka stuck out his ear.

"1839, I told you."

"What's your name? What regiment did you serve in?"

"Maxim Bogatiriev. I was a corporal in Baklanov's regiment."

"Are you of Melekhov's family?"

"What?"

"Your family, I asked."

"Aha! I'm the bridegroom's grandfather on his mother's side."

"In Baklanov's regiment, did you say?"

The old man gazed at Grishaka with faded eyes and nodded.

"So you must have been through the Caucasian campaign?"

"I served under Baklanov himself and helped in the Caucasian conquest. We had some rare Cossacks in our regiment. They were as tall as the guards, but stooped a little, long-armed and broad-shouldered. That's the men we had, my son! His Excellency the dead general was good enough to give me the cat for stealing a carpet. . . ."

"And I was in the Turkish campaign. Eh? Yes, I was there." Grishaka threw out his sunken chest, jingling with medals.

". . . We took a village at dawn, and at midday the bugler sounded the alarm," the old man continued without heeding Grishaka.

"We were fighting around Rossitz, and our regiment, the Twelfth Don Cossack, was engaged with the janizaries," Grishaka told him.

"As I was in a hut the bugler sounded the alarm. . . ."

"Yes," Grishaka went on, beginning to get annoyed and angrily waving his hand. "The Turkish janizaries wear white sacks on their heads. Eh? White sacks on their heads."

". . . The bugler sounded the alarm, and I said to my comrade: 'We'll have to retreat, Timofei, but first we'll have that carpet off the wall.' "

"I have been decorated with two Georges, awarded for heroism under fire. I took a Turkish major alive." Grandfather Grishaka began to weep and bang his withered fist on his neighbour's spine. But the latter, dipping a piece of chicken in the cherry jelly, lifelessly stared at the soiled tablecloth and mumbled:

"And listen what sin the unclean spirit led me into, my son! I'd never before taken anything that wasn't mine, but now I happened to see that carpet, and I thought: 'That would make a good horse-cloth.' "

"I've seen those parts myself. I've been in lands across the sea as well," Grishaka tried to look his neighbour in the eyes, but the deep sockets were overgrown with a shaggy bush of eyebrows and beard. So he resorted to craft. He wanted to win his neighbour's attention for the climax of his story, and he plunged into the middle of it without any preliminaries: "And the captain gives the order: 'In troop columns at the gallop! Forward!' "

But the old Baklanov regiment Cossack threw back his head like a charger at the sound of the trumpet and, dropping his fist on the table, whispered: "Lances at the ready; draw sabres, Baklanov's men!" His voice suddenly grew stronger, his faded eyes glittered and burned. "Baklanov's boys!" he roared, opening wide his toothless yellow jaws. "Into attack—forward!"

And he gazed at Grishaka with a youthful and intelligent look and let the tears trickling over his beard fall unwiped.

Grishaka also grew excited:

"He gave us this command and waved his sword. We galloped forward, and the janizaries were drawn up like this," he drew an irregular square on the tablecloth with his finger, "and firing at us. Three times we charged them. Each time they beat us back. Whenever we tried, their cavalry came out of a little wood on their flank. Our troop commander gave the order and we turned and went at them. We smashed them. Rode them down.

What cavalry in the world can stand up against Cossacks? They fled into the wood; I see their officer just in front of me, riding on a bay. A good-looking officer, black-whiskered. He looks back at me and draws his pistol. He shot, but he missed me. I spurred my horse and caught up with him. I was going to cut him down, but then I thought better of it. After all, he was a man too. I seized him round the waist with my right arm, and he flew out of the saddle. He bit my arm, but I took him all the same. . . ."

Grishaka glanced triumphantly at his neighbour, but the old man's great angular head had fallen on his chest and he was snoring comfortably.

CHAPTER 7

Sergei Platonovich Mokhov could trace his ancestry a long way back.

During the reign of Peter I a State barge was travelling down the Don to Azov with a cargo of biscuit and gunpowder. The Cossacks of the little robber town of Chigonak, nestling on the bank of the upper Don, fell on the barge by night, destroyed the sleepy guards, pillaged the biscuit and gunpowder, and sank the vessel.

The Czar ordered out soldiers from Voronezh, and they burned down the town of Chigonak, ruthlessly put the guilty Cossacks to the sword, and hanged forty of them on a floating gallows, which, as a warning to the unruly villages, was sent sailing down the Don.

Some ten years later the spot where the hearths of the Chigonak huts had smoked began again to be inhabited. At the same time, on the Czar's instructions, a secret agent, a Russian peasant named Mokhov, came to live there. He traded in knife-hafts, tobacco, flints, and the other odds and ends necessary to the Cossacks' everyday life. He bought up and resold stolen goods, and once or twice a year journeyed to Voronezh, ostensibly to replenish his stocks, but in reality to report to the authorities on the state of the district.

From this Russian peasant, Nikitka Mokhov, descended the merchant family of Mokhovs. They took deep root in the Cossack earth; they multiplied and grew into the district like a sturdy field bush, reverently preserving the half-rotten credentials given to their ancestor by the Governor of Voronezh. The credentials might have been preserved until this day but for a great fire which occurred during the lifetime of Sergei Mokhov's grandfather. This Mokhov had already ruined himself once by card-playing, but was getting on his feet again when the fire engulfed everything. After burying his paralytic father, Sergei Platonovich had to begin afresh, starting by buying bristles and feathers. For five years he lived miserably, swindling and squeezing the Cossacks of the district out of every kopek. Then he suddenly jumped from "cattle-dealer Seriozhka" to "Sergei Platonovich," opened a little haberdashery shop, married the daughter of a half-demented priest, received no small dowry with her, and set up as a retail dealer in linen goods. Sergei Platonovich began to trade in textiles at just the right moment. On the instruction of the army authorities, about this time the Cossacks were migrating in entire villages from the left bank of the Don, where the ground was unproductive and sandy, to the right bank. And instead of having to journey thirty miles or more for goods, they found Sergei Mokhov's shop, packed with attractive commodities, right on the spot. Sergei extended his business widely, like a three-tiered accordion, and traded in everything requisite to simple village life. He even began to supply agricultural machinery. Evidently his trading yielded the quick-witted Sergei considerable profit, for within three years he had opened a grain elevator, and two years after the death of his first wife he began the construction of a steam flour-mill.

He squeezed Tatarsk and the neighbouring villages tightly in his swarthy fist. There was not a hut free from debt to Sergei Mokhov. Nine hands were employed at the mill, seven in the shop, and four watchmen: all together twenty mouths dependent on the merchant's pleasure for their daily bread. He had two children by his first wife: the girl Elizabieta and the sluggish, scrofulous Vladimir. His second wife, Anna, was childless. All her belated mother-love and accumulated spleen were poured out on the children. Her nervous temperament had a bad influence on them, and their father paid them no more attention than he gave his stable-hand or cook. His business activities occupied all his time. The children grew up uncontrolled. His insensitive wife made no attempt to penetrate into the secrets of the child mind, and the brother and sister were alien to each other, different in character and unlike their parents. Vladimir was sullen, sluggish, with a sly look and an unchildish seriousness. Liza, who lived in the society of the maid and the cook (the latter a dissolute, much too experienced woman), early saw the seamy side of life. The women aroused an unhealthy curiosity in her, and while still an angular and bashful adolescent she had grown as wild as a spurge.

The impatient years slipped by. The old grew older and the young grew green of leaf.

Vladimir Mokhov, a slender, sickly yellow lad now in the fifth class of the high school, was walking through the mill yard. He had recently returned home for the summer vacation, and, as usual, he had gone to look at the mill and jostle among the crowd. It ministered to his vanity to hear the respectful murmur of the Cossack carters:

"The master's heir. . . ."

Carefully picking his way among the wagons and the heaps of dung, Vladimir reached the gate. Then he remembered he had not been to see the power plant and turned back.

Close to the red oil-tank, at the entrance to the machine room, Timofei, the mill-hand, Valet, the scalesman, and Timofei's assistant, David, were kneading a great ring of clay with bare feet, their trousers turned up above their knees.

"Ah! Here's master!" the scalesman jokingly greeted him.

"Good afternoon. What is it you're doing?"

"We're mixing clay," David said with an unpleasant smile, with difficulty drawing his feet out of the clinging mass. "Your father is careful of the rubles and won't hire women to do it. Your father's stingy," he added.

Vladimir flushed. He suddenly felt an invincible dislike for the ever smiling David and his contemptuous tone.

"What do you mean, 'stingy'?"

"He's terribly mean," David explained with a smile.

The others laughed approvingly. Vladimir felt all the smart of the insult. He stared coldly at David.

"So you're—dissatisfied?" he asked.

"Come into this mess and mix it for yourself, and then you'll know. What fool would be satisfied? It would do your father good to do some of this. It would give him a pain in the belly," David replied. He trod heavily around the ring of clay, kneading it with his feet, and now smiling gaily. Foretasting a sweet revenge, Vladimir turned over a fitting reply in his mind.

"Good!" he said slowly. "I'll tell Papa you're not satisfied with your work."

He glanced sidelong at the man's face

and was startled by the impression he had caused. David was smiling miserably and forcedly, and the faces of the others were clouded over. All three went on kneading the clay in silence for a moment. Then David tore his eyes away from his muddy feet and said in a wheedlingly spiteful tone:

"I was only joking, Volodia."

"I'll tell Papa what you said." Affronted, with tears in his eyes for his father and himself, Vladimir walked away.

"Volodia! Vladimir Sergeivich!" David called after him in alarm, and stepped out of the clay, dropping his trousers over his bespattered legs.

Vladimir halted. David ran to him, breathing heavily.

"Don't tell your father! Forgive me, fool that I am. True God, I said it without thinking."

"All right, I won't tell him," Vladimir replied with a frown, and walked on towards the gate.

"What did you want to say that for?" Valet's bass voice reached his ears. "Don't stir them up and they won't trouble you."

"The swine!" Vladimir thought indignantly. "Shall I tell Father or not?" Glancing back, he saw David wearing his everlasting smile and decided: "I will tell him!"

Vladimir went up the stairs of the house. Over him swayed the leaves of the wild vine, thickly enlaced in the porch and veranda. He went to his father's private room and knocked. Sergei Platonovich was sitting on a cool leather couch, turning over the pages of a June magazine. A yellow bone paper-knife lay at his feet.

"Well, what do you want?"

"As I was coming back from the mill—" Vladimir began uncertainly. But then he recalled David's dazzling smile, and gazing at his father's corpulent belly, he resolutely continued:

"I heard David, the mill-hand, say . . ."

Sergei Platonovich listened attentively to his son's story, and said: "I'll fire him." He bent with a groan to pick up the paper-knife.

Of an evening the intelligentsia of the village were in the habit of gathering at Sergei Mokhov's house. There was Boyarishkin, a student of the Moscow Technical School; the teacher Balanda, eaten up with conceit and tuberculosis; his assistant and cohabitant, Martha Gerasimovna, a never-ageing girl with her petticoat always showing indecently; the postmaster, a bachelor smelling of sealing-wax and cheap perfumes. Occasionally the young troop commander Eugene Listnitsky rode over from his father's estate. The company would sit drinking tea on the veranda, carrying on a meaningless conversation, and when there was a lull in the talk, one of the guests wound up and set going the host's expensive inlaid phonograph.

On rare occasions, during the great holidays, Sergei Platonovich liked to cut a dash: he invited guests and regaled them on expensive wines, fresh caviar, and the finest of hors-d'œuvres. At other times he lived frugally. The one thing in regard to which he exercised no self-restraint was the purchase of books. He loved reading and had a mind quick to assimilate all he read.

The two village priests, Father Vissarion and Father Pankraty, were not on friendly terms with Sergei Platonovich. They had a long-standing quarrel with him. Nor were they on very amicable terms with each other. The fractious, intriguing Father Pankraty cleverly perverted his fellow human beings, and the naturally affable, syphilitic widower Father Vissarion, who lived with a Ukrainian housekeeper, held himself aloof and had no love for Father Pankraty because of his inordinate pride and intriguing character.

All except the teacher Balanda owned their own houses. Mokhov's blue-painted house stood on the square; right opposite, at the heart of the square, straddled his shop with its glass door and faded signboard. Attached to the shop was a long, low shed with a cellar, and a hundred yards farther on rose the brick wall of the church garden and the church itself with its green, onion-shaped cupola. Beyond the church were the whitewashed, authoritatively severe walls of the school, and two smart-looking houses, one blue, with blue-painted palisades, belonging to Father Pankraty; the other brown (to avoid any resemblance), with carved fencing and a broad balcony, belonging to Father Vissarion. Then came another two-storeyed house, then the post office, the thatched and iron-roofed huts of the Cossacks, and finally the sloping back of the mill, with rusty iron cocks on its roof.

The inhabitants of the village lived behind their barred and bolted shutters, cut off from all the rest of the world, both outside and inside the village. Every evening, unless they were paying a visit to a neighbour, each family shot the bolts of their doors, unchained their dogs in the yards, and only the sound of the night watchman disturbed the silence.

One day towards the end of August, Mitka Korshunov happened to meet Elizabieta Mokhov down by the river. He had just rowed across from the other side, and as he was tying up his boat he saw a gaily decorated, light craft skimming the stream. The skiff was being rowed by the young student Boyarishkin. His bare head glistened with perspiration, and the veins stood out on his forehead.

Mitka did not recognize Elizabieta in the skiff at first, for her straw hat threw her face into shadow. Her sunburnt hands were pressing a bunch of yellow water-lilies to her breast.

"Korshunov!" she called, as she saw Mitka. "You've deceived me."

"Deceived you?"

"Don't you remember, you promised to take me fishing?"

Boyarishkin dropped the oars and straightened his back. The skiff thrust its nose into the shore with a scrunch.

"Do you remember?" Elizabieta laughed as she jumped out.

"I haven't had the time. Too much work to do," Mitka said apologetically as the girl approached him.

"Well, then, when shall we go fishing?" she asked as she shook his hand.

"Tomorrow if you like. We've done the threshing and I've got more time now."

"You're not deceiving me this time?"

"No, I'm not!"

"I'll be waiting for you. You haven't forgotten the window? I'm going away soon, I expect. And I'd like to go fishing first." She was silent a moment, then, smiling to herself, she asked:

"You've had a wedding in your family, haven't you?"

"Yes, my sister."

"Whom did she marry?" Then, without waiting for an answer, she smiled again mysteriously and fleetingly. "Do come, won't you?" Once more her smile stung Mitka like a nettle.

He watched her to the boat. Boyarishkin impatiently pushed off, while Elizabieta smilingly gazed across his head at Mitka and nodded farewell.

When the boat was well out, Mitka heard Boyarishkin quietly ask:

"Who is that lad?"

"Just an acquaintance," she replied.

"Not a love affair?"

Mitka did not catch her answer above the creak of the rowlocks. He saw Boyarishkin throw himself back with a laugh, but could not see Elizabieta's face. A lilac ribbon, stirring gently in the breeze, hung from her hat to the slope of her bare neck.

Mitka, who rarely went fishing with rod and line, had never prepared for the occasion with such zeal as on that evening. When he had finished he went into the front room. Grandfather Grishaka was sitting by the window, with round, copper-rimmed spectacles on his nose, studying the Gospels.

"Grand-dad!" Mitka said, leaning his back against the doorframe.

The old man looked at him over his spectacles.

"Eh?"

"Wake me up at the first cock."

"Where are you off to so early?"

"Fishing."

The old man had a weakness for fish, but he made a pretence of opposing Mitka's designs.

"Your father said the hemp must be beaten tomorrow. There's no time to laze around."

Mitka stirred from the door and tried strategy.

"Oh, all right, then. I wanted to give you a treat, but as there's the hemp to be done, I won't go."

"Stop, where are you off to?" The old man took alarm and drew off his spectacles. "I'll speak to your father. You'll go. I'll give you a call."

At midnight the old man, his linen trousers held up with one hand and his stick gripped on the other, groped his way down the stairs and across the yard to the barn. Mitka was sleeping on a rug in a corn-bin. Grishaka poked at him with his stick, but could not rouse him for some time. At first he poked lightly, whispering:

"Mitka! Mitka! Hey, Mitka!"

But Mitka only sighed and drew his legs up. Grishaka grew more ruthless and began to bore into Mitka's stomach with the stick. Mitka woke up suddenly and seized the end of the stick.

"How you do sleep!" the old man cursed.

The lad made his way quietly out of the yard and hurried to the square. He reached the Mokhovs' house, set down his fishing tackle, and on tiptoe, so as not to disturb the dogs, crept into the porch. He tried the cold iron latch. The door was shut fast. He clambered across the balustrade of the veranda and went up to the casement window. It was half-closed. Through the black gap came the sweet scent of a warm, womanly body and unfamiliar perfumes.

"Elizabieta Sergeevna!"

Mitka thought he had called very loudly. He waited. Silence. Supposing he was at the wrong window! What if Mokhov himself was asleep in there! He'd use a gun!

"Elizabieta Sergeevna, coming fishing?"

If he'd mistaken the window there'd be some fish caught all right!

"Are you getting up?" he asked, irritatedly, and thrust his head through the window opening.

"Who's that?" a voice sounded quietly and a little alarmed in the darkness.

"It's me, Korshunov. Coming fishing?"

"Ah! One moment!"

There was a sound of movement inside. Her warm, sleepy voice seemed to smell of mint. Mitka saw something white and rustling moving about the room. After a while her smiling face, bound in a white kerchief, appeared at the window.

"I'm coming out this way. Give me your hand." As she squeezed his hand in hers she glanced closely into his eyes.

They went down to the Don. During the night the river had risen, and the boat, which had been left high and dry the evening before, was now rocking on the water a little way out.

"I'll have to take off my shoes," Elizabieta sighed.

"Let me carry you," Mitka proposed.

"No, I'd better take my shoes off."

"Carrying you would be pleasanter."

"I'd rather not," she said, with embarrassment in her voice.

Without further argument Mitka embraced her legs above the knees with his left arm and, lifting her easily, splashed through the water. She involuntarily clutched at his stout neck and laughed quietly.

If Mitka had not stumbled over a stone used by the village women when washing clothes, there would not have been a brief, accidental kiss. She groaned and pressed her face against Mitka's lips, and he came to a halt two paces away from the boat. The water swirled over the legs of his boots and chilled his feet.

Unfastening the boat, he pushed it off and jumped in. He rowed standing. The boat gently breasted the stream, making for the opposite bank. The keel grated on the sandy shore. Without asking permission he picked the girl up in his arms and carried her into a clump of hawthorn. She bit at his face, scratched, screamed faintly once or twice, and feeling her strength ebbing, she wept angrily, but without tears.

They returned about nine o'clock in the morning. The sky was wrapped in a ruddy yellow haze. A wind was dancing over the river, lashing the waves into foam. The boat danced over the waves, and the ice-cold, sprinkling drops struck Elizabieta's pallid face and clung to her lashes and the strands of her hair. She wearily screwed up her dreary eyes and listlessly broke the stalk of a flower in her hands. Mitka rowed without looking at her. A small carp and a bream lay at his feet. His face wore an expression of mingled guilt, content, and anxiety.

"I'll take you to Semionov's landing-place. It will be nearer for you," he told her as he turned the boat into the stream.

Along the shore the dusty wattle fences pined in the hot wind. The heavy caps of the sunflowers, pecked by sparrows, were completely ripe and were scattering swollen seeds over the ground. The meadowland was emeralded with newly springing young grass. In the distance stallions were kicking up their heels; the burning southerly wind blew across the river.

As Elizabieta was getting out of the boat, Mitka picked up a fish and held it out to her.

"Here, take your share of the catch," he said.

She raised her eyebrows in astonishment, but took the fish.

"Well, I'm going," she replied.

Holding the fish suspended by a twig, she turned miserably away. All her recent assurance and gaiety had been left behind in the hawthorn bush.

"Elizabieta!"

She turned round, concealing her surprise and irritation. When she came closer, annoyed at his own embarrassment he said:

"Your dress at the back—there's a hole in it. It's quite small. . . ."

She flamed up, blushing down to her collar-bone. After a moment's silence Mitka advised her:

"Go by the back ways."

"I'll have to pass through the square in any case. . . . And I wanted to put my black skirt on," she whispered with regret and unexpected hatred in her voice.

"Shall I green it a bit with a leaf?" Mitka suggested simply, and was surprised to see the tears come into her eyes.

Like the rustling whisper of a zephyr the news ran through the village. "Mitka Korshunov's been out all night with Sergei Platonovich's daughter!" The women talked about it as they drove out the cattle to join the village herd of a morning, as they stood around the wells, or as they beat out their washing on the flat stones down by the river.

"Her own mother is dead, you know."

"Her father never stops working for a moment, and her stepmother just doesn't trouble."

"The store watchman says he saw a man tapping at the end window at midnight. He thought at first it was someone trying to break in. He ran to see who it was and found it was Mitka."

"The girls these days, they're in sin up to their necks. They're good for nothing."

"Mitka told my Michael he is going to marry her."

"He forced her, they say."

"Ah, my dear, a dog doesn't worry an unwilling bitch!"

The rumours finally came to the ears of Mokhov himself. They struck him like a beam falling from a building and crushing a man to the ground. For two days he went neither to the store nor to the mill.

On the third day Sergei Platonovich had his dappled grey stallion harnessed into his droshky and drove to the district centre. The droshky was followed by a highly lacquered carriage drawn by a pair of prancing black horses. Behind the coachman Elizabieta was sitting. She was as pale as death. She held a light suitcase on her knees and was smiling sadly. At the gate she waved her glove to Vladimir and her stepmother.

Pantaleimon Prokoffievich happened to be limping out of the store at the moment, and he stopped to ask the yardman:

"Where's the master's daughter going?"

And Nikita, condescending to the simple human weakness, replied:

"To Moscow, to school."

The next day an incident occurred which was long the subject of talk down by the river, around the wells, and when the cattle were being driven out to graze. Just before dusk (the village herd had already returned from the steppe) Mitka went to see Sergei Platonovich. He had waited until evening in order to avoid people. He did not go merely to make a friendly call, but to ask for the hand of Mokhov's daughter, Elizabieta.

He had seen her perhaps four times, not more. At the last meeting the conversation had taken the following course:

"Elizabieta, will you marry me?"

"Nonsense!"

"I shall care for you, I'll love you. We have people to work for us; you shall sit at the window and read your books."

"You're a fool!"

Mitka took umbrage and said no more. That evening he went home early, and in the morning he announced to his astonished father:

"Father, arrange for my wedding."

"Cross yourself!" Miron replied.

"Really, Father; I'm not joking."

"In a hurry, aren't you? Who's caught you, crazy Martha?"

"Send the matchmakers to Sergei Platonovich."

Miron Gregorievich carefully set down the cobbling tools with which he was mending harness and roared with laughter.

"You're in a funny vein today, my son."

But Mitka stood to his guns, and his father flared up: "You fool! Sergei Platonovich has a capital of over a hundred thousand rubles. He's a merchant, and what are you? Clear off or I'll leather you with this strap."

"We've got twelve pairs of bullocks, and look at the land we own. Besides, he's a peasant, and we're Cossacks."

"Clear off!" Miron said curtly.

Mitka found a sympathetic listener only in his grandfather. The old man attempted to persuade Miron in favour of his son's suit.

"Miron," old Grishaka said, "why don't you agree? As the boy's taken it into his head. . . ."

"Father, you're a great baby, God's truth you are! Mitka's just silly, but you're . . ."

"Hold your tongue!" Grishaka rapped his stick on the floor. "Aren't we equal to them? He ought to take it as an honour for a Cossack's son to wed his daughter. We're known all around the countryside. We're not farm-hands, we're masters. Go and ask him, Miron. Let him give his mill as the dowry."

Miron flared up again and went out into the yard. So Mitka decided to wait until evening and then go to Mokhov himself. He knew that his father's obstinacy was like an elm at the root: you might bend it, but you could never break it. It wasn't worth trying.

He went whistling as far as Mokhov's front door, then grew timid. He hesitated a moment and finally went through the yard to the side door. On the steps he asked the maid:

"Master at home?"

"He's drinking tea. Wait."

He sat down and waited, lit a cigarette, smoked it, and crushed the end on the floor. Mokhov came out, brushing crumbs off his waistcoat. When he saw Mitka he knitted his brows, but said: "Come in."

Mitka entered Mokhov's cool private room, feeling that the courage with which he had been charged so far had been sufficient to last only to the threshold. The merchant went to his table and turned round on his heels: "Well?" Behind his back his fingers scratched at the top of the table.

"I've come to find out—" Mitka plunged into the cold slime of Mokhov's eyes and shuddered. "Perhaps you'll give me Elizabieta?" Despair, anger, fear, all combined to bring the perspiration in beads to his face.

Mokhov's left eyebrow quivered, and the upper lip writhed back from the gums. He stretched out his neck and leaned all his body forward.

"What? Wha-a-at? You scoundrel! Get out! I'll haul you before the ataman! You son of a swine!"

At the sound of Mokhov's shout Mitka plucked up courage.

"Don't take it as an insult. I only thought to make up for my wrong."

Mokhov rolled his bloodshot eyes and threw a massive iron ashtray at Mitka's feet. It bounced up and struck him on the knee. But he stoically bore the pain and, throwing open the door, shouted, baring his teeth with shame and pain:

"As you wish, Sergei Platonovich, as you wish, but upon my soul—who would want her now? I thought I'd cover her shame. But now—a dog won't touch a gnawed bone."

Pressing his crushed handkerchief to his lips, Mokhov followed on Mitka's heels. He barred the way to the main door, and Mitka ran into the yard. Here the master had only to wink to Yemelian, the coachman, and as Mitka was struggling with the stout latch at the wicket gate, four unleashed dogs tore round the corner of the barn. Seeing Mitka, they sped across the yard straight at him. He had not had time to turn round when the foremost dog was up at his shoulders with its teeth fastened into his jacket. All four rent and tore at him. Mitka thrust them off with his hand, endeavouring to keep his feet. He saw Yemelian, his pipe scattering sparks, disappear into the kitchen and heard the door slam behind him.

At the steps, his back against a drainpipe, stood Sergei Platonovich, his white, hairy fists clenched. Swaying, Mitka tore open the door and dragged the bunch of clamorous, hot-smelling dogs after him on his bleeding legs. He seized one by the throat and choked it off, and passing Cossacks with difficulty beat off the others.

CHAPTER 8

The Melekhovs found Natalia of great use on the farm. Although he was rich and employed labourers, her father had made his children work. Hard-working Natalia won the hearts of her husband's parents. Ilinichna, who secretly did not like her elder daughter-in-law, Daria, took to Natalia from the very first.

"Sleep on, sleep on, little one! What are you out so early for?" she would grumble kindly. "Go back to bed, we'll manage without you."

Even Pantaleimon, who was usually strict in regard to household matters, said to his wife:

"Listen, wife, don't wake Natalia up. She'll work hard enough as it is. She's going with Grishka to plough today. But whip up that Daria. She's a lazy woman, and bad. She paints her face and blacks her brows, the bitch."

Gregor could not grow accustomed to his newly married state; within two or three weeks he realized with fear and vexation that he had not completely broken with Aksinia. The feeling which, in the excitement of the marriage, he had dismissed with a contemptuous wave of the hand had taken deep root. He thought he could forget, but it refused to be forgotten, and the wound bled at the memory. Even before the wedding Piotra had asked him:

"Grishka, but what about Aksinia?"

"Well, what about her?"

"Pity to throw her over, isn't it?"

"If I do, someone else will pick her up!" Gregor had smiled.

But it had not worked out like that. As, burning with his youthful, amorous ardour, he forcedly caressed his wife, he met with only coldness and an embarrassed submission from her. Natalia shrank from bodily delights; her mother had given her her own sluggish, tranquil blood, and as he recalled Aksinia's passionate fervour Gregor sighed:

"Your father must have made you of ice, Natalia."

When he met Aksinia one day, she laughed and exclaimed:

"Hello, Grishka! How do you find life with your young wife?"

"We live!" Gregor shook her off with an evasive reply and escaped as quickly as possible from Aksinia's caressing glance.

Stepan had evidently made up his quarrel with his wife. He visited the tavern less frequently, and one evening, as he was winnowing grain in the threshing-floor, he suggested, for the first time since the beginning of the trouble:

"Let's sing a song, Aksinia!"

They sat down, their backs against a heap of threshed, dusty wheat. Stepan began an army song, Aksinia joined in with her full, throaty voice. Gregor heard the Astakhovs singing, and while he was threshing (the two threshing-floors adjoined) he could see Aksinia as self-assured as formerly and apparently happy.

Stepan exchanged no greeting with the Melekhovs. He worked in the threshing-floor, occasionally making a jesting remark to Aksinia. And she would respond with a smile, her black eyes flashing. Her green skirt rippled like rain before Gregor's eyes. His neck was continually being twisted by a strange force which turned his head in the direction of Stepan's yard. He did not notice that Natalia, who was assisting Pantaleimon repair the fence, intercepted his every involuntary glance; he did not see Piotra, who was driving the horses round the threshing-circle, grimacing with an almost imperceptible smile as he watched his brother.

From near and distant threshing-floors came the sound of threshing: the shouts of drivers, the whistle of knouts, the rattle of the winnowing drums. The village had waxed fat on the harvest and was threshing in the September warmth that stretched over the Don like a beaded snake across the road. In every farmyard, under the roof of every hut, each was living a full-blooded, bitter-sweet life, separate and apart from the rest. Old Grishaka was suffering with his teeth; Mokhov, crushed by his shame, was stroking his beard, weeping, and grinding his teeth; Stepan nursed his hatred for Gregor in his heart and tore at the shaggy blanket with his iron fingers in his sleep; Natalia ran into the shed and fell to the ground, shaking and huddling into a ball as she wept over her lost happiness; Gregor sighed, oppressed by gloomy presentiments and his continually returning pain; as Aksinia caressed her husband she flooded her undying hatred for him with tears. David had been discharged from the mill and sat night after night with Valet in the boiler-shed, while Valet, his evil eyes sparkling, would declare:

"David, you're a fool! They'll have their throats cut before long. One revolution isn't enough for them. Let them have another 1905, and then we'll settle scores. We'll settle scores!" he threatened with his scarred finger, and with a shrug adjusted the coat flung across his shoulders.

And over the village slipped the days, passing into the nights; the weeks flowed by, the months crept on, the wind howled, and, glassified with an autumnal, translucent, greenish-azure, the Don flowed tranquilly down to the sea.

One Sunday at the end of October, Fiodot Bodovskov drove to the district village on business. He took with him four brace of fattened ducks and sold them at the market; he bought his wife some cotton print and was on the point of driving home when a stranger, obviously not of those parts, came up to him.

"Good afternoon," he greeted Fiodot, putting his fingers to the edge of his black hat.

"Good afternoon," said Fiodot inquiringly.

"Where are you from?"

"From a village."

"And which village is it you're from?"

"From Tatarsk."

The stranger drew a silver cigarette-case out of his pocket and offered Fiodot a cigarette. "Is yours a big village?" he asked.

"Pretty large. Some three hundred families."

"Any smiths there?"

"Yes." Fiodot fastened the rein to his horse's bit and looked distrustfully at the man's black hat and the furrows in the large white face. "What do you want to know for?" he added.

"I'm coming to live in your village. I've just been to the district ataman. Will you take me back with you? I have a wife and a couple of boxes."

"I can take you."

They collected the wife and the boxes and set out on the return journey. Fiodot's passengers sat quietly behind him. Fiodot first asked for a cigarette, then he queried:

"Where do you come from?"

"From Rostov."

"Born there?"

"Yes."

Fiodot twisted himself round to study his passengers more closely. The man was of average height, but thin; his close-set eyes glittered intelligently. As he talked he smiled frequently, his upper lip protruded over the lower. His wife, wrapped in a knitted shawl, was dozing.

"What are you coming to live in our village for?"

"I'm a locksmith. I'm thinking of starting a workshop. I can do carpentry too."

Fiodot stared suspiciously at the man's plump hands, and, catching his gaze, the stranger added:

"I'm also an agent for the Singer Sewing Machine Company."

"What is your name?" Fiodot asked him.

"Stockman."

"So you're not Russian, then?"

"Yes, I'm a Russian. But my grandfather was a German by birth."

In a brief while Fiodot had learned that Osip Davidovich Stockman had formerly worked at a factory, then somewhere in the Kuban, then in the South-Eastern Railway workshops. After a while the conversation flagged. Fiodot gave his horse a drink at a wayside spring, and, drowsy with the journey and a good meal, he began to doze. He fastened the reins to the wagon and lay down comfortably. But he was not allowed to go to sleep.

"How's life in your parts?" Stockman asked him.

"Not so bad, we have enough to eat."

"And the Cossacks generally, are they satisfied?"

"Some are, some aren't. You can't please everybody."

"True, true," the man assented, and went on with his questioning.

"You live pretty well, you say?"

"Pretty well."

"The annual army training must be a trouble, eh?"

"Army training? We're used to it."

"But the officers are bad?"

"Yes, the sons of swine!" Fiodot grew animated and glanced fearfully at the woman. "Our authorities are a bad lot. . . . When I went to do my service I sold my bullocks and bought a horse, and they rejected him."

"Rejected him?" Stockman said with assumed amazement.

"Right off. His legs were no good, they said. I argued with them, but no, they wouldn't pass him. It's a shame!"

The conversation went on briskly. Fiodot jumped off the wagon and began to talk freely of the village life. He cursed the village ataman for his unjust division of the meadowland and praised the state of affairs in Poland, where his regiment had been stationed. Stockman smoked and smiled continually, but the frown furrowing his white forehead stirred slowly and heavily, as though driven from within by secret thoughts.

They reached the village in the early evening. On Fiodot's advice Stockman went to the widow Lukieshka and rented two rooms from her.

"Who is that you brought back with you?" Fiodot's neighbour asked him as he drove past.

"An agent."

"What kind of angel?"

"You're a fool, that's what you are. An agent, I said. He sells machines. He gives them away to the handsome ones, but to such fools as you, Aunty Maria, he sells them."

Next day the locksmith Stockman visited the village ataman. Fiodor Manitskov, who was in his third year as ataman, turned the newcomer's black passport over and over, then handed it to the secretary, who also turned it over and over. They exchanged glances, and the ataman authoritatively waved his hand:

"You can stay."

The newcomer bowed and left the room. For a week he did not put his nose outside Lukieshka's hut. He was to be heard pounding with an axe, preparing a workshop in the outdoor kitchen. The women's interest in him died away; only the children spent all day peeping over the fence and watching the stranger with an unabashed animal curiosity.

Some three days before the Intercession of the Holy Virgin, Gregor and his wife drove out to the steppe to plough. Pantaleimon was unwell; he leaned heavily on his stick and wheezed with pain as he stood in the yard seeing them off. As Ilinichna wrapped Natalia in her jacket she whispered:

"Don't be long away; come back soon."

Her slender waist bent under the weight of a load of damp washing, Dunia went past on her way to the Don to rinse the clothes. As she went by she called to Natalia:

"Natalia, in the red glade there is lots of sorrel. Pull some up and bring it home."

The three pairs of bullocks dragged the upturned plough out of the yard. Gregor, who had caught a cold while fishing, adjusted the handkerchief bound round his neck and walked along at the roadside, coughing. Natalia walked at his side, a sack of victuals swinging on her back.

A transparent silence enveloped the steppe. Beyond the fallow land, on the other side of the rolling hill the earth was being scratched with ploughs, the drivers were whistling; but here along the highroad was only the blue-grey of low-growing wormwood, the roadside clover, and the ringingly glassy, chilly heaven above, criss-crossed by flying threads of natural-coloured web.

After seeing the ploughers on their way Piotra and Daria made ready to drive to the mill. Piotra sifted the wheat in the granary, Daria sacked it and carried it to the wagonette. Pantaleimon harnessed the horses.

When they arrived at the mill they found the yard crowded with wagons. The scales were surrounded by a dense throng. Piotra threw the reins to Daria and jumped down from the cart.

"How soon will my turn be?" he asked Valet, the scalesman.

"You're the thirty-eighth."

Piotra turned to fetch his sacks. As he did so he heard cursing behind him. A hoarse, unpleasant voice barked:

"You oversleep and then you want to get in before your turn. Get away, Hokhol,[1] or I'll give you one."

Piotra recognized the voice of "Horseshoe" Yakob. He stopped to listen. There was a shout from the weighing-room and the sound of a blow. The blow was well aimed, and an elderly, bearded Ukrainian, with his cap crushed on the back of his head, came tumbling out through the doorway.

"What's that for?" he shouted, holding his cheek.

"I'll wring your neck, you son of a whore!"

"Mikifor, help!" the Ukrainian shouted.

"Horseshoe" Yakob, a desperate, solidly built artillery-man, who had earned his nickname because of the horseshoe marks left by the kick of a horse on his cheek, came running out of the weighing-room, rolling up his sleeves. Behind him a tall Ukrainian in a rose-coloured shirt struck hard at him. But Yakob kept on his feet.

"Brothers, they're attacking Cossacks!" he cried.

From all sides Cossacks and Ukrainians, who were at the mill in large numbers, came running. A fight began, centring in the main entrance to the mill. The door groaned under the pressure of the struggling bodies. Piotra threw down his sack and went slowly towards the mêlée. Standing up in the wagonette, Daria saw him press into the middle of the crowd, pushing the others aside. She groaned as she saw him carried to the

[1] *Hokhol:* familiar name for Ukrainians.

mill wall and flung down and trampled underfoot.

Mitka Korshunov came running round the corner from the machine-room, waving a bar of iron. The same Ukrainian who had struck at Yakob from behind burst out of the struggling crowd, a torn sleeve fluttering on his back like a bird's broken wing. Bent double, his hands touching the ground, he ran to the nearest wagon and snatched up a shaft. The three Shamil brothers came at a run from the village. One-armed Alexei fell at the gate, catching his feet in reins lying abandoned on the ground. He jumped up and leaped across the cart-shafts, pressing his armless sleeve to his breast. His brother Martin's trousers came out of their socks; he bent down to tuck them in, but a cry floated high over the mill roof, and Martin straightened up and tore after his brothers.

Daria stood watching from the wagon, panting and wringing her hands. Sergei Mokhov ambled past, pale and chewing his lips, his belly shaking like a round ball beneath his waistcoat. Daria saw the Ukrainian with the torn shirt cut Mitka down with the shaft, only himself to be sent headlong by one-armed Alexei's iron fist. She saw Mitka Korshunov, on his hands and knees, sweep Mokhov's legs from under him with the iron bar, and she was not surprised. Mokhov threw out his arms and slipped like a crab into the weighing-shed, there to be trodden underfoot. Daria laughed hysterically, the black arches of her painted brows broken with her laughter. But she stopped abruptly as she saw Piotra; he had succeeded in making his way out of the swaying, howling mob and was lying under a cart, spitting up blood. With a shriek Daria ran to him. From the village Cossacks came hurrying with stakes; one of them carried a crowbar. At the door of the weighing-shed a young Ukrainian lay with a broken head in a pool of blood; bloody strands of hair fell over his face. It looked as though he was departing this pleasant life.

Herded together like sheep, the Ukrainians were slowly being driven towards the boiler-shed. There was every prospect of the fight ending seriously, but an old Ukrainian had an inspiration. Jumping into the boiler-shed, he pulled a flaming brand out of the furnace and ran towards the granary where the milled grain was stored: eighteen tons and more of flour.

"I'll set it afire!" he roared savagely, raising the crackling brand towards the thatched roof.

The Cossacks shuddered and came to a halt. A dry, boisterous wind was blowing from the east, carrying the smoke away from the roof of the granary towards the group of Ukrainians. One spark in the dry thatch, and the whole village would go up in flames.

A brief, stifled howl of rage arose from the Cossacks. Some of them began to retreat towards the mill, while the Ukrainian, waving the brand above his head and scattering fiery rain, shouted:

"I'll burn it! I'll burn it! Out of the yard!"

Horseshoe Yakob, the cause of the fight, was the first to leave the yard. The other Cossacks streamed hurriedly after him. Throwing their sacks hastily into their wagons, the Ukrainians harnessed their horses; then, standing up in their wagons, waving the ends of the leather reins around their heads, whipping up their horses frantically, they tore out of the yard and away from the village.

Standing in the middle of the yard, his eyes and cheeks twitching, one-armed Alexei cried:

"To horse, Cossacks!"

"After them!" the cry was taken up.

Mitka Korshunov was on the point of dashing out of the yard, and the other Cossacks were about to act on the advice. But at that moment an unfamiliar figure in a black hat approached the group with hasty steps and raised his hand, crying:

"Stop!"

"Who are you?" Yakob asked.

"Where did you spring from?" another demanded.

"Stop, villagers!"

"Who are you calling villagers?"

"The peasant! Give him one, Yakob!"

"That's right, close up his eyes for him!"

The man smiled anxiously, but without a sign of fear. He took off his hat, wiped his brow with a gesture of ineffable simplicity, and finally disarmed them with his smile.

"What's the matter?" he asked, waving his hat at the blood by the door of the weighing-shed.

"We've been fighting the Hokhols," one-armed Alexei replied peaceably.

"But what for?"

"They wanted to get in ahead of their turn," Yakob explained.

"One of them would have set fire to the place in his desperation," Afonka Ozierov smiled. "The Hokhols are a terribly bad-tempered lot."

The man waved his hat in Ozierov's direction. "And who are you?" he asked.

Ozierov spat contemptuously and answered, as he watched the flight of the spittle:

"I'm a Cossack. And you—you're not a gypsy, are you?"

"You and I are both of us Russians."

"You lie!" Afonka declared deliberately.

"The Cossacks are descended from the Russians. Do you know that?" the stranger declared.

"And I tell you the Cossacks are the sons of Cossacks."

"Long ago," the man explained, "serfs ran away from the landowners and settled along the Don. They came to be known as Cossacks."

"Go your own way, man!" Alexei advised, restraining his anger. "The swine wants to make peasants of us! Who is he?"

"He's the newcomer living with cross-eyed Lukieshka," another explained.

But the moment for pursuit of the Ukrainians was past. The Cossacks dispersed, animatedly discussing the fight.

That night, in the steppe some five miles from the village, as Gregor wrapped himself in his prickly linen coat he said querulously to Natalia:

"You're a stranger, somehow! You're like that moon, you don't warm and you don't chill a man. I don't love you, Natashka; you mustn't be angry. I didn't want to say anything about it, but there it is; clearly we can't go on like this. I'm sorry for you; we've been married all these days, and still I feel nothing in my heart. It's empty. Like the steppe tonight."

Natalia glanced up at the inaccessible, starry pastures, at the shadowy, translucent cloak of the clouds floating above her, and was silent. From somewhere in the bluish-black upper wilderness belated cranes called to one another with voices like little silver bells. The grass had a yearning, deathly smell. On the hillock glimmered the ruddy glow of the dying camp-fire.

Gregor awoke just before dawn. Snow lay on his coat to the depth of three inches. The steppe was hidden beneath the freezing, virginal blue of the fresh snow; the clearly marked tracks of a hare ran close by where he was lying.

For many years past if a Cossack rode alone along the road to Millerovo and fell in with Hokhols (the Ukrainian villages began with Lower Yablonska and stretched for some fifty miles, as far as Millerovo), he had to yield them the road or they would set upon him. So the Cossacks were in the habit of driving to the district village in groups, and then they were not afraid of falling in with Hokhols on the steppe and exchanging invective:

"Hey, Hokhol! Give us the road! You live on the Cossacks' land, you swine, and you don't want to let them pass!"

It was not pleasant for the Ukrainians, who had to bring their grain to the central granaries at Paramonov on the Don. Fights would break out without cause, simply because they were Hokhols, and as they were Hokhols the Cossacks had to fight them.

Hundreds of years previously a diligent hand had sown the seeds of national discord in the Cossack land, and the seed had yielded rich fruit. In the inter-racial struggles the blue blood of the Cossacks and the crimson blood of the immigrant Muscovites and Ukrainians were poured out liberally over the Don country.

Some two weeks after the battle of the mill a district police officer and an investigating official arrived in the village. Stockman was the first to be cross-examined. The investigator, a young official from the Cossack nobility, asked him:

"Where were you living before you came here?"

"At Rostov."

"What were you imprisoned for in 1907?"

"For disorders."

"Hm! Where were you working then?"

"In the railway workshops."

"What as?"

"Locksmith."

"You're not a Jew, are you? Or a converted Jew?"

"No. I think—"

"I'm not interested in what you think. Have you been in exile?"

"Yes, I have."

The investigator raised his head, and chewed his lips. "I advise you to clear out of this district," he said, adding in an undertone: "and I'll see that you do."

"Why?"

"What did you say to the Cossacks on the day of the fight at the mill?" he answered with a question.

"Well . . ."

"All right, you can go."

Stockman went on to the veranda of Mokhov's house (the authorities always made the merchant's house their headquarters), and although a frown furrowed his brow, he glanced back at the door with a smile.

CHAPTER 9

Winter came on slowly. After some days the snow melted and the herds were driven out to pasture again. For a week a southern wind blew, warming the earth; a late, straggling green sprang up over the steppe. The thaw lasted until St. Michael's Day, then the frost returned and snow fell, and the gardens by the Don, through the fences, were criss-crossed with the marks of hares' feet. The streets were deserted.

Just after the snowfall a village assembly was held to arrange for the allotment and cutting of brushwood. Long before the hour fixed for the meeting the Cossacks crowded around the steps of the village administration in their sheepskins and greatcoats, and the cold drove them inside. Behind a table, at the side of the ataman and the secretary, the respected village elders were gathered; the younger Cossacks squeezed together in a group and muttered out of the warmth of their coat collars. The secretary covered sheet after sheet of paper with close writing, while the ataman watched over his shoulder, and a restrained hum arose in the chilly room.

"The hay this year . . ."

"You're right. The meadow hay is good, but the steppe hay is all clover."

"What about the wood-cutting?"

"Quiet, please!"

The meeting began. Stroking his beard, the ataman called out the names of the families and their assignments of wood.

"You can't fix the wood-cutting for Thursday." Ivan Tomilin attempted to shout down the ataman.

"Why not?"

"On Thursday half the village will be going out to bring in hay."

"You can leave that till Sunday!"

"The better the day . . ." A howl of derision arose from the assembly.

Old Matvey Kashulin leaned across the rickety table and pointed his smooth ash stick at Tomilin.

"The hay can wait! You're a fool, brother! And that's that! You . . ."

"You've got no brains to boast about, anyway . . ." one-armed Alexei joined in. For six years he had been quarreling with old Kashulin over a piece of land. Every spring Alexei asserted his right to it, but each time Kashulin ploughed it up again.

"Shut up, St. Vitus!"

"Pity you're so far away, or I'd give you something to remember me by," Alexei stormed.

The ataman banged the table with his fist.

"I'll call the militia in in a moment if there isn't silence." When order was restored, he added: "Wood-cutting will begin on Thursday at dawn."

"A fine time!" "God grant it!" arose the jeering remarks.

"And one other thing: I've received an instruction from the district ataman." The village ataman raised his voice. "Next Saturday the youngsters are to go to be sworn in at the district ataman's office. They are to be there by afternoon."

Pantaleimon Prokoffievich was standing by the window nearest the door. At his side Miron Gregorievich was sitting on the windowsill, screwing up his eyes and smiling into his beard. Close by them the younger Cossacks were crowded, winking and smiling at one another. In the middle of their group, the fur cap of the ataman's regiment thrust back on his smooth bald head, his unageing face everlastingly blushing like a ruddy winter apple, stood Avdeich Senilin.

Avdeich had served in the ataman's Life Guards and had come back with the nickname of "Bragger." He had been one of the first in the village to be assigned to the ataman's regiment. While he was on service a strange thing had happened to him, and from the very first day of his return he had begun to tell astonishing stories of his extraordinary adventures in Petersburg. His astounded listeners at first believed him, drinking it all in with gaping mouths, but then they discovered that Avdeich was the biggest liar the village had ever produced, and they openly laughed at him. But he was not to be abashed and did not cease his lying. As he grew old he began to get annoyed when nailed down to a lie and would resort to his fists; but if his listeners only laughed and said nothing he grew more and more fervent in his story-telling.

Avdeich stood in the middle of the room, rocking on his heels. Glancing around the assembled Cossacks, he observed in a ponderous bass voice:

"Speaking of service, these days the Cossacks aren't at all what they were. They're small and good-for-nothing. But—" and he smiled contemptuously—"I once saw some dead bones! Ah, they were Cossacks in those days!"

"Where did you dig the bones up, Avdeich?" smooth-faced Anikushka asked, nudging his neighbour.

"Don't start telling any of your lies, Avdeich, with the holy days so near." Pantaleimon wrinkled up his nose. He did not like Avdeich's bragging habits.

"It isn't my nature to lie, brother," Avdeich replied truculently, and stared in astonishment at Anikushka, who was shaking as though with fever. "I saw these dead bones when we were building a hut for my brother-in-law. As we were digging the foundations we came to a grave. The arms were as long as this—" he extended both arms wide—"and the head was as big as a copper."

"You'd better tell the youngsters how you caught a robber in St. Petersburg," Miron suggested as he rose from the window-sill.

"There's nothing really to tell," Avdeich replied, with a sudden attack of modesty.

"Tell us, tell us, Avdeich!" arose a shout.

"Well, it was like this." Avdeich cleared his throat and drew his tobacco-pouch out of his trouser pocket. He poured a pinch of tobacco on his palm and stared around his audience with eyes beaming. "A thief had escaped from prison. They looked for him everywhere, but do you think they could find him? They just couldn't. All the authorities were beaten. Well, one night the officer of the guard calls me to him. 'Go into that room,' he says. 'His Imperial Majesty is in there. The Sire Emperor himself wants to see you.' Of course I was taken aback a bit, but I went in. I stood at attention, but he claps me on the shoulder and says: 'Listen,' he says, 'Ivan Avdeich, the biggest thief in our Empire has escaped. Look for him and find him or never let me set eyes on you again!' 'Very good, Your Imperial Majesty!' I said. So I took three of the best horses in the Czar's stables and set out. I rode all day and I rode all night, until on the third day I came up with the thief near Moscow. I take him into my coach and haul him back to Petersburg. I arrive at midnight, all covered with mud, and go straight to His Imperial Majesty himself. All sorts of counts and princes tried to stop me, but I march on. Yes. . . . I knock at the door. 'May I come in, Your Imperial Majesty?' 'Who is it?' 'It's me,' I said, 'Ivan Avdeich Senilin.' I heard a noise in the room and heard His Majesty himself cry out: 'Maria Fiodorovna, Maria Fiodorovna! Get up quickly and get a samovar going, Ivan Avdeich has arrived.' "

There was a roar of laughter from the Cossacks at the back of the crowd. The secretary, who was reading a notice concerning a lost animal, stopped in the middle of a sentence, and the ataman stretched out his neck like a goose and stared hard at the crowd rocking with laughter.

Avdeich's face clouded and his eyes wandered uncertainly over the faces before him.

"Wait a bit!" he said.

"Ha-ha-ha!"

"Oh, he'll be the death of us!"

"Get a samovar going! Avdeich has arrived! Ha-ha-ha!"

The assembly began to break up. On the trampled snow outside the administration hut Stepan Astakhov and a tall, long-shanked Cossack, the owner of the windmill, were stamping about to get themselves warm.

When Pantaleimon returned from the meeting he went at once to the room which he and his wife occupied. Ilinichna had been unwell for some days, and her swollen face reflected her weariness and pain. She lay propped up on a plump feather bed. At the sound of Pantaleimon's footsteps she turned her head; her eyes rested on his beard, damp with his breath, and her nostrils dilated. But the old man smelt only of the frost and the sour sheepskin. "Sober today," she thought, and contentedly laid down her knitting-needles.

"Well, what of the wood-cutting?" she asked.

"They've decided to begin on Thursday." Pantaleimon stroked his beard. "Thursday morning," he added, sitting down on a chest at the side of the bed. "Well, feeling any better?"

"Just the same. A shooting pain in all my joints."

"I told you not to go into the water," Pantaleimon fumed. "There were plenty of other women to steep the hemp. . . . And how's Natalia?" he asked suddenly, bending towards the bed.

There was a note of anxiety in Ilinichna's voice as she replied:

"I don't know what to do. She was crying again a day or two ago. I went out into the yard and found someone had left the barn door wide open. I went inside, and she was standing by the millet-bin. I asked her what was the matter, but she said she only had a headache. I can't get the truth out of her."

"Perhaps she's ill?"

"I don't think so. Either someone's given her the evil eye, or else it's Grishka. . . ."

"He hasn't been with that . . . You haven't heard anything, have you?"

"What are you saying, father?" Ilinichna exclaimed in alarm. "And what about Stepan? He's no fool! No, I haven't heard anything."

Pantaleimon sat with his wife awhile longer, then went out. Gregor was in his room sharpening hooks with a file. Natalia was smearing them with pork grease and carefully wrapping each in a separate rag. As Pantaleimon limped by he stared inquisitively at her. Her yellow cheeks were flushed like an autumn leaf. She had grown noticeably thinner during the past month, and there was a new unhappy look in her eyes. The old man halted at the door. "He's killing the girl!" he thought as he glanced back at Natalia bowed over the bench.

"Drop that, the devil take it!" the old man shouted, turning livid with his sudden frenzy. Gregor looked at his father in astonishment.

"I want to sharpen both ends, Father."

"Drop it, I tell you! Get ready for the wood-cutting. The sledges aren't ready at all, and you sit there sharpening hooks," he added more quietly, and hesitated at the door, evidently wanting to say something else. But he went out. Gregor heard him giving vent to the rest of his anger on Piotra.

A good two hours before dawn on the Thursday, Ilinichna got up and called Daria: "Get up! Time to light the fire!"

Daria ran in her shift to the stove and struck a light with the flint.

"Get a move on with it!" Piotra hurried his wife as he lit a cigarette.

"They don't go and wake that Natashka up! Am I to tear myself in two?" Daria fumed.

"Go and wake her up yourself," Piotra advised her. But the advice was unnecessary, for Natalia was already up. Flinging on her jacket, she went out to get fuel for the fire.

The kitchen smelt of fresh kvass, harness, and the warmth of human bodies. Daria bustled about, shuffling in her felt boots; under her rose-coloured shift her little breasts quivered. Her married life had not soured or withered her. Tall and slender, supple as a willow switch, she was as fresh as a young girl.

Dawn broke before the meal was ready. Pantaleimon hurried over his breakfast, blowing on the thick porridge. Gregor ate slowly, his face clouded, and Piotra amused himself with teasing Dunia, who was suffering with toothache and had her face bound up.

There was the sound of sledge-runners in the street. Bullock sledges were moving down to the Don in the grey dawn. Gregor and Piotra went out to harness their sledges. As he went Gregor wound a soft scarf, his wife's gift, around his neck. A crow flew overhead with a full, throaty cry. Piotra watched its flight and remarked:

"Flying to the south, to the warmth."

Behind a rosy little cloud, as gay as a maiden smile, a tiny slip of moon gleamed dimly. The smoke from the chimneys rose in columns, reaching towards the inaccessibly distant, golden slip of the young moon. The river was not completely frozen over opposite the Melekhovs' hut. Along the edges of the stream the ice was firm, and green with accumulated drift snow. But beyond the middle, towards the Black Cliff, the ice-holes yawned sombre and menacing out of the white snow.

Pantaleimon drove off first with the old bullocks, leaving his sons to follow later. At the slope down to the river-crossing Piotra and Gregor caught up with Anikushka. He was walking at the side of his bullocks, and his wife, a stocky, sickly woman, held the reins. Piotra called out to him:

"Hello, neighbour, surely you're not taking your woman with you?"

Anikushka smiled and turned to talk to the brothers.

"Yes, I am, to keep me warm," he replied.

"You'll get no warmth from her, she's too lean."

"That's true; and I feed her with oats, but still she doesn't fatten!"

The three drove on together. The forest was laced with rime, and of a virgin whiteness. Anikushka went in front, lashing his whip against the branches overhead. The needly and crumbling snow fell in showers, sprinkling over his wife.

"Don't play about, you devil!" she shouted at him as she shook the snow off.

"Drop her into the snow," Piotra advised.

At a turn of the road they met Stepan Astakhov, driving two yoked bullocks back towards the village. His curly hair hung below his fur cap like a bunch of white grapes.

"Hey, Stepan, lost your way?" Anikushka exclaimed as he passed.

"Lost my way be damned! We swung over, and the sledge struck a stump and snapped a runner in two. So I've got to go back." Stepan cursed and his eyes suddenly darkened as he passed Piotra.

"Left your sledge behind?" Anikushka asked, turning round.

Stepan waved his hand, cracked his whip, and gave Gregor a hard stare. A little farther on, the group came to a sledge abandoned in the middle of the road. Aksinia was standing by it. Holding the edge of her sheepskin with her hand, she was gazing along the road in their direction.

"Out of the way or I'll drive over you. You're not my wife!" Anikushka snorted. Aksinia stepped aside with a smile and sat down on the overturned sledge.

"I'd take you along, but I've got my own wife with me," Anikushka explained as he drove by.

As Piotra came up to her he gave a quick glance back at Gregor, who was some distance behind. Gregor was smiling uncertainly, anxiety and expectation expressed in all his movements.

"What, sledge broken?" Piotra asked.

"Yes," she replied, and rising to her feet, turned away from Piotra towards Gregor. "Gregor Pantalievich, I'd like a word with you," she said as he came up to her.

Asking Piotra to look after his bullocks for a moment, Gregor turned to her. Piotra laughed suggestively and drove on.

The two stood silently regarding each other. Aksinia glanced cautiously around, then turned her humid black eyes again to Gregor's face. Shame and joy flamed in her cheeks and dried her lips. Her breath came in sharp gasps.

At a turn in the road Anikushka and Piotra disappeared behind the brown oak trunks.

"Well, Grishka, it's as you wish, but

I've no strength left to live without you," she said firmly, and pressed her lips together in expectation of his answer.

Gregor made no reply. The silence fettered the forest in its grip. The glassy emptiness rang in his ears. The smooth surface of the road, polished with sledge-runners, the grey rag of sky, the dumb, mortally drowsy forest. . . . A sudden cry of a raven near by seemed to arouse Gregor from his momentary lethargy. He raised his head and watched the bird winging its silent flight. Unexpectedly to himself he said:

"It's going to be warm. He's flying towards the warmth." Starting, he laughed hoarsely. "Well—" He turned his intoxicated eyes to Aksinia and suddenly snatched her towards himself.

During the winter evenings a little group of villagers gathered in Stockman's room at Lukieshka's hut. There were Christonia, and Valet from the mill, ever smiling David (now three months a loafer), the engine-man, Ivan Alexeivich Kotliarov, occasionally Filka the cobbler, and always Misha Koshevoi, a young Cossack who had not yet done his regular army service.

At first the group played cards. Then Stockman casually brought out a book of Nekrasov's poetry. They began to read the volume aloud, and liked it. Then they went on to Nikitin, and about Christmas-time Stockman suggested the reading of a dog-eared, unbound and well-bethumbed brochure. Koshevoi, who had been to the church school, read aloud from it as he contemptuously glanced through the greasy pages.

"You could make vermicelli of it, it's so greasy!" he said in disgust.

Christonia roared with laughter; David smiled dazzlingly. But Stockman waited for the merriment to die away and then said:

"Read it, Misha. It's interesting. It's all about the Cossacks."

Bending his head over the table, Koshevoi spelt out laboriously: *Short History of the Don Cossacks,* and then glanced around expectantly.

"Read it!" Kotliarov, the engine-man, ordered.

They laboured through the book for three evenings, reading about the free life of the past, about Pugachov, Stenka Razin and Vasily Bulovin. Finally they came down to recent times. The unknown author poured scorn on the Cossacks' miserable existence, he jeered intelligently and powerfully at the authorities and the system, the Czar's government, and the Cossackry itself, which had hired itself out to the monarchs as their bodyguard. The listeners grew excited and began to quarrel among themselves. Stockman sat at the door smoking a pipe and smiling.

"He's right! It's all true!" Christonia would burst out.

The engineer Kotliarov was steeped to the backbone in Cossack traditions, and he defended the Cossacks vigorously, his bulging round eyes glittering:

"You're a peasant, Christan, your Cossack blood's a drop in a bucket. Your mother was mated with a peasant from Voronezh."

"You're a fool, you're a fool, brother!" Christonia replied vigorously.

"Shut up, peasant!"

"And aren't the peasants just as much men as you?"

"They're peasants, made of bast and stuffed with brushwood."

"When I was serving in Petersburg, brother, I saw many things," Christonia said. "Once it happened that we were on guard at the Czar's palace, inside the rooms and around the walls outside. We rode around, two this way and two that. When we met we used to ask: 'All quiet, no risings anywhere?' and then we'd ride on. We weren't allowed to stop and talk. And they chose us for our looks; when we had to take our turn on guard at the doors, they chose each pair so as they should be alike in their faces and their figures. The barber once had to dye my beard because of it. I had to take a turn at guard duty with some Cossack whose beard was a bay colour. They searched all through the regiment and there wasn't another like him. So the troop commander sent me to the barber to have my beard dyed. When I looked in the glass afterwards my heart almost broke. I burned, absolutely burned!"

"Yes, Christonia, but what's all this to do with the question? What were you going to tell us?" Kotliarov interrupted him.

"About the people. I was just telling you I once had to take a turn on guard outside. We were riding along, me and my comrade, when some students came running round the corner. As soon as they saw us they roared: 'Ha!' and then again: 'Ha!' We hadn't time to call out before they had surrounded us. 'What are you riding about for, Cossacks?' they asked. And I said: 'We're keeping guard, you let go of the reins,' and clapped my hands on my sword. 'Don't distrust me, Cossack, I'm from Kamienska district myself, and I'm studying in the university,' one said. We start to ride on, and he pulls out a ten-ruble piece and says: 'Drink to the health of my dead father.' And he draws a picture out of his pocket. 'Look, that's my father,' he says, 'take it as a keepsake.' Well, we took it, we couldn't refuse. And they went off again. Just then an officer comes running out of the back door of the palace with a troop of men. 'Who was that?' he shouts. And I tell him students had come and begun talking to us, and we had wanted to sabre them according to instructions, but as they had set us free we had ridden off. When we went off duty later, we told the corporal we'd earned ten rubles and wanted to drink them to the health of the old man, showing him the portrait. In the evening the corporal brought some vodka, and we had a good time for a couple of days. Then it turned out that this student had given us the portrait of the chief rebel of Germany. I had hung it above my bed; he had a grey beard and was a decent sort of man, looked like a merchant. The troop commander saw it and asked: 'Where did you get that picture from?' So I told him, and he began to roar: 'Do you know who that is? He's their ataman Karl—' Drat it, I've forgotten his name. What was it . . . ?"

"Karl Marx?" Stockman suggested with a smile.

"That's it, Karl Marx," Christonia exclaimed joyfully. "But we drank the ten rubles. It was the bearded Karl we drank to, but we drank them!"

"He deserves to be drunk to." Stockman smiled, playing with his cigarette-holder.

"Why, what good did he do?" Kotliarov queried.

"I'll tell you another time, it's getting late now." Stockman held the holder between his fingers and ejected the dead cigarette-end with a slap from the other hand.

After long selection and testing, a little group of ten Cossacks began to meet regularly in Stockman's workshop. Stockman was the heart and soul of the group and went straight towards the end he had in mind. He ate into the simple understandings and conceptions like a worm into wood, instilling repugnance and hatred towards the existing system. At first he found himself confronted with the cold steel of distrust, but he was not to be repulsed.

On the sandy slope of the left bank of the Don lies the centre of Vieshenska, the most ancient of the district centres of the upper Don, transferred from the town of Chigonak, which was destroyed during the reign of Peter the Great, and renamed Vieshenska. It was formerly an important link along the great waterway from Voronezh to Azov.

Opposite Vieshenska the Don bends like a Tatar bow, turns sharply to the right, and by the little village of Bazka majestically straightens again, carries its greenish-blue waters over the chalky feet of the hills on the west bank, past the thickly clustered villages on the right and the rare hamlets on the left, down to the sea, to the blue Sea of Azov.

Vieshenska stands among dunes of yellow sands. It is a bare, unhappy village without gardens or orchards. On the square stands an old church, grey with age, and six streets run out of the square in lines parallel with the river. Where the Don bends towards Bazka a lake, as broad as the Don at low tide, runs like a sleeve into willows. The far end of Vieshenska runs down to this lake, and on a smaller square, overgrown with golden prickly thorn, is a second church, with a green cupola and green roof, standing under the green of the willows.

Beyond the village, to the north stretches a saffron waste of sands, a miserable pine plantation, and groves flooded with rust-coloured water. Here and there in the sandy wilderness are rare oases of villages, meadowland, and a grey scrub of willows.

One Sunday in December a dense crowd of fifteen hundred young Cossacks from all the villages in the district was assembled in the square outside the old church. Mass ended, the senior sergeant, a brave-looking, elderly Cossack with long-service decorations, gave an order, and the youngsters drew up in two long, unequal ranks. Followed by his staff, the ataman entered the church enclosure, dressed according to form and wearing a new officer's cloak, his spurs jingling.

Falling back a pace or two, the senior sergeant swung on his heels and shouted:

"By the right, quick march!"

The two lines filed through the wide-open gate, and the church rang to the cupola with the sound of tramping feet.

Gregor paid no attention to the words of the oath of allegiance being read by the priest. By his side stood Mitka Korshunov, his face contorted with the pain of his tight new boots. Gregor's upraised arm grew numb, a jumbled train of thought slipped through his mind. As he passed under the crucifix and kissed the silver, damp with the moisture of many lips, he thought of Aksinia, of his wife. He had a fleeting vision of the forest, its brown trunks and branches lined with white down, and the humid gleam of Aksinia's black eyes beneath her kerchief. . . .

When the ceremony was ended they were marched out into the square and again drawn up in ranks. Blowing his nose and stealthily wiping his fingers on the lining of his coat, the sergeant addressed them:

"You're not boys any longer now, you're Cossacks. You've taken the oath and you ought to understand what it means and what you've sworn to do. You're grown up into Cossacks now and you must watch over your honour, obey your fathers and mothers, and so on. You were boys, you played about, you may even have played tipcat in the road, but now you must think about your future service. In a year's time you will be called up into the army." Here the sergeant blew his nose again, brushed his hands, and ended, as he drew on his fur gloves: "And your father or mother must think about getting you your equipment. They must provide you with an army horse, and . . . in general. . . . And now, home you go and God be with you, boys."

Gregor and Mitka picked up the rest of

the lads from their village, and they set off together for Tatarsk.

It was dusk when they reached the village. Gregor went up the steps of the hut and glanced in at the window. The hanging lamp shed a dim yellow light through the room. Piotra was standing in its light with his back to the window. Gregor brushed the snow off his boots with the twig broom at the door and entered the kitchen amid a cloud of steam.

"Well, I'm back," he announced.

"You've been quick. You must be frozen," Piotra replied in an anxious and hurried tone.

Pantaleimon was sitting with his head bowed in his hands, his elbows on his knees. Daria was spinning at the droning spinning-wheel. Natalia was standing at the table with her back to Gregor and did not turn round on his entry. Glancing hastily around the kitchen, Gregor rested his eyes on Piotra. By his brother's agitatedly expectant face he guessed that something had happened.

"Taken the oath?" Piotra asked.

"Ah-ha."

Gregor took off his outdoor clothes slowly, playing for time and turning over in his mind all the possibilities which might have led to this chilly and silent welcome. Ilinichna came out of the best room, her face expressing her agitation.

"It's Natalia!" Gregor thought as he sat down on the bench beside his father.

"Get him some supper," his mother said to Daria, indicating Gregor with her eyes. Daria stopped in the middle of her spinning-song and went to the stove. The kitchen was engulfed in a silence broken only by the heavy breathing of a goat and her newly-born kid.

As Gregor sipped his soup he glanced at Natalia. But he could not see her face. She was sitting sideways to him, her head bent over her knitting-needles. Pantaleimon was the first to be provoked into speech by the general silence. Coughing artificially, he said:

"Natalia is talking about going back to her parents."

Gregor wiped his plate clean with his bread and said nothing.

"What's the reason?" his father asked, his lower lip quivering—the first sign of a coming outburst of frenzy.

"I don't know," Gregor replied as he rose and crossed himself.

"But I know," his father raised his voice.

"Don't shout, don't shout!" Ilinichna interposed.

"Yes, there's no cause for shouting." Piotra moved from the window to the middle of the room. "It all depends on love. If you want to, you live together; if you don't, well—God be with you!"

"I'm not judging her. Even if she was a wanton hussy and sinful in the sight of God, still I'd not judge her, but that swine there—" Pantaleimon pointed to Gregor, who was warming himself at the stove.

"Who have I done wrong to?" Gregor asked.

"You don't know? You don't know, you devil?"

"No, I don't."

Pantaleimon jumped from his seat, overturning the bench, and went right up to Gregor. Natalia threw down her stocking, the needles clattered to the floor. At the sound a kitten jumped down from the stove and began to play with the ball of wool.

"What I say to you is this," the old man began slowly and deliberately; "if you won't live with Natalia, you can clear out of this house and go wherever your feet will carry you. That's what I say to you. Go where your feet will carry you," he repeated in a calm voice, and turned and picked up the bench.

"What I say to you, Father, I don't say in anger." Gregor's voice was jarringly hollow. "I didn't marry of my own choice, it was you who married me off. And I have no feeling for Natalia. Let her go back to her father if she wants to."

"You clear out yourself."

"And I will go!"

"And go to the devil!"

"I'm going, I'm going, don't be in a hurry." Gregor stretched out his hand for his short fur coat lying on the bed, distending his nostrils and trembling with the same boiling anger as his father. The same mingled Turkish and Cossack blood flowed in their veins, and at that moment their resemblance to each other was extraordinary.

"Where are you going?" Ilinichna groaned, seizing Gregor's arm. But he forcibly threw her off and snatched up his fur cap.

"Let him go, the sinful swine! Let him go, curse him! Go on, go! Clear out!" the old man thundered, throwing the door wide open.

Gregor ran out on to the steps, and the last sound he heard was Natalia's weeping.

The frosty night held the village in its grip, a needly powder was falling from the inky sky, the ice on the Don was cracking like pistol-shots. Gregor ran panting out of the gate. At the far end of the village, dogs were barking in chorus; yellow points of light shone through the frosty haze.

He walked aimlessly down the street. Astakhov's windows sparkled like diamonds through the darkness.

"Grishka!" he heard Natalia's yearning cry from the gate.

"Go to hell, you fickle bitch!" Gregor grated his teeth and hastened his steps.

"Grishka, come back!"

He turned into the first cross-lane and for the last time heard her distant, bitter cry:

"Grishenka, dearest! . . ."

He swiftly crossed the square and stopped at a fork in the road, wondering with whom he could spend the night. He decided on Misha Koshevoi. Misha lived with his mother and sister in a lonely straw-thatched hut right by the hill. Gregor entered their yard and knocked at the tiny window.

"Who's there?"

"Is Misha in?"

"Yes, who is it wants him?"

"It's me, Gregor Melekhov."

After a moment Misha, awakened from his first sleep, opened the door.

"You, Grishka?"

"Me."

"What do you want at this time of night?"

"Let me in, and I'll tell you inside."

In the porch Gregor seized Misha by the elbow and whispered:

"I want to spend the night with you. I've fallen out with my people. Have you got room for me? Anywhere will do."

"We'll fix you up somewhere. What's the row all about?"

"I'll tell you later."

They made Gregor a bed on the bench. He lay thinking, his head wrapped in his sheepskin to muffle the snores of Misha's mother. What was happening at home now, he wondered. Would Natalia go back to her father or not? Well, life had taken a new turn. Where should he go? And the answer came swiftly. He would send for Aksinia tomorrow and go with her to the Kuban, far away from the village . . . far away . . . away.

His sleep was troubled by the approaching unknown. Before he finally dropped off he tried hard to recall what it was that oppressed him. In his drowsy state his thoughts would flow easily and smoothly, like a boat downstream, then suddenly they would come up against something, as though the boat had struck a sandbank. He wrestled with the baffling obstacle. What was it that lay across the road?

In the morning he awoke and at once

remembered his army service. That was it! How could he go away with Aksinia? In the spring there was the training camp, and in the autumn the army draft.

He had some breakfast and called Misha into the porch.

"Misha, go to the Astakhovs' for me, will you?" he asked. "Tell Aksinia to go to the windmill this evening after dark."

"But what about Stepan?" Misha stammered.

"Say you've come on some business or other."

"All right, I'll go."

"Tell her to be sure to go there."

In the evening Gregor went and sat down by the windmill. He lit a cigarette. Beyond the windmill the wind was stumbling over withered cornstalks. The torn linen flapped on the motionless sails. He thought it sounded like a great bird winging around the mill and unable to fly away, and it was unpleasant and disturbing. Aksinia did not come. The sun had set in the west in a fading, gilded lilac, the wind began to flow freshly from the east, the darkness overtook the moon stranded among the willows. Above the windmill the sky was deathly dark, with blue streaks. From the village came the last sounds of the day's activities.

He smoked three cigarettes in succession, thrust the last butt into the trodden snow, and gazed around in anxious irritation. There was no one in sight. He rose, stretched himself, and moved towards the light twinkling invitingly in Misha's window. He was approaching the yard when he stumbled into Aksinia. She had evidently been running: she was out of breath, and the scent of the winter wind, or perhaps of fresh steppe hay, came from her cold mouth.

"I waited and waited and thought you weren't coming," he said.

"I had to get rid of Stepan."

"I'm frozen through, you, you accursed woman!"

"I'm hot, I'll warm you." She flung open her wool-lined coat and wrapped herself around Gregor like hops around an oak.

"Why did you send for me?" she asked.

"Wait, take my arm. There are likely to be people around here."

"You haven't quarrelled with your people?"

"I've left them. I spent the night with Misha. I'm a homeless dog now."

They turned off the road, and Gregor, sweeping away the drift-snow, leaned against a wattle fence.

"You don't know whether Natalia has gone home, do you?" he asked.

"I don't. . . . She'll go, I expect."

Gregor slipped Aksinia's frozen hand up the sleeve of his coat, and squeezing her slender fingers, he asked:

"And what about us?"

"I don't know, dear. Whatever you think best."

"Will you leave Stepan?"

"Without a sigh. This evening, if you like."

"And we'll find work somewhere, and live somehow."

"I'll sleep with the cattle to be with you, Grishka. Anything to be with you."

They stood close together, each warming the other. Gregor did not want to stir; he stood with his head towards the wind, his nostrils quivering, his eyelids closed. Her face pressed into his armpit, Aksinia breathed in the familiar, intoxicating scent of his sweat; and on her shamelessly avid lips, hidden from Gregor's eyes, trembled a joyous smile.

"Tomorrow I'll go and see Mokhov. He may be able to give me work," Gregor said, gripping Aksinia's moist arm above the hand.

Aksinia did not speak, nor did she raise her head. The smile slipped from her face like a dying wind, anxiety and fear started to her dilated eyes like a frightened animal. "Shall I tell him or not?" she thought, as she remembered that she was pregnant. "I must tell him," she decided, but immediately, trembling with fear, she drove away the terrible thought. Her woman's instinct divined that this was not the moment to tell him; she realized that she might lose Gregor for ever; and uncertain whether the child leaping beneath her heart was Gregor's or Stepan's, she temporized and did not tell him.

"What did you tremble for? Are you cold?" Gregor asked, wrapping her in his coat.

"I am a little. . . . I must go, Grishka. Stepan will come back and find me not there."

"Where's he gone?"

"I took him along to Anikey to play cards."

They parted. The agitating scent of her lips remained on Gregor's lips: the scent of the winter wind, or perhaps the intangible scent of rain-sprinkled steppe hay.

Aksinia turned into a by-way, bowed and almost running. By a well, where the cattle had churned up the autumn mud, she stumbled awkwardly, her foot slipping on a frozen clod; and feeling a lacerated pain in her bowels, she caught at the fence. The pain died away, but in her side something living, turning, knocked angrily and strongly time and again.

Next morning Gregor went to see Mokhov. Sergei Platonovich had just returned from the shop and was sitting in the dining-room, sipping strong, claret-coloured tea. Gregor left his cap in the anteroom and went in.

"I'd like to have a word with you, Sergei Platonovich," he said.

"Ah, Pantaleimon Melekhov's son, isn't it? What do you want?"

"I've come to ask whether you could take me on as a workman."

As Gregor spoke, the door creaked and a young officer in a green tunic with a troop commander's epaulets entered. Gregor recognized him as the young Listnitsky, whom Mitka Korshunov had outraced the previous summer. Sergei Platonovich gave the officer a chair and turned back to Gregor.

"Has your father come down in the world, that he is putting his son out to work?" he inquired.

"I'm no longer living with him."

"Left him?"

"Yes."

"Well, I'd gladly take you on, I know your family to be a hardworking lot, but I'm afraid I haven't any work for you to do."

"What's the matter?" Listnitsky inquired, pulling his chair up to the table.

"This lad is looking for work."

"Can you look after horses? Can you drive a pair?" the officer asked as he stirred his tea.

"I can. I've had the care of our own six horses."

"I want a coachman. What wage do you require?"

"I'm not asking for much."

"In that case go to my father at our estate tomorrow. You know the house? At Yagodnoe, some eight miles from here."

"Yes, I know it."

Gregor went to the door. As he turned the handle he hesitated and said:

"I'd like to have a word with you in private, sir."

Listnitsky followed Gregor out into the twilit passage. A rosy light filtered dimly through the Venetian glass of the door leading to the balcony.

"Well, what is it?" the officer asked.

"I'm not alone." Gregor flushed darkly. "I've a woman with me. Perhaps you can find something for her to do?"

"Your wife?" Listnitsky inquired, smiling and raising his eyebrows.

"Someone else's wife."

"Ah, so that's it, is it? All right, we'll fix her up as cook for the servants. But where is her husband?"

"Here in the village."

"So you've stolen another man's wife?"

"She came of her own accord."

"A romantic story! Well, don't fail to come tomorrow. You can go now."

Gregor arrived at Yagodnoe at about eight the next morning. The great house stood in a broad valley, and was surrounded by a brick wall. Outbuildings straggled over the yard: a wing with a tiled roof, the date 1910 picked out with tiles of a different colour; the servants' quarters, a bath-house, stables, poultry-house, and cattle-shed, a long barn, and a coach-house. The main building was old, and nestled in an orchard. Beyond the house rose bare poplars and the willows of the meadows, empty crows' nests swinging in their brown tops.

As he entered the yard Gregor was welcomed by a pack of Crimean borzois. An old lame bitch was the first to snuff at him and follow him with drooping head. In the servants' quarters a cook was quarrelling with a young, freckled maid. Sitting in a cloud of tobacco-smoke at the threshold was an old bowed man. The maid conducted Gregor to the house. The anteroom smelt of dogs and uncured pelts. On a table lay the case of a double-barrelled gun and a fringed game-bag.

"The young master will see you," the maid called to Gregor through a side door.

Gregor looked anxiously at his muddy boots and entered. Listnitsky was lying on a bed under the window. The officer rolled a cigarette, buttoned up the collar of his white shirt, and remarked:

"You're in good time. Wait; my father will be here in a minute."

Gregor stood by the door. After a moment or two there was the sound of footsteps in the anteroom, and a deep bass voice asked through the door:

"Are you asleep, Eugene?"

"Come in," Listnitsky replied.

An old man wearing a black Caucasian cloak entered. Gregor gave him a stealthy glance. He was immediately struck by the fine hooked nose and the white, tobacco-stained arch of whiskers. Old Listnitsky was tall and broad-shouldered, but gaunt. Beneath the cloak a long coat of camel-hair hung on him. His eyes were set close to his nose.

"Pàpa, here is the coachman I spoke to you about," Eugene remarked.

"Whose son is he?"

"Pantaleimon Melekhov's."

"I knew Prokoffey, he was in the army with me. I remember Pantaleimon, too. Lame, isn't he?"

"Yes, Your Excellency," Gregor replied, mentally recalling his father's stories of the retired General Listnitsky, a hero of the Russo-Turkish war.

"Why are you seeking work?" the old man inquired.

"I'm not living with my father, Your Excellency."

"What sort of Cossack will you make if you hire yourself out? Didn't your father provide for you when you left him?"

"No, Your Excellency."

"Hm, that's another matter. You want work for your wife as well?"

The younger Listnitsky's bed creaked heavily. Gregor turned his eyes in that direction and saw the officer winking.

"That's right, Your Excellency," he answered.

"Without any 'Excellencies.' I don't like them. Your wage will be eight rubles a month. For both of you. Your wife will cook for the yard and seasonal workers. Is that satisfactory?"

"Yes."

"Come along tomorrow morning. You will occupy the room the previous coachman had. And now quick march. Be here at eight."

Gregor went out. On the far side of the barn the borzois were sunning themselves on a patch of ground bare of snow. The old bitch followed Gregor a little way with head still drooping mournfully, then turned back.

That same morning Aksinia finished cooking early. She raked out the fire, washed the dishes, and glanced out of the window looking on to the yard. Stepan was standing by the wood-pile close to the fence bordering on the Melekhovs' yard. The left-hand corner of the shed was tumbling down, and he was selecting posts suitable for its repair.

Aksinia had arisen with two rosy blushes in her cheeks and a youthful glitter in her eyes. Stepan noticed the change, and as he was having breakfast he could not forbear to ask:

"What's happened to you?"

"What's happened?" Aksinia echoed him.

"Your face is shining as though you had smeared yourself with butter."

"It's the heat of the fire," and turning round, she glanced stealthily out of the window to see whether Misha Koshevoi's sister was coming.

But the girl did not arrive until late in the afternoon. Tormented with waiting, Aksinia started up, asking:

"Do you want me, Mashutka?"

"Come out for a moment," the girl replied.

Stepan was combing his hair before a scrap of mirror fixed above the stove. Aksinia looked at him nervously.

"You aren't going out, are you?" she asked.

He did not answer immediately, but put the comb into his trouser pocket and picked up a pack of cards and his pipe, lying on the stove ledge. Then he said:

"I'm going along to Anikushka's for a while."

"And when are you ever at home? You spend every night at cards. You're not going to play for points?"

"Enough of that, Aksinia. There's someone waiting for you."

Aksinia went out. Mashutka welcomed her with a smile and a droop of her eyelashes.

"Grishka's come back," she said.

"Well?"

"He told me to tell you to come along to our hut as soon as it's dark."

Seizing the girl's hand, Aksinia drew her towards the outer door.

"Softer, softer, dear! Did he tell you to say anything else?"

"He said you were to get your things together and bring them along."

Burning and trembling, stepping from foot to foot like a mettlesome horse, Aksinia turned and glanced at the kitchen door:

"Lord, how am I to—so quickly? Well—wait; tell him I'll be along as soon as I can. . . . But where will he meet me?"

"You're to come to our hut."

"Oh, no!"

"All right, I'll tell him to come out and wait for you."

Stepan was drawing on his coat as Aksinia went in. "What did she want?" he asked between two puffs at a cigarette.

"Oh, she came to ask me—to cut out a skirt for her."

Blowing the ash off his cigarette, Stepan went to the door. "Don't wait up for me," he said as he went out.

Aksinia ran to the frosted window and dropped to her knees before the bench. Stepan's footsteps sounded along the path trodden out in the snow to the gate. The wind caught a spark from his cigarette and carried it back to the window. Through the melted circle of glass Aksinia caught a glimpse of his fur cap and the profile of his face.

She feverishly turned jackets, skirts, and kerchiefs—her dowry—out of the great chest and threw them into a large shawl. Panting, her eyes wandering, she passed through the kitchen for the last time and, putting out the light, ran on to the steps. She fastened the kitchen door by the chain. Someone emerged from the Melekhovs' hut to see to the cattle. She waited until the footsteps had died away, then ran down to the Don. Strands of hair escaped from her kerchief and tickled her cheeks. Clutching her bundle she made her way by side lanes to the Koshevois' hut, her strength ebbing, her feet feeling like cast iron. Gregor was waiting for her at the gate. He took the bundle and silently led the way into the steppe.

Beyond the hut Aksinia slowed her pace and caught at Gregor's sleeve. "Wait a moment," she asked him.

"What is there to wait for? The moon will be late tonight, so we must hurry."

"Wait, Grishka!" She halted, doubled up with pain.

"What's the matter?" Gregor turned back to her.

"Something—in my belly. I carried too much away with me." She licked her dry lips and clutched at her bowels. She stood a moment bowed and miserable and then, poking her hair under her kerchief, set off again.

"You haven't asked where I'm taking you to. I might be leading you to the nearest cliff to push you over." Gregor smiled in the darkness.

"It's all the same to me now. I can't go back." Her voice trembled with an unhappy smile.

That night Stepan returned at midnight as usual. He went first to the stable, threw the scattered hay back into the manger, removed the horse's halter, then went to the hut. "She must have gone out for the evening," he thought, as he unfastened the chain. He entered the kitchen, closed the door fast, and struck a match. He had been in a winning vein that evening and so was quiet and drowsy. He lit the lamp and gaped at the disorder of the kitchen, not divining the reason. A little astonished, he went into the best room. The open chest yawned blackly. On the floor lay an old jacket which Aksinia had forgotten in her hurry. Stepan tore off his sheepskin and ran back to the kitchen for the light. He stared around the best room, and at last he understood. He dropped the lamp, tore his sabre down from the wall, gripped the hilt until the veins swelled in his fingers, raised Aksinia's blue and yellow jacket on its point, threw the jacket up in the air, and with a short swing of the sabre cut it in two as it fell.

Grey, savage, in his wolfish yearning he threw the pieces of old jacket up to the ceiling again and again; the sharp steel whistled as it cut them in their flight.

Then, tearing off the sword-knot, he threw the sabre into a corner, went into the kitchen, and sat down at the table. His head bowed, with trembling fingers he stroked the unwashed table-top time after time.

Troubles never come singly.

The morning after Gregor had left home, through Getka's carelessness Miron Korshunov's pedigree bull gored the throat of his finest mare. Getka came running into the kitchen, white, distracted, and trembling.

"Trouble, master! The bull, curse him, the damned bull!"

"Well, what about the bull?" Miron asked in alarm.

"He's done the mare in. Gored her. . . ."

Miron ran half-undressed into the yard. By the well Mitka was beating the red five-year-old bull with a stick. The bull, his head down and dewlap dragging over the snow, was churning up the snow with his hoofs and scattering a silvery powder around his tail. He would not yield before the drubbing, but danced about on his hind legs as though intending to charge. Mitka beat him on his nose and sides, cursing the while and paying no heed to the labourer who was trying to drag him back by his belt.

Miron Gregorievich ran to the well. The mare was standing by the fence, her head drooping and a fine shiver running over her body. Her heaving flanks were wet with sweat, and blood was running down her chest. A rose-coloured wound a hand-breadth deep and revealing the windpipe gaped on her neck. Miron seized her by the forelock and raised her head. The mare fixed her glazing eyes on her master as though mutely asking: "What next?" As if in answer to the question Miron shouted:

"Run and tell someone to scald some oak bark. Hurry!"

Getka ran to strip some bark from a tree, and Mitka came across to his father, one eye fixed on the bull circling and bellowing about the yard.

"Hold the mare by her forelock," his father ordered. "Someone run for some twine. Quickly!"

They tied string round the mare's upper lip so that she should not feel the pain, and then washed the wound. With freezing fingers Miron threaded raw thread through a darning-needle and sewed up the edges, making a neat seam. He had hardly turned away to go back to the house when his wife came running from the kitchen, alarm written large on her face. She called her husband aside:

"Natalia's here, Gregorich! . . . Ah, my God!"

"Now what's the matter?" Miron demanded, his face paling.

"It's Gregor. He's left home!" Lukinichna flung out her arms like a rook preparing for flight, clapped her hands against her skirt, and broke into a whine:

"Disgraced before all the village! Lord, what a blow! Oh! . . ."

Miron found Natalia standing in the middle of the kitchen. Two tears welled in her eyes, her cheeks were deeply flushed.

"What are you doing here?" her father blustered as he ran into the room. "Has your husband beaten you? Can't you get on together?"

"He's gone away!" Natalia groaned, and she swayed and fell on her knees before her father. "Father, my life is blighted. . . . Take me back. . . . Gregor's gone away with that woman. . . . He's left me. Father, I've been crushed into the dust!" she sobbed, gazing imploringly up at her father's grey beard.

"Wait, wait now. . . ."

"I can't go on living there! Take me back!" She crawled on her knees to the chest and dropped her head on her arms. Tears at such a time are like rain in a May drought. Her mother pressed Natalia's head against her skirt, whispering soothing, motherly words; but Miron, infuriated, ran out to the steps:

"Harness two horses to the sleigh!" he shouted.

A cock pattering importantly around behind its hen on the steps took alarm at the shout, jumped away, and fluttered agitatedly off towards the barn, squawking indignantly.

"Harness the horses!" Miron kicked again and again at the fretted balustrade of the steps until it was hopelessly ruined. He returned to the kitchen only when Getka hurried out from the stables with the pair of horses, harnessing them as he went.

Mitka drove with Getka to the Melekhovs' for Natalia's possessions. In his abstraction Getka sent a young pig in the road flying. "Maybe the master will forget all about the mare now," he was thinking, and rejoiced, letting the reins hang loose. "But he's such an old devil, he'll never forget," and Getka brought the whip-lash hard down across the horses' backs.

CHAPTER 10

Eugene Listnitsky held a commission as troop commander in the ataman's Life Guard regiment. Having had a tumble during the officers' hurdle races and broken his left arm, when he came out of the hospital he took a furlough and went to stay with his father for six weeks.

The old general lived alone in Yagodnoe. He had lost his wife while driving in the suburbs of Warsaw in the eighties of the nineteenth century. Revolutionaries had attempted to shoot the Cossack general, had missed him, but had killed his wife and coachman. Listnitsky was left with his two-year-old son, Eugene. Soon after this event the general retired, went to live at Yagodnoe, and lived a lonely, harsh life.

He sent his son Eugene to the Cadets' corps as soon as the lad was old enough, and occupied himself with farming. He purchased blood stock from the Imperial stables, crossed them with the finest mares from England and from the famous Provalsky stables, and reared a new stock. He raised cattle and livestock on his own and rented land, sowed grain (with hired labour), hunted with his borzois in the autumn and winter, and occasionally locked himself into the hall and drank for a week on end. He was troubled with a stomach complaint, and his doctor had strictly forbidden him to swallow anything; he had to extract the goodness from all his food by mastication, spitting out the residue on a silver tray held by his personal servant, Benyamin.

Benyamin was a half-witted, swarthy young peasant, with a shock of thick black hair. He had been in Listnitsky's service for six years. When he first had to wait on the general he could not bear to watch the old man spitting out the chewed food. But after a time he grew accustomed to it. After some months he thought as he watched his master chewing the white meat of a turkey: "What a waste of good food! He doesn't eat it himself, and my belly is turning over with hunger. I'll try it after he's finished with it." After that he made a practice of carrying the silver tray into the anteroom when his master had dined, and there hurriedly gulping down all that was left. Perhaps it was for this reason that he began to grow fat and double-chinned.

The other inhabitants of the farm were the maid, the pock-marked cook, Lukeria, the ancient stableman, Sashka, and the shepherd, Tikhon. From the very first Lukeria would not allow Aksinia to help in the cooking for the master, and Aksinia was set to work washing the floors of the house three times a week, feeding the innumerable fowls, and keeping the chicken-house clean. Gregor spent much of his time in the spacious stables with Sashka, the stableman. The old man was one mass of grey hair, but everybody still familiarly called him Sashka. Probably even old Listnitsky, for whom he had worked more than twenty years, had forgotten his surname. In his youth Sashka had been the coachman, but as he grew old and feeble and his sight began to fail he was made stableman. Stocky, covered with greenish-grey hair, with a nose that had been flattened by a stick in his youth, he wore an everlasting childish smile and gazed out on the world with twinkling, artless eyes. The reverend, apostolic expression of his face was marred by his broken nose and his hanging, scarred underlip. Sashka was fond of vodka, and when he was in his cups he would wander about the yard as though he were master. Stamping his feet, he would stand beneath old Listnitsky's bedroom and call loudly and sternly:

"Mikolai Lexievich! Mikolai Lexievich!"

If old Listnitsky happened to be in his

bedroom he would come to the window.

"You're drunk, you scoundrel!" he would thunder.

Sashka would hitch up his trousers and wink and smile. His smile danced right across his face.

"Mikolai Lexievich, Your Excellency, I know you!" He would shake his lean, dirty finger threateningly.

"Go and sleep it off!" his master would smile pacifyingly.

"You can't take in Sashka!" the stableman would laugh, going up to the railings of the fence. "Mikolai Lexievich, you're like me. Me and you—we're like fish in the water. You and me—we're rich, ah!" Here he would fling his arms wide open to show how rich. "We're known by everybody, all over the Don district. We . . ." Sashka's voice would suddenly sound miserable and surreptitious: "Me and you—Your Excellency, we're good to everybody, only we've both got rotting noses."

"What with?" his master would ask, turning purple with laughter.

"With vodka!" Sashka would stamp out the words, winking and licking his lips. "Don't drink, Mikolai Lexievich, or we'll be ruined, you and me. We'll drink everything away."

"Go and drink this away!" Old Listnitsky would throw out a twenty-kopek piece, and Sashka would catch it and hide it in his cap, crying:

"Well, good-bye, general."

"Have you watered the horses yet?" his master would ask with a smile.

"You lousy devil! You son of a swine!" Sashka would turn livid and in his anger would stutter and shake as though with the ague. "Sashka forget to water the horses? Eh? If I was dying I'd still crawl for a pail to water the horses. And he thinks . . ."

The old man would march off fuming at the undeserved reproach, cursing, and shaking his fist. Everything came naturally to him, even drinking and his familiarity with his master. He was irreplaceable as a stableman. Winter and summer he slept in the stables, in an empty stall. He was ostler and blacksmith; he cut grass for the horses in the spring and dug up medicinal roots on the steppe and in the valleys. Bunches of dried herbs, remedies for all the various horse ailments and diseases, hung high up on the stable walls.

Winter and summer a fine tingling aroma hung like a spider's web about the stall in which Sashka slept. Hay packed as hard as a board, covered with a horsecloth and his coat, smelling of horse sweat, served as mattress and bedding to his plank bed. The coat and a sheepskin were all the old man's worldly goods.

Tikhon, a healthy and dull-witted Cossack, lived with Lukeria and was needlessly jealous of her and Sashka. Regularly once a month he would take the old man by the button of his greasy shirt and lead him aside.

"Old man, don't you set your cap at my woman," he would say.

"That depends. . . ." Sashka would wink significantly.

"You ought to be ashamed of yourself at your age. . . . And you a doctor, too; you look after the horses . . . you know the Holy Book!"

"I like them pockmarked. Say good-bye to Lukeria, I'll be taking her away from you. She's like a currant pudding. . . ."

"Don't let me catch you or I'll kill you!" Tikhon would say, sighing and drawing some copper coins out of his pocket.

Life mouldered away in a sleepy torpor at Yagodnoe. The estate lay in a valley remote from all frequented roads, and from the autumn onward all connection with the neighbouring villages was broken. In the winter nights the wolf packs emerged from their forest lairs and terrified the horses with their howling. Tikhon used to go to the meadow to frighten them off with shot from his master's double-barrelled gun, and Lukeria would wait in suspense for the sound of the shot. At such times her imagination transformed bald-headed Tikhon into a handsome and desperately brave youth, and when the door of the servants' quarters slammed and Tikhon entered, she warmly embraced his frozen old bones.

In summer-time Yagodnoe was alive until late in the evening with the sound of labourers' voices. The master sowed some hundred acres with grain of various kinds. Occasionally Eugene came home and would wander boredly through the orchard and over the meadow or sit all the morning with rod and line by the lakeside. Eugene was of medium height and broad-chested. He arranged his hair Cossack-fashion, brushing it on the right side. His officer's tunic was always a perfect fit.

During the first ten days of Gregor's life on the estate he was frequently in the young master's company. One day Benyamin came smiling into the servants' quarters and announced:

"The young master wants you, Gregor."

Gregor went to Eugene's room and stood at the door. The master pointed to a chair. Gregor seated himself on the very edge.

"How do you like our horses?" Listnitsky asked.

"They're good horses. The grey is very good."

"Give him plenty of exercise, but don't gallop him."

"So Grand-dad Sashka told me."

Screwing up his eyes, the young master said:

"You have to go to the training camp in May, don't you?"

"Yes."

"I'll speak to the ataman about it. You won't need to go."

"Thank you, sir."

There was a momentary silence. Unbuttoning the collar of his uniform, Eugene scratched his womanishly white breast.

"Aren't you afraid of Aksinia's husband taking her from you?" he asked.

"He's thrown her over; he won't take her back."

"How do you know?"

"I saw one of the men from the village the other day, and he told me Stepan had said so to him."

"Aksinia's a fine-looking woman," Listnitsky remarked thoughtfully, staring over Gregor's head and smiling.

"Not bad," Gregor agreed, and his face clouded.

During the last few days of his furlough Eugene spent a great deal of his time in Gregor's room. Aksinia kept the little room spotlessly clean and made it gay with feminine gewgaws. The officer chose times for his visit when Gregor was occupied with the horses. He would first go into the kitchen and stand joking with Lukeria for a minute or two, then would pass into the farther room. One day he sat down on a stool, hunching his shoulders, and fixed a shamelessly smiling gaze on Aksinia. She was embarrassed by his presence, and the knitting-needles trembled in her fingers.

"Well, Aksinia, how are you getting on?" he asked, puffing at his cigarette until the room was filled with blue smoke.

"Very well, thank you." Aksinia raised her eyes, and meeting Eugene's transparent gaze silently telling of his desire, she turned crimson. She replied disconnectedly to his questions, avoiding his eyes and seeking an opportunity to leave the room.

"I must go and feed the ducks now," she told him.

"Sit a little longer. The ducks can wait," he smiled, and continued to ply her with questions concerning her past life, while his crystal-clear eyes pleaded obscenely.

When Gregor came in, Eugene offered him a cigarette, and went out soon after.

"What did he want?" Gregor asked Aksinia, not looking at her.

"How should I know?" Remembering the officer's look, Aksinia laughed forcedly. "He came in and sat there, just like this, Grishka" (she showed him how Eugene had sat with hunched back), "and sat and sat until I was sick of him."

"You made yourself pleasant to him, of course?" Gregor screwed up his eyes angrily. "You watch out, or I shall send him flying down the steps some day."

Aksinia gazed at Gregor with a smile on her lips and could not be sure whether he was speaking in jest or earnest.

CHAPTER 11

The winter broke during the fourth week of Lent. Open water began to fringe the edges of the Don; the ice, melting from the top, turned grey and swelled spongily. Of an evening a howling noise came from the hills, indicating frost according to the time-honoured saying, but in reality presaging the approaching thaw. In the morning the air tingled with the light frost, but by noon the earth was bare in patches, and in the nostrils was a scent of March, of the frozen bark of cherry trees, and rotting straw.

Miron Gregorievich leisurely made ready for the ploughing season, spending his days under the shed sharpening the teeth of the harrows and preparing for the thaw. During the fourth week of Lent old Grishaka fasted. He returned blue with cold from the church and complained to his daughter-in-law, Lukinichna:

"The priest starved me. He's no good. He's as slow as a carter with a load of eggs."

"You'd have been wiser to have fasted during Passion Week; it's warmer by then," she told him.

"Call Natalia," he replied. "Let her make me a pair of warmer stockings."

Natalia still lived in the belief that Gregor would return to her; her heart waited for him and would not listen to the warning whisper of sober reason. She spent the nights in a weary yearning, tosson her bed, crushed by her undeserved and unexpected shame. Another woe was now added to the first, and she awaited its sequel in a cold terror, casting about in her maiden room like a shot lapwing in a forest glade. From the earliest days of her return home her brother Mitka began to give her queer glances, and one day, catching her in the porch, he asked frankly:

"Are you still yearning after Grishka?"

"What has it to do with you?"

"I want to help you get rid of your pain."

Natalia glanced into his eyes and was terrified by what she saw there. Mitka's green cat's eyes glittered and their slits gleamed oilily in the dim light of the porch. Natalia slammed the door and ran to her grandfather's room, standing and listening to the beating of her heart. Two days later Mitka came up to her in the yard. He had been turning over fresh hay for the cattle, and green stalks of grass hung from his straight hair and his fur cap.

"Don't torture yourself, Natalia. . . ."

"I'll tell Father," she cried, raising her hands to protect herself.

"You're an idiot! What are you shouting for?"

"Go away, Mitka! I'll go at once and

tell Father. What eyes you make at me! It's a wonder the earth doesn't open and swallow you up. Don't come near me, Mitka," she pleaded.

"I won't now, but I'll come at night. By God, I'll come!" he replied.

Trembling, Natalia left the yard. That evening she made her bed on the chest and took her younger sister to sleep with her. All night she tossed and turned, her burning eyes seeking to pierce the darkness, her ears alert to the slightest sound, ready to scream the house down. But the silence was broken only by the snores of Grishaka sleeping in the next room and an occasional grunt from her sister.

Mitka had not got over the shame of his recent attempt at marriage, and he went about morose and ill-tempered. He went out every evening, and rarely arrived home again before dawn. He formed associations with women of undesirable reputation in the village and went to Stepan Astakhov's to play cards for stakes. His father watched his behaviour, but said nothing.

Just before Easter, Natalia met Pantaleimon Prokoffievich close to Mokhov's shop. He called to her:

"Wait a moment!"

She halted. Her heart yearned as she saw her father-in-law's face, mournfully reminding her of Gregor.

"Why don't you come and see us sometimes?" the old man asked her diffidently, avoiding her eyes as though he himself had been guilty of some offence against her. "The wife is longing to see you. . . . Well, perhaps you will come some day?"

Natalia recovered from her embarrassment. "Thank you," she said, and after a moment's hesitation (she wanted to say "Father") she added: "Pantaleimon Prokoffiech. I've been very busy at home."

"Our Grishka—ah!" the old man shook his head bitterly. "He's tricked us, the scoundrel. How well we'd have got on together!"

"Oh, well, Father"—Natalia spoke in a high-pitched, grating voice—"clearly it wasn't to be."

Pantaleimon fiddled about embarrassedly as he saw Natalia's eyes fill with tears. Her lips were pressed together to restrain her desire to weep.

"Good-bye, my dear," he said. "Don't grieve over him, the son of a swine! He's not worth the nail on your little finger. Maybe he'll come back. I'm thinking of going to see him, but it's difficult."

Natalia walked away with her head sunk on her breast. Pantaleimon stood dancing from foot to foot as though about to break into a run. As she turned the corner Natalia glanced back; the old man was limping across the square, leaning heavily on his stick.

As spring approached, the meetings in Stockman's workshop were held less frequently. The villagers were preparing for the field work, and only Ivan Alexievich, the engine-man, and Valet came from the mill, bringing David with them. On Maundy Thursday they gathered at the workshop in the early evening. Stockman was sitting at his bench, cleaning a silver ring made from a fifty-kopek piece. A broad bar of rays from the setting sun streamed through the window. The engine-man picked up a pair of pincers and turned them over in his hand.

"I had to go to the master the other day to ask about a piston," he remarked. "It will have to be taken to Millerovo, we can't mend it here. There's a crack in it as long as this." Ivan Alexievich measured the length on his little finger.

"There's a works at Millerovo, isn't there?" Stockman asked, scattering a fine silver rain as he filed the coin.

"A steel-foundry. I had to spend some days there last year," Ivan replied.

"Many workers?"

"Some five hundred."

"And what are they like?" The words came deliberately from Stockman.

"They're well off. They're none of your proletariat, they're muck."

"Why is that?" Valet asked.

"Because they're too well off. Each has his own little house, his wife, and every comfort. And a good half of them are Baptists into the bargain. The master himself is their preacher, and they suck one another's noses, and the dirt on them is so thick you couldn't scrape it off with a rake. Well, and I went to Sergei Platonovich," Ivan Alexievich continued his story, "and he had company with him, so he told me to wait outside. I sat down and waited and heard them talking through the door. Mokhov was saying there was going to be a war with the Germans very soon; he had read it in a book. But someone else said there couldn't be a war between Germany and Russia, because Germany needed our grain. Then I heard a third voice; I found out afterwards it was that of the officer, old Listnitsky's son. 'There will be a war,' he said, 'between Germany and France, over vineyards, but it's nothing to do with us.' What do you think, Osip Davidovich?" Ivan asked, turning to Stockman.

"I'm no good at prophecies," Stockman replied, staring fixedly at the ring in his hand.

"Once they do start we'll have to go. Like it or not, they'll drag us there by the hair," Valet declared.

"It's like this, boys," Stockman said, gently taking the pincers out of the engine-man's hands. He spoke seriously, evidently intending to explain the matter thoroughly. Valet sat himself comfortably on the bench, and David's lips shaped into an "O," revealing his strong teeth.

In definite, well-chosen words Stockman outlined the struggle of the capitalist states for markets and colonies. When he had finished, Ivan Alexievich asked anxiously:

"Yes, but where do we come in?"

"Your heads will ache for the drunken orgies of others." Stockman smiled.

"Don't talk like a child," Valet said venomously. "You know the saying: 'The master tugs at the leash, but the dog shakes its head.' "

"And what was Listnitsky visiting Mokhov for?" David changed the subject.

"He was on his way to the station. Yes, and here's some more news. When I went out of the house I saw—who do you think? Gregor Melekhov! He was standing outside with a whip in his hand."

"He's Listnitsky's coachman," David explained.

It was getting late, and Ivan Alexievich initiated a general movement to depart. Stockman accompanied his guests to the gate, then locked up the workshop and went into the hut.

Gregor returned on Palm Sunday from his journey with Eugene to the station. He found the thaw had eaten away the snow; the road had broken up within a couple of days.

At a Ukrainian village some twenty miles back from the station he all but lost his horses as he was crossing a stream. He arrived at the village early in the evening. During the previous night the ice of the rivulet had broken and floated away, and the stream was swollen and foaming with muddy brown water. The tavern at which he had stopped to feed the horses on the way out lay on the farther side of the stream. The water might easily rise still higher during the night, and Gregor decided to cross.

He drove to the point where he had crossed over the ice on the outward journey and found the stream had overflowed its banks. A piece of fencing and half a cartwheel were eddying in the middle. There were fresh traces of sledge-runners on the bare sand at the edge. He halted the horses and jumped down to look at the marks more closely. At the water's edge the tracks turned a little to the left and disappeared into the stream. He measured the distance to the other side with his eyes: fifty yards at the most. He went to the horses to see that the harness was in good order. At that moment an aged Ukrainian came towards him from the nearest hut.

"Is there a good crossing here?" Gregor asked him, waving his reins at the seething brown flood.

"People crossed there this morning."

"Is it deep?"

"No. It might flow into the sleigh."

Gregor gathered up the reins and, holding his knout ready, urged on the horses with a curt, imperative command. They moved unwillingly, snorting and snuffing at the water. Gregor cracked his whip and stood up on the seat.

The bay on the left shook its head and suddenly pulled on the traces. Gregor glanced down at his feet; the water was swirling over the front of the sleigh. At first the horses were wading up to their knees, but suddenly the stream rose to their breasts. Gregor tried to turn them back, but they refused to answer the rein and began to swim. The tail of the sleigh was swung round by the current, and the horses' heads were forced upstream. The water flowed in waves over their backs, the sleigh rocked and pulled them back strongly.

"Hey! Hey! to the right!" the Ukrainian shouted, running along the bank and waving his three-cornered cap in his hands.

Savagely raging, Gregor incessantly shouted and urged on the horses. The water foamed in eddies behind the dragging sleigh. The runners struck against a jutting pile, the remains of the bridge which had been swept away overnight, and the sleigh turned over with extraordinary ease. With a groan Gregor plunged in headfirst, but he did not lose his grip of the reins. He was dragged by the edges of his sheepskin, by his feet, drawn with gentle insistence, rocking and turning over and over at the side of the sleigh. He succeeded in clutching a runner, dropped the reins, and hauled himself along hand over hand, making his way to the singletrees. He was about to seize the iron-shod end of the singletree when one horse, in its struggle against the current, lashed out with its hind leg and struck him on the knee. Choking, Gregor threw out his hands and caught at the traces. His body fierily tingling with the cold, he managed to reach the horse's head, and the animal fixed the maddened, mortally terrified gaze of its bloodshot eyes right into his dilated pupils.

Again and again he grasped at the slippery leather reins, but they eluded his fingers. Somehow he managed at last to seize them. Abruptly his legs scraped along ground. Dragging himself to the edge of the water, he stumbled forward and fell in the foaming shallows, knocked off his feet by the horses' breasts.

Trampling over him, the horses tugged the sleigh violently out of the water and halted a few paces away, exhausted, shuddering, and steaming. Unconscious of any pain, Gregor jumped to his feet; the cold enveloped him as though in unbearably hot dough. He was trembling even more than the horses, feeling that he was as weak on his legs as an unweaned infant. He gathered his wits and, turning the sleigh on to its runners, drove the horses off at a gallop to get them warm. He flew into the street of the village as though attacking an enemy and turned into the first open gate without slackening his pace.

Fortunately he had chanced upon a hospitable Ukrainian, who sent his son to attend to the horses and himself helped Gregor to undress. In a tone permitting of no question he ordered his wife to light the stove. Until his own clothes were dry Gregor stretched himself out on top of the stove in his host's trousers. After a supper of cabbage soup he went to sleep.

He set off again long before dawn came. A good eighty-five miles of travel lay before him, and every minute was precious. The untracked confusion of the flooded spring steppe was at hand; every little ravine or gully had become a roaring torrent of snow-water.

The black, bare road exhausted the horses. Over the hard road of the early morning frost he reached a village lying three miles off his route and stopped at a crossroad. The horses were smoking with sweat; behind him lay the gleaming track of the sleigh-runners in the ground. He abandoned the sleigh and set off again, riding one horse bareback and leading the other by the reins. He arrived at Yagodnoe in the morning of Palm Sunday.

Old Listnitsky listened attentively to his story of the journey and went to look at the horses. Sashka was leading them up and down the yard, angrily eyeing their sunken flanks.

"How are they?" the master asked. "They haven't been overdriven, have they?"

"No. The bay has a sore on the chest where the collar has rubbed, but it's nothing."

"Go and get some rest." Listnitsky indicated Gregor with his hand. Gregor went to his room. But he had only one night's rest. The next morning Benyamin came and called to him:

"Gregor, the master wants you. At once."

The general was shuffling about the hall in felt slippers. Only after Gregor had coughed twice did he look up.

"Ah, yes! Go and saddle the stallion and my horse. Tell Lukeria not to feed the dogs. They're going hunting."

Gregor turned to leave the room. His master stopped him with a shout:

"Do you hear? And you're going with me."

Gregor led the saddled horses to the palisade and whistled to the dogs. Listnitsky came out, attired in a jerkin of blue cloth and girdled with an ornamental leather belt. A nickel cork-lined flask was slung at his back; the whip hanging from his arm trailed behind him like a snake.

As he held the rein for his master to mount, Gregor was astonished at the ease with which old Listnitsky hoisted his bony body into the saddle. "Keep close behind me," the general curtly ordered as he gathered the reins in his gloved hand.

Gregor rode the stallion. It was not shod on the hind hoofs, and as it trod on the shards of ice it slipped and sat on its hindquarters. It called for strong use of the bridle, for it arched its short neck and glanced askance at its rider, trying to bite his knees. When they reached the top of the hill from Yagodnoe, Listnitsky put his horse into a fast trot. The chain of hounds followed Gregor; one black old bitch ran with her muzzle touching the end of the stallion's tail. The horse tried to reach her by falling back on its hindquarters, but the bitch dropped behind, giving Gregor a yearning, grandmotherly glance.

They reached their objective, the Olshansky ravine, in half an hour. Listnitsky rode through the undergrowth along the brow of the ravine. Gregor dropped down into the valley, cautiously avoiding the numerous holes. From time to time he looked up, and through the steely blue of a straggling and naked alder grove he saw Listnitsky's clearly defined figure standing in the stirrups. Behind him the hounds were running in a bunch along the undulating ridge. Pulling off his glove, Gregor fumbled in his pocket for some cigarette paper, thinking to have a smoke.

"After him!" a shout came like a pistol-shot from the other side of the ridge.

Gregor raised his head and saw Listnitsky galloping along with upraised whip.

"After him!"

Crossing the rushy and reedy bottom of the ravine, slipping along with body close to the ground, a shaggy, dirty brown wolf was running swiftly. Leaping the bed of the stream, it stopped and, turning quickly, caught sight of the dogs. They were coming after it stretched in horseshoe formation, to cut it off from the wood at the end of the ravine.

With a springy stride the wolf made for the wood. The old bitch came almost straight towards it, another hound behind her. The wolf hesitated for a moment, and as Gregor rode up out of the ravine he lost sight of it. When next he had a good view from a hillock, the wolf was far away in the steppe, making for a neighbouring ravine. Gregor could see the hounds running through the undergrowth behind it, and old Listnitsky riding slightly to the side, plying his horse with the butt of his whip. As the wolf reached the ravine the hounds were beginning to overtake it, and one was almost on top of the hunted animal.

Gregor put his horse into a gallop, vainly trying to see what was happening ahead of him. His eyes were streaming with tears, and his ears were deafened by the whistling wind. He was suddenly possessed by the excitement of the hunt. Bending over his horse's neck, he flew along like the wind. When he reached the ravine neither wolf nor dogs were to be seen. A moment or two later Listnitsky overtook him. Reining in his horse sharply, he shouted:

"Which way did they go?"

"Into the ravine, I think."

"You overtake them from the left. After them!" The old man dug his heels into his horse's flanks and rode off to the right. Gregor dropped into a hollow, and with whip and shout rode his horse hard for a good mile. The damp, sticky earth flew up under the hoofs, striking him on the face. The long ravine bent to the right and branched into three. Gregor crossed the first fork and caught sight of the dark chain of hounds chasing the wolf across the steppe. The animal had been headed off from the heart of the ravine, which was densely overgrown with oaks and alders, and was now making for a dry, brush- and thistle-covered valley.

Rising in his stirrups, and wiping the tears from his eyes with his sleeve, Gregor watched them. Glancing momentarily to the left, he realized that he was in the steppe close to his native village. Near by lay the irregular square of land which he and Natalia had ploughed in the autumn. He deliberately guided the stallion across the patch, and during the few moments in which the animal was sliding and stumbling over the clods the zest for the hunt died to ashes within him. He now calmly urged on the heavily sweating horse and, glancing round to see whether Listnitsky was looking, dropped into an easy trot.

Some distance away he could see the empty camping-quarters of ploughers; a little farther off three pairs of bullocks were dragging a plough across the fresh, velvety soil.

"From the village, surely. Whose land is that? That's not Anikushka, is it?" Gregor screwed up his eyes as he recognized the man following the plough.

He saw two Cossacks drop the plough and run to head off the wolf from the near-by ravine. One, in a visored, red-banded cap, chin-strap under his chin, was waving an iron bar. Suddenly the wolf squatted down in a deep furrow. The foremost hound flew right over it and fell with its forelegs tucked beneath it; the old bitch following tried to stop, her hindquarters scraping along the cloddy, ploughed ground; but unable to halt in time, she tumbled against the wolf. The hunted animal shook its head violently, and the bitch ricocheted off it. Now the mass of hounds fastened on the wolf, and they all dragged for some yards over the ploughed land. Gregor was off his horse half a minute before his master. He fell to his knees, his hand on his hunting-knife.

"There! In the throat!" the Cossack with the iron bar cried in a voice which Gregor knew well. Panting heavily, he ran up and lay down at Gregor's side and, dragging away the hound which had fastened on the hunted animal's belly, tied the wolf's forelegs with a cord. Gregor felt under the animal's shaggy fur for its windpipe and drew the knife across it.

"The dogs! The dogs! Drive them off!" old Listnitsky cried as he dropped from his saddle.

Gregor managed with difficulty to drive away the dogs, then glanced towards his master. Standing a little way off was Stepan Astakhov. His face working strangely, he was turning the iron bar over and over in his hands.

"Where are you from, my man?" Listnitsky turned to Stepan.

"From Tatarsk," Stepan answered after a momentary hesitation, and he took a step in Gregor's direction.

"What's your name?" Listnitsky asked.

"Astakhov."

"When are you going home, my lad?"

"Tonight."

"Bring us that carcass." Listnitsky pointed to the wolf with his foot. "I'll pay whatever it costs." He wiped the sweat from his purple face with his scarf, turned away, and slipped the flask off his back.

Gregor went to his stallion. As he set foot in the stirrup he glanced back. Trembling uncontrollably, Stepan was coming towards him, pressing his great, heavy hands against his chest. He walked up to the horse and seized the stirrup, pressing himself right against the stallion's side.

"You're looking well, Gregor!" Stepan said.

"Praise be!"

"What are your thoughts about it? Eh?"

"What is it I'm to think about?"

"You've carried off another man's wife—and you're having your will of her?"

"Let go of the stirrup."

"Don't be afraid! I won't beat you."

"I'm not afraid. Stop that talk!" Gregor flushed and raised his voice.

"I shan't fight you today; I don't want to. . . . But mark my words, Grishka; sooner or later I shall kill you."

" 'We shall see,' said the blind man!"

"Mark my words well. You've brought shame on me. You've castrated my life as if I was a pig. You see there—" he stretched out his hands palms-upward. "I'm ploughing, and the Lord knows what for. Do I need it for myself? I could shift around a bit and get through the winter that way. It's only the dreariness of it all that gets me down. You've brought terrible shame on me, Gregor."

"Don't complain to me. I shan't understand. The full man doesn't understand the hungry."

"That's true," Stepan agreed, staring up into Gregor's face. And suddenly he broke into a simple, boyish smile which wrinkled the corners of his eyes into tiny furrows. "I'm sorry only for one thing, lad, very sorry. You remember how the year before last we boxed together at Shrovetide?"

"No, I don't."

"Why, it was when the single men fought the married, do you remember? And how I chased after you? You were thinner then, a green rush as against me. I spared you that time, but if I'd hit you as you were running away, I'd have split you in two. You ran quickly, all springy-like; if I'd struck you hard on the side you wouldn't have been alive in the world today."

"Don't grieve over it, we may yet come up against each other."

Stepan rubbed his forehead with his hand as though trying to recall something. Still holding the stirrup with his left hand, he walked alongside the stallion. Gregor watched his every movement. He noticed Stepan's drooping flaxen moustaches, the heavy scrub of his long unshaven chin. His dirty face, marked with whiter runnels of sweat, was sad and strangely unfamiliar. As he looked Gregor felt that he might well be gazing from a hilltop at the distant steppe veiled in a rainy mist. A grey weariness and emptiness ashened Stepan's features. He dropped behind without a word of farewell. Gregor touched up his horse into a canter.

"Wait a bit. And how is—how is Aksinia?"

Knocking a lump of earth off his boot with the whip, Gregor replied:

"Oh, she's all right."

He halted the stallion and glanced back. Stepan was standing with his feet planted wide apart, chewing a piece of twig between his teeth. For a moment Gregor had a feeling of immeasurable pity for him, but jealousy rose uppermost. Turning in his saddle, he shouted:

"She doesn't yearn for you, don't worry!"

"Is that so?"

Gregor brought the whip down between his horse's ears and rode away without replying.

The night before Easter Sunday the sky was overcast with masses of black cloud, and rain began to fall. A raw darkness enveloped Tatarsk. At dusk the ice of the Don began to crack with a protracted, rolling groan, and crushed by a mass of broken ice, the first floe emerged from the water. The ice broke suddenly over a length of three miles and drifted downstream. The floes crashed against one another and against the banks, to the sound of the church-bell ringing measuredly for the service. At the first bend, where the Don sweeps to the left, the ice was dammed up. The roar and scraping of the moving floes reached the village. The lads had gathered in the church enclosure. Through the open doors came the muffled tones of the service, light streamed gaily through the windows, while outside in the darkness the lads surreptitiously tickled and kissed the girls and whispered dirty stories to one another.

From the Don came a flowing whisper, rustle, and crunch, as though a strongly-built, gaily-dressed woman as tall as a poplar were passing by, her great, invisible skirts rustling.

At midnight Mitka Korshunov, riding a horse bareback, clattered through the Egyptian darkness up to the church. He tied the reins to the horse's mane and with a smack of the hand on her flanks sent her back home. He listened to the sound of the hoofs for a moment; then, adjusting his belt, he went into the church. At the porch he removed his cap, bent his head devoutly, and thrusting aside the women, pressed up to the altar. The Cossacks were crowded in a black mass on the left; on the right was an azure throng of women. Mitka found his father in the front row and, seizing him by the elbow, whispered into his ear:

"Father, come outside for a moment."

As he pressed out of the church through the dense curtain of mingled odours, Mitka's nostrils quivered. He was overwhelmed by the vapour of burning wax, the stench of women's sweaty bodies, the deathly odour of clothes brought out only at Christmas and Easter-time, the smell of damp leather, naphthaline, and other indistinguishable scents.

In the porch Mitka put his mouth close to his father's ear and said:

"Natalia is dying."

On Good Friday the women gathered in the hut of Korshunov's neighbour Pelagea Maidannikov for a talk. Her husband, Gavrila, had written from Lodz that he was trying to get furlough for Easter. Pelagea had whitewashed the walls and tidied up the hut as early as the Monday before Easter, and from Thursday onward she waited expectantly, running to the gate and standing at the fence, straight-haired and gaunt, the signs of her pregnancy showing in her face. Shading her eyes with her palm, she stared down the road. Perhaps he was coming! She was pregnant, but lawfully so. Gavrila had returned from his regiment the previous year, bringing his wife a present of Polish chintz. He had spent four nights with his wife, and on the fifth day had got drunk, cursed in Polish and German, and with tears in his eyes had sat singing an old Cossack song about Poland. His friends and brothers had sat with him, singing and drinking vodka before dinner. After dinner he had said good-bye to his family and had ridden off. And from that day Pelagea had begun to watch the hem of her skirt.

She explained to Natalia Korshunov how she came to be pregnant. "A day or two before Gavrila arrived, I had a dream," she said. "I was going through the meadow, and I saw our old cow in front of me, the one we sold last August. She was walking along, and milk was dripping from her teats. Lord, I thought, how did I ever come to milk her so badly? Next day old woman Drozdikha came for some hops, and I told her my dream. And she told me to break a piece of wax off a candle, roll it into a ball, and to take and bury it in some cow-dung, for misfortune was watching at the window. I ran to do as she said, but I couldn't find the candle. I had had one, I knew, but the children had taken it or else the cockroaches had eaten it. Then Gavrila arrived, and the misfortune with him. Before that I had gone for three years without trouble, and now look at me!" She thrust her fingers into her belly.

Pelagea fretted while waiting for her husband. She was bored with her own company, and so on the Friday she invited her women neighbours to come and spend the evening with her. Natalia came with an unfinished stocking, for when spring came Grand-dad Grishaka felt the cold all the more. She was unnaturally full of high spirits and laughed more than necessary at the others' jokes, trying to hide her yearning for her husband from them. Pelagea was sitting on the stove with her bare, violet-veined legs dangling, and bantering the young and shrewish Frossia.

"How was it you beat your husband, Frossia?" she asked.

"Don't you know how? On the back, on the head, and wherever I could lay my hands on him."

"I didn't mean that, but why you did it."

"I had to," Frossia answered unwillingly.

"If you were to catch your husband with another woman would you keep your tongue quiet?" a gaunt woman asked deliberately.

"Tell us all about it, Frossinia."

"There's nothing to tell."

"Don't be afraid, we're all friends here."

Spitting out a sunflower-seed husk into her hand, Frossia smiled. "Well, I'd noticed his goings-on for a long time, and then someone told me he was at the mill with a loose woman from across the Don. I went out and found them by the—"

"Any news of your husband, Natalia?" another woman interrupted, turning to Natalia.

"He's at Yagodnoe," she replied in a whisper.

"Do you expect to live with him or not?"

"She might expect to, but he doesn't," their hostess intervened. Natalia felt the hot blood surging to her face. She bent her head over her stocking and glanced from beneath her eyelids at the women. Realizing that she could not hide her flush of shame from them, she deliberately, yet so clumsily that everybody noticed it, sent the ball of wool rolling from her knees and then bent down and fumbled with her fingers over the cold floor.

"Spit on him, woman! He would only be a yoke to you," one woman advised her with unconcealed pity in her voice.

Natalia's artificial animation died away like a spark in the wind. The women's conversation turned to the latest scandal, to tittle-tattle and gossip. Natalia knitted in silence. She forced herself to sit on until the party broke up, and then went home turning over an unformulated decision in her mind. Shame for her uncertain situation (for she still would not believe that Gregor had gone for ever, and was ready to forgive him and take him back) drove her on to a further step. She resolved to send a letter secretly to him, in order to learn whether he had gone altogether or whether he was changing his mind. When she reached home she found Grishaka sitting in his little room reading an old leather-bound, grease-stained copy of the Gospels. Her father was in the kitchen mending a fish-net. Her mother had put the children to bed and was asleep on the stove. Natalia took off her jacket and wandered aimlessly from room to room. She stopped for a moment in her grandfather's room, staring listlessly at the pile of devotional books under the ikons.

"Grand-dad, have you any paper?" she asked him.

"What sort of paper?" Grishaka asked, puckering his forehead into frowns.

"Paper to write on."

The old man fumbled in a Psalter and drew out a crumpled sheet of paper that smelt strongly of incense.

"And a pencil?"

"Ask your father. Go away, my dear, and don't bother."

She obtained a stump of pencil from her father and sat down at the table, laboriously formulating her long-pondered thought and evoking a numb, gnawing pain in her heart.

Gregor Pantalievich,

Tell me, will you, how I am to live, and whether my life is quite lost or not. You left home and you didn't say a single word to me. I haven't done you any wrong, and I waited for you to untie my hands and to say that you have gone for good, but you've gone away and are as silent as the grave.

I thought you had gone off in the heat of the moment, and waited for you to come back, but I don't want to part from you. Better one should be trodden into the ground than two. Have pity at last and write. Then I shall know what to think, but now I stand in the middle of the road.

Don't be angry with me, Grishka, for the love of Christ.

Natalia

Next morning she promised Getka vodka and persuaded him to ride with the letter to Yagodnoe. Moody with expectation of his promised drink, Getka led a horse into the yard and, without informing Miron Gregorievich, rode off to Yagodnoe.

He returned in the afternoon. He brought with him a piece of blue sugar-bag paper, and as he drew it out of his pocket he winked at Natalia.

"The road was terrible. I got such a

shaking that it upset my kidneys," he informed her.

Natalia read the letter, and her face turned grey. The four words scribbled on the paper entered her heart like sharp teeth rending a weave.

Live alone.

Gregor Melekhov

Hurriedly, as though not trusting her own strength, Natalia went into the house and lay down on her bed. Her mother was lighting the stove for the night, in order to have the place tidy early on Easter Sunday morning and to get the Easter curd cake ready in time.

"Natalia, come and give me a hand," she called to her daughter.

"I've got a headache, Mamma; I'll lie a little longer."

Her mother put her head in at the door. "A fine time to fall sick," she remarked.

Natalia licked her cold lips with her dry tongue and made no reply.

She lay until evening, her head covered with a warm woollen shawl, a light tremor shaking her huddled body. Miron Gregorievich and Grishaka were about to go off to church when she got up and went into the kitchen. Beads of perspiration shone on the strands of her smoothly combed hair, her eyes were dim with an unhealthy, oily film.

As Miron Gregorievich buttoned up the long row of buttons on his trousers he glanced at his daughter. "You've fallen ill suddenly, daughter. Come along with us to the service."

"You go; I'll come along later," she replied.

The men went out. Lukinichna and Natalia were left in the kitchen. Natalia went listlessly backward and forward from the chest to the bed, looked with unseeing eyes through the heap of clothing in the chest, painfully thinking of something, her lips whispering. Lukinichna thought she could not make up her mind which clothes to wear, and with motherly kindness she suggested:

"Wear my blue skirt, my dear. It will just fit you. Shall I get it for you?"

"No, I'll go in this!" Natalia carefully drew out her green skirt and suddenly remembered that she had been wearing it when Gregor first visited her as her future bridegroom, when he had shamed her with a flying kiss. Shaking with sobs, she fell breast-forward against the raised lid of the chest.

"Natalia, what's the matter?" Her mother clapped her hands.

Natalia choked down her desire to scream and, mastering herself, laughed with a grating, wooden laugh.

"I'm all unwell today."

"Oh, Natalia, I've noticed."

"Well, and what have you noticed, Mamma?" she cried with unexpected irritation, crumpling the green skirt in her fingers.

"You're not well at all; you need a husband."

"Enough of that talk; I've had one!"

She went to her room, and quickly returned to the kitchen, dressed, girlishly slender, her face an azure pallor, a mournful flush in her cheeks.

"You go on, I'm not ready yet," her mother said.

Pushing a handkerchief into her sleeve, Natalia went out. The wind brought the rumble of the floating ice and the scent of the damp thaw to her nostrils. Holding up her skirt in her left hand, picking her way across the pearly-blue puddles, she reached the church. On the way she attempted to recover her former comparatively tranquil state of mind, thinking of the holiday, of everything vaguely and in snatches. But her thoughts turned straight back to the scrap of blue sugar-bag paper hidden at her breast, to Gregor and the happy woman who was now condescendingly laughing at her, perhaps even pitying her.

As she entered the church enclosure some lads barred her way. She passed round them and heard the whisper:

"Whose is she? Did you see?"

"It was Natalia Korshunov."

"She's ruptured, they say. That's why her husband left her."

"That's not true. She got playing about with her father-in-law, lame Pantaleimon."

"Ah, so that's it! And that's why Gregor ran away from home?"

Stumbling over the uneven stones, followed by a shameful, filthy whisper, she reached the church porch. The girls standing in the porch giggled as she turned and made her way to the farther gate. Swaying drunkenly, she ran home. At the yard gate she took breath and then entered, stumbling over the hem of her skirt, biting her lips till the blood came. Through the lilac darkness the open doorway of the shed yawned blackly. With evil determination she gathered her last strength, ran to the door, and hastily stepped across the threshold. The shed was dry and cold, smelling of leather harness and long-lying straw. Gropingly, without thought or feeling, in a sombre yearning which scratched at her shamed and despairing soul, she made her way to a corner. There she picked up a scythe by the handle, removed the blade (her movements were deliberately assured and precise), and throwing back her head, with all the force and joyous resolution that possessed her she slashed her throat with its point. She fell as though struck down before the burning, savage pain, and feeling, mournfully realizing, that she had not completely carried out her intention, she struggled on to all fours, then on to her knees. Hurriedly (she was terrified by the blood pouring over her chest) with trembling fingers she tore off the buttons of her jacket, and with one hand she drew aside her taut, unyielding breast, with the other she guided the point of the scythe over the floor. She crawled on her knees to the earthen wall, thrust the blunt end of the scythe blade into it, and, throwing her arms above her head, pressed her chest firmly forward, forward. . . . She clearly heard and felt the resisting, cabbage-like scrunch of the rending flesh; a rising wave of intense pain flowed over her breast to her throat and pressed with ringing needles into her ears. . . .

The kitchen door scraped. Lukinichna came down the stairs, feeling for the steps with her feet. From the belfry came the measured beat of the church-bell. With an incessant grinding the giant floes were floating end-up down the Don. The joyous, full-flowing, liberated river was carrying its icy fetters away down to the Sea of Azov.

CHAPTER 12

Aksinia confessed her pregnancy to Gregor only during the sixth month, when she was no longer able to conceal it from him. She had kept silent so long because she was afraid he would not believe it was his child she was carrying.

She told him agitatedly one evening, anxiously scanning his face the while for any change in its expression. But he turned away to the window and coughed with vexation.

"Why didn't you tell me before?" he demanded.

"I was afraid to, Gregor. I thought you might throw me over. . . ."

Drumming his fingers on the back of the bed, he asked:

"Is it to be soon?"

"The beginning of August, I think."

"Is it Stepan's?"

"No, it's yours."

"So you say."

"Reckon up for yourself. From the day of the wood-cutting it is . . ."

"Don't lie, Aksinia! Even if it was Stepan's, where would you go to now?"

Weeping angry tears, Aksinia sat down on the bench and broke into a burning whisper:

"I lived with him so many years and nothing ever happened! Think for yourself! I'm not an ailing woman. . . . I must have got it from you. . . . And you . . ."

Gregor talked no more about the matter. A new thread of anxious aloofness and a light mocking pity entered into his attitude to Aksinia. She withdrew into herself, asking for no favours. Since the summer she had lost her good looks, but pregnancy hardly affected her shapely figure; her general fullness concealed her condition, and although her face was thinner, it gained a new beauty from her warmly glowing eyes. She easily managed her work as cook, especially as that year fewer labourers were employed on the farm.

Eugene had arranged for Gregor to be freed from the spring training camp, and he worked at the mowing, occasionally drove old Listnitsky to the district centre, and spent the rest of the time hunting with him after bustards. The easy-going, comfortable life began to spoil him. He grew lazy and stout and looked older than his years. He was troubled only by the thought of his forthcoming army service. He had neither horse nor equipment, and he could hope for nothing from his father. He saved the wages he received for himself and Aksinia and spent nothing ever on tobacco, hoping to be able to buy a horse without having to beg from his father. Old Listnitsky also promised to help him. Gregor's presentiment that his father would give him nothing was quickly confirmed. At the end of June, Piotra visited his brother and in the course of conversation mentioned that his father was as angry with him as ever and had declared that he would not help him to get a horse. "Let him go to the local command for one," he had said.

"He needn't worry, I'll go to do my service on my own horse," Gregor declared, stressing "my own."

"Where will you get it from?" Piotra asked.

"I'll beg for it, or dance for it, and if I don't get it that way, I'll steal it."

"Brave lad!"

"I shall buy a horse with my wages," Gregor said more seriously.

Piotra sat on the steps, asking about Gregor's work and chewing the ends of his moustache. Having completed his inquiries, as he turned to go he said to his brother:

"You should come back; there's no point in knocking your head against a brick wall."

"I'm not intending to."

"Are you thinking of staying with her?"

"With who?"

"With this one."

"At present I am, but what of it?"

"Oh, I'm just interested."

As Gregor went to see his brother off, he had to ask at last: "How is everything at home?"

Piotra laughed as he untied his horse from the balustrade of the steps. "You've got as many homes as a rabbit has holes! Everything is all right. Your mother longs to see you. We've got in the hay—three loads of it."

Agitatedly Gregor scanned the old mare his brother was riding. "No foal this year?" he inquired.

"No, brother, she's barren. But the bay which we got from Christonia has foaled. A stallion it is, a good one too. High on the legs, sound pasterns, and strong in the chest. It'll be a good horse."

Gregor sighed. "I pine for the village, Piotra," he said. "I pine for the Don. You never see running water here. It's a dreary place!"

"Come and see us," Piotra replied as he hoisted his body on to the mare's bony spine.

"Some day."

"Well, good-bye."

"A good journey."

Piotra had ridden out of the yard when, remembering something, he called to Gregor, who was still standing on the steps:

"Natalia—I'd forgotten—a misfortune. . . ."

The wind blowing round the farm carried the end of the sentence away from Gregor's ears. Piotra and the horse were enveloped in velvety dust, and Gregor shrugged his shoulders and went off to the stables.

The summer was dry. Rain fell but rarely, and the grain ripened early. As soon as the rye was garnered the barley was ripe and yellow. The four day-labourers and Gregor went out to reap it.

Aksinia had finished work early that day, and she asked Gregor to take her with him. Despite his attempt to dissuade her, she quickly threw a kerchief over her head, ran out, and caught up with the wagon in which the men were riding.

The event which Aksinia anticipated with yearning and joyous impatience, which Gregor awaited with apprehension, happened during the harvesting. Feeling certain symptoms, she threw down the rake and lay under a shock of corn. Her travail came on quickly. Biting her blackened tongue, she lay flat on the ground. The labourers with the reaping machine drove in a circle around her. As they passed, one of them called out to her:

"Hey, you! You've lain yourself down to bake in an awkward spot, haven't you? Get up, or you'll melt!"

Gregor got one of the men to take his place at the machine and went across to her.

"What's the matter?" he asked.

Her lips writhing uncontrollably, she said hoarsely:

"I'm in labor. . . ."

"I told you not to come, you devilish bitch! Now what are we to do?"

"Don't be angry with me, Grishka! . . . Oh! . . . Oh! . . . Grishka, harness the horse to the wagon. I must get home. . . . How could I, here? . . . with the Cossacks . . ." she groaned, gripped in an iron band of pain.

Gregor ran for the horse. It was grazing in a hollow a little way off, and by the time he drove up, Aksinia had struggled on to all fours, thrust her head into a pile of dusty barley, and was spitting out the prickly beards she had chewed in her pain. She fixed her dilated eyes vacantly on Gregor and set her teeth into her crumbled handkerchief to prevent the labourers from hearing her horrible, rending cry.

Gregor tumbled her into the wagon and drove the horse fast towards the estate.

"Oh! Don't hurry. . . . Oh, death! You're—shaking—me. . . ." Aksinia screamed as her head knocked on the bottom of the wagon.

Gregor silently plied the whip and swung the reins around his head, without a glance back at her.

Pressing her cheeks with her palms, her staring, frenzied eyes rolling wildly, Aksinia bounced about in the wagon, tumbling from side to side over the bumpy, unworn road. Gregor kept the horse at a gallop. For a moment Aksinia ceased her shrieking howl. The wheels rattled, and her head thudded heavily against the bottom board. At first her silence did not impress itself on Gregor, but then, taking thought, he glanced back.

Aksinia was lying with horribly distorted face, her cheek pressed hard against the side of the wagon, her jaws working like a fish flung ashore. The sweat was pouring from her brow into her sunken eyes. Gregor turned and raised her head, putting his crumpled cap beneath it. Glancing sidelong at him, she said firmly:

"I shall die, Grishka. And that's all there is to it!"

Gregor shuddered; a chill ran down his body to his toes. Suddenly alarmed, he sought for words of encouragement, of comfort, but could not find them. From his trembling lips came:

"You're lying, you fool!" He shook his head and, bending over her, awkwardly squeezed her foot.

"Aksinia, my little pigeon . . ."

The pain died away and left Aksinia for a moment, then returned with redoubled force. Feeling something rending and bending in an arch under her belly, she pierced Gregor's ears with an inexpressibly horrible, rising scream. Gregor frantically whipped up the horse.

"Oh! . . . Ah! . . ." Aksinia shrieked in her agony.

Then above the rattle of the wheels Gregor just heard her thin, yearning voice:

"Grishka!"

He reined in the horse and turned his head. Aksinia lay in a pool of blood, her arms flung out. Below her skirt, between her legs, a white and crimson living thing was stirring. Gregor frenziedly jumped down from the wagon and stumbled to the back. Staring into Aksinia's panting, burning mouth, he rather guessed than caught the words:

"Bite through the cord . . . tie it with cotton . . . from the shirt. . . ."

With trembling fingers he tore a bunch of threads from the sleeve of his own cotton shirt, and screwing up his eyes until they pained him, he bit through the cord and carefully tied up the bleeding end with cotton.

The estate of Yagodnoe lay in a spacious valley. The wind blew changeably from north or south, summer advanced on the valley, the autumn rustled with falling leaves, winter flung its forces of frost and snow against it, but Yagodnoe remained sunk in its wooden torpor. So the days passed, crawling over the high wall that cut off the estate from the rest of the world.

The farmyard was always alive with black ducks wearing red spectacles; the guinea-fowls scattered like a beady rain; gaily-feathered peacocks called hoarsely from the roof of the stables. The old general was fond of all kinds of birds and even kept a maimed crane. In November it wrung the heart-strings with its copper-tongued, yearning cry as it heard the call of the wild cranes flying south. But it could not fly, for one wing hung uselessly at its side. As the general stood at the window and watched the bird stretching out its neck and jumping, fluttering off the ground, he laughed; and the bass tones of his laughter rocked through the empty hall like clouds of tobacco-smoke.

During all the time of Gregor's stay at Yagodnoe only two events disturbed the sleepy, monotonous life: the coming of Aksinia's child, and the loss of a prize gander. The inhabitants of Yagodnoe quickly grew accustomed to the baby girl, and they found some of the gander's feathers in the meadow and concluded that a fox had carried her off.

One day in December Gregor was summoned to the district administration at Vieshenska. There he was given a hundred rubles to buy a horse and was instructed to report on two days after Christmas at the village of Mankovo for the army draft.

He returned to Yagodnoe in considerable agitation. Christmas was approaching, and he had nothing ready. With the money he had received from the authorities plus his own savings he bought a horse for a hundred and forty rubles. He took Sashka with him and they purchased a presentable animal enough, a six-year-old bay with one hidden blemish. Old Sashka combed his beard with his fingers and advised:

"You won't get one cheaper, and the authorities won't see the fault! They're not smart enough!"

Gregor rode the horse bareback to Yagodnoe, trying out its paces.

A week before Christmas Pantaleimon arrived unexpectedly at Yagodnoe. He did not drive into the yard, but tied up his horse and basket sledge at the gate and limped into the servants' quarters, rubbing the icicles off his beard. As through the window he saw his father approaching, Gregor exclaimed in confusion:

"Well I'm— Father!"

For some reason Aksinia ran to the cradle and wrapped up the child. Pantaleimon entered, bringing a breath of cold air with him. He removed his three-cornered cap and crossed himself to the ikon, then gazed slowly around the room.

"Good health!" he greeted his son.

"Good morning, Father!" Gregor replied, rising from the bench and striding to the centre of the room.

Pantaleimon offered Gregor his ice-cold hand and sat down on the edge of the bench, wrapping his sheepskin around him. He would not look at Aksinia.

"Getting ready for your service?" he asked.

"Of course."

Pantaleimon was silent, staring long and questioningly at Gregor.

"Take your things off, Father, and we'll get a samovar going."

"Thank you"; the old man scraped an old spot of mud off his coat with his fingernail, and added: "I've brought your equipment; two coats, a saddle, and trousers. You'll find them all there in the sledge."

Gregor went out and removed the two sacks of equipment from the sledge. When he returned, his father rose from the bench.

"When are you going off?" he asked his son.

"The day after Christmas. You aren't going already, are you, Father?"

"I want to get back early."

He took leave of Gregor and, still avoiding Aksinia's eyes, went towards the door. As he lifted the latch he turned his eyes in the direction of the cradle and said:

"Your mother sends her greetings. She's in bed with trouble in her legs." After a momentary pause he said heavily: "I shall ride with you to Mankovo. Be ready when I come."

He went out, thrusting his hands into warm knitted gloves. Aksinia, pale with the humiliation she had suffered, said nothing. Gregor followed his father, trying to avoid a creaking floorboard and giving Aksinia a sidelong glance as he passed.

On Christmas Day Gregor drove his master to Vieshenska. Listnitsky attended Mass, had breakfast with his cousin, a local landowner, and then ordered Gregor to get the sleigh ready for the return journey. Gregor had not finished his bowl of greasy soup, but he rose at once, went to the stable, and harnessed the grey trotting-horse into the light sleigh.

The wind was blowing the crumbling, tingling snow into spray; a silvery froth whirled hissingly through the yard; on the trees beyond the palisade hung a tender, scalloped hoarfrost. The wind sent it flying, and as it fell and scattered, it reflected a marvelous variety of colours from the sun. On the roof close to the smoking chimney, rooks were chattering

coldly. Startled by the sound of footsteps, they flew off, circled round the house like dove-coloured snowflakes, then flew to the east, to the church, clearly outlined against the violet morning sky.

"Tell the master we're ready," Gregor shouted to the maid that came to the steps of the house.

Listnitsky came out and entered the sleigh, his whiskers buried in the collar of his raccoon-fur coat. Gregor wrapped up his legs and buttoned the shaggy wolfskin over him.

They arrived at Yagodnoe within two hours. Listnitsky held no communication whatever with Gregor during the journey, except for an occasional tap on the back with his finger, to order him to stop while he rolled and lit a cigarette. Only as they were descending the hill to the house did he ask:

"Early in the morning?"

Gregor turned sideways in his seat and with difficulty opened his frozen lips. His tongue, bursting and stiff with cold, stuck to the back of his teeth.

"Yes," he managed to reply.

"Received all your money?"

"Yes."

"Don't be anxious about your wife; she'll be all right. Be a good soldier. Your grandfather was a fine Cossack; you must conduct yourself in a manner worthy of your grandfather and father. Your father received the first prize for trick riding at the Imperial Review in 1883, didn't he?"

"Yes, it was my father."

"Well, well!" the old man ended with a stern note in his voice, as though admonishing Gregor. And he buried his face once more in his fur coat.

At the yard Gregor handed over the horse to Sashka and turned to go to the servants' quarters.

"Your father's arrived," Sashka shouted after him.

Gregor found Pantaleimon sitting at the table, eating cranberry jelly. "Drunk!" Gregor decided as he glanced at his father's sodden face.

"So you're back, soldier?" Pantaleimon exclaimed.

"I'm all frozen," Gregor answered, clapping his hands together. Turning to Aksinia, he added: "Untie my hood, my fingers are too cold to do it."

On this occasion his father was much more affable and told Aksinia curtly, as though he were master in the house:

"Cut me some more bread; don't spare it!"

When he had finished he rose from the table and went towards the door to have a smoke in the yard. As he passed the cradle he rocked it once or twice, pretending that the action was accidental, and asked:

"A Cossack?"

"A girl," Aksinia replied for Gregor; and catching the expression of dissatisfaction that passed over the old man's face, she hurriedly added:

"She's so handsome! Just like Grishka!"

Pantaleimon attentively examined the dark little head sticking out of the clothes and declared, not without a touch of pride:

"She's of our blood! . . . Ah, you! . . ."

"How did you come, Father?" Gregor asked.

"With the mare and Piotra's horse."

"You need only have used one, and we could have harnessed mine for the journey to Mankovo."

"Let him go light. He's a good horse, too."

Disturbed by the one common thought, they talked about various matters. Aksinia took no part in the conversation, but sat on the bed. She had noticeably grown stouter since the birth of the child and had a new, confidently happy air.

It was late when they went to bed. As she lay pressed against Gregor, Aksinia wet his shirt with her tears.

"I shall die of pining for you. How shall

I be able to live without you? The long nights . . . the child awake. . . . Just think, Grishka! Four years!"

"In the old days service lasted twenty-five years, they say."

"What do I care about the old days? Curse your army service, say I."

"I shall come home on furlough."

"On furlough!" Aksinia groaned, blowing her nose on her shift. "Much water will flow down the Don before then."

"Don't whine so! You're like rain in autumn—one continual drizzle."

"You should be in my skin," she retorted.

Gregor fell asleep a little before dawn. Aksinia got up and fed the child, then lay down again. Leaning on her elbows and gazing unwinkingly into Gregor's face, she took a long farewell of him. She recalled the night when she had tried to persuade him to go with her to the Kuban: once more the yard outside the window was flooded with the white light of the moon. So they had lain then, and Gregor was still the same, yet not the same. Behind them both lay a long track trodden out by the passing days.

He turned over, muttered something about Olshansky village, and then was silent. Aksinia tried to sleep, but her thoughts drove all sleep away as wind does a haycock. Until daybreak she lay thinking over his disconnected phrases, seeking its meaning. Pantaleimon awoke as soon as the faintest glimmer of daylight peered through the window.

"Gregor, get up!" he cried.

By the time they had breakfasted and packed, dawn had fully come. Pantaleimon went to harness his horses, while Gregor tore himself away from Aksinia's passionate kisses and went to say good-bye to Sashka and the other servants.

Wrapping the child up warmly, Aksinia took her out with her for a last farewell. Gregor lightly touched his daughter's damp little forehead with his lips and went to his horse.

"Come in the sledge," his father called as he touched up his horses.

"No, I'll ride my horse."

With calculated deliberation Gregor fastened the saddle-girths, mounted his horse, gathered the reins in his hand. More than once Aksinia repeated:

"Grishka, wait—there's something I wanted to say"; puckering her brow, she tried to remember what it was.

"Well, good-bye. . . . Look after the child. . . . I must be off; see how far Father's got already."

"Wait, dear!" With her left hand Aksinia seized the icy iron stirrup; her right arm pressed the baby to her breast; and she had no free hand with which to wipe away the tears streaming from her staring, unwinking eyes.

Benyamin came to the steps of the house.

"Gregor, the master wants you!" he called.

Gregor cursed, waved his whip, and dashed out of the yard. Aksinia ran after him, stumbling in the drifted snow.

He overtook his father at the top of the hill. Then he turned and looked back. Aksinia was standing at the gate, the child still pressed to her breast, the ends of her crimson shawl fluttering in the wind.

He rode his horse alongside his father's sledge. After a few moments the old man turned his back to his horses and asked:

"So you're not thinking of living with your wife?"

"That old story again? I've already told you . . ."

"So you're not thinking . . ."

"No, I'm not!"

"You haven't heard that she laid hands on herself?"

"Yes, I've heard. I happened to meet a man from the village."

"And in the sight of God?"

"Why, Father, after all—what falls from the wagon is lost."

"Don't use that devil's talk to me. What I'm saying to you I'm saying for your good," Pantaleimon flared up.

"You see I have a child. What is there to talk about? You can't push the other on to me now. . . ."

"Take care you're not feeding another man's child."

Gregor turned pale; his father had touched a sore spot. Ever since the child was born he had tormentedly nursed the suspicion in his mind, while concealing it from Aksinia. At night, when Aksinia was asleep, he had more than once gone to the cradle and stared down at the child, seeking his own features in its swarthily rosy face, and had turned back to bed as uncertain as before. Stepan also was dark red, almost black of complexion, and how was he to know whose blood flowed in the child's veins? At times he thought the child resembled him; at other times she was painfully like Stepan. Gregor had no feeling for her, except perhaps of hostility as he recalled the moments he had lived through as he drove Aksinia back from the steppe. Only once Aksinia was busy elsewhere, and he had had to change the child's wet diaper. As he did so he had felt a sharp, pinching agitation. Afterwards he had bent stealthily over the cradle and pressed the baby's great toe between his teeth.

His father probed mercilessly at the wound, and Gregor, his palm resting on the saddle-bow, numbly replied: "Whoseever it is, I won't leave the child."

Pantaleimon waved his whip at the horses without turning round. "Natalia's spoilt her good looks. She carries her head on one side like a paralytic. It seems she cut a large tendon." He lapsed into silence.

"And how is she now?" Gregor asked, studiously picking a bur out of his horse's mane.

"She's got over it somehow or other. She lay sėven months. On Trinity Sunday she was all but gone. Father Pankraty performed the last rites. Then she got better, rose, and walked. She thrust the scythe at her heart, but her hand trembled, and it missed."

"Quicker up the hill!" Gregor proposed, and waved his whip and outdistanced his father, sending a shower of snow from his horse's hoofs over the sledge. He broke into a trot, standing in his stirrups.

"We're taking Natalia back into our home," Pantaleimon shouted, chasing after him. "The woman doesn't want to live with her own folks. I saw her the other day and told her to come to us."

Gregor made no reply. They drove as far as the first village without exchanging a word, and his father made no further reference to the subject.

That day they covered forty-five miles. They arrived at Mankovo as dusk was falling the next day, and spent the night in the quarters allotted to the Vieshenska recruits.

Next morning the district ataman conducted the Vieshenska recruits before the medical commission. Gregor fell in with the other young men from his own village. In the morning Mitka Korshunov, riding a high bay horse equipped with a new and gaily ornamented saddle, had passed Gregor standing at the door of his quarters, but had gone by without a word of greeting.

The men undressed in turn in the cold room of the local civil administration. Military clerks bustled around, and the adjutant to the provincial ataman hurried past. From an inner room came the sound of the doctors' orders and snatches of remarks.

A clerk came out and curtly called Gregor and another into the examination room. Gregor went in, his back all goose-flesh with the cold. His swarthy body was the colour of oak. He was embarrassed as he glanced down at his hairy legs. The humiliating procedure of the medical examination irritated him. A grey-haired doctor in white overalls sounded him with the aid of a stethoscope. A younger doctor turned up his eyelids, and looked at his tongue. Behind him a third in horn-rimmed spectacles bustled about, rubbing his hands.

"On the scales!" an officer ordered.

Gregor stepped on to the cold platform.

"A hundred eighty-five and a half."

"Wha-a-at? He's not particularly tall, either," the grey-haired doctor drawled, turning Gregor round by the arm.

"Astonishing!" the younger man coughed.

"How much?" an officer sitting at the table asked in surprise.

"A hundred eighty-five and a half pounds," the grey-haired doctor replied.

"How about the Life Guards for him?" the district military commissary asked, bending towards his neighbour at the table.

"He has a brigand's face. . . . Very savage-looking. . . ."

"Hey, turn round! What's that on your back?" an official wearing colonel's epaulets shouted, impatiently tapping his finger on the table. Turning to face the colonel, trying to restrain the trembling of his body, Gregor replied:

"I got frozen in the spring. They're the marks."

Towards the end of the examination the officials at the table decided that Gregor would have to be drafted into an ordinary regiment.

"The 12th Regiment, Melekhov. Do you hear?" he was told. And as he went towards the door he heard a whispered:

"It's impossible. Just consider; the Emperor would see a face like that, and then what? His eyes alone . . ."

"He's a crossbreed. From the East undoubtedly."

"And his body isn't clean. Those marks . . ."

Buttoning up his coat as he went, he ran down the steps. Horses were being mustered in the square. The warm wind breathed of thaw; the road was bare in places, and steaming. Clucking hens fluttered down the street, geese were splashing in a puddle.

The examination of the horses took place the following day. A long line of mounts was drawn up in the square against the church wall. A veterinary surgeon and his assistant passed along the line. The Vieshenska ataman went running from the scales to the table in the middle of the square, where the results of the examination were being entered. The military commissary went by, deep in conversation with a young captain.

When his turn came, Gregor led his horse to the scales. The surgeon and his assistant measured every part of the animal's body, and weighed it. Before it could be led from the platform the surgeon had deftly taken it by the upper lip, looked down its throat, felt its chest muscles, and running his fine fingers like spider's legs over its body, turned to its legs. He felt the knee joints, tapped the tendons, squeezed the bone above the fetlocks. When he had finished his examination he passed on, his white overalls flapping in the wind and scattering the scent of carbolic acid.

Gregor's horse was rejected. Sashka's hopes proved unjustified, and the experienced surgeon discovered the secret blemish of which the old man had spoken. Gregor at once held an agitated consultation with his father, and before half an hour had elapsed he led Piotra's horse on to the scales. The surgeon passed it almost without an examination.

Gregor led the horse a little way off,

found a comparatively dry spot, and spread out his saddle-cloth on the ground. His father held his horse. Past them strode a tall, grey-haired general in a light grey cloak and a silver astrakhan-fur cap, followed by a group of officers.

"That's the provincial ataman," Pantaleimon whispered, digging Gregor from behind.

Gregor stared inquisitively at the unfamiliar features of the officers and officials. An adjutant fixed a bored gaze on him and turned away as he met Gregor's attentive eyes. An old captain went by almost at a run, agitated by something and biting his upper lip with his yellow teeth.

On his saddle-cloth Gregor had set out his saddle, adorned with a green ribbon, with its saddlebags at the pommel and the back; two army coats, two pairs of trousers, a tunic, two pairs of leg-boots, a pound and a half of biscuit, a tin of corned beef, grits, and other food in the regulation quantities. In the open saddlebags were four horseshoes, shoe-nails wrapped in a greasy rag, a soldier's sewing-kit with a couple of needles and thread and towels.

He gave a last glance over his accoutrements, and squatted down to rub some mud off the ends of the pack-strings with his sleeve. From the end of the square the army commission slowly passed along the rows of Cossacks drawn up behind their saddle-cloths. The officers and the ataman closely examined the equipment, stooping and feeling the edges of the greatcoats, fumbling in the saddlebags, turning out the contents of the sewing-kits, and weighing the bags of biscuit in their hands.

The talk gradually died away as the commission approached. Gregor drew himself up. Behind him his father coughed. The wind carried the scent of horses' urine and melted snow over the square. The sun looked unhappy, as though after a drinking bout.

The group of officers halted by the man next to Gregor, then came on to him one by one.

"Your surname, Christian name?"

"Melekhov, Gregor."

The commissary picked up the greatcoat by its edge, smelled at the lining, and hurriedly counted the fastenings; another officer, wearing a cornet's epaulets, felt the good cloth of the trousers between his fingers. A third stooped and rummaged in the saddlebags. With his thumb and forefinger the commissary cautiously poked at the rag of shoe-nails as though afraid it might be hot, and counted the nails with whispering lips.

"Why are there only twenty-three nails? What is this?" He angrily pulled at the corner of the rag.

"Not at all, Your Excellency. Twenty-four."

"What, am I blind?"

Gregor hastily turned back a folded corner and revealed the twenty-fourth nail. As he did so, his hairy black fingers lightly touched the officer's white hand. The commissary snatched his hand away as though struck, rubbed it on the edge of his greatcoat, frowning fastidiously, and drew on his glove.

Gregor noticed his action and smiled evilly. Their eyes met, and the commissary flushed and raised his voice.

"What's all this, what's all this, Cossack? Why aren't your pack-strings in order? Why aren't your snaffles right? And what does this mean? Are you a Cossack or a peasant? Where's your father?"

Pantaleimon pulled on the horse's rein and stepped forward a pace, his lame leg dragging.

"Don't you know the Cossack regulations?" the commissary poured out the vials of his wrath upon him.

The provincial ataman came up, and the commissary quieted down. The ataman thrust the toe of his boot into the padding of the saddle and passed on to the next man. The draft officer of the regiment to which Gregor had been drafted politely turned out all his belongings down to the contents of the sewing-kit and passed on last of all.

A day later a train of red wagons loaded with horses, Cossacks and forage left for Voronezh. In one of them stood Gregor. Past the open door crawled an unfamiliar flat landscape; in the distance a blue and tender thread of forest whirled by. Behind him the horses were munching hay and stepping from hoof to hoof as they felt the unstable floor beneath them. The wagon smelt of wormwood, horses' sweat, the spring thaw; and on the horizon lurked the distant thread of forest, blue, pensive, and as inaccessible as the faintly shining evening star.

CHAPTER 13

It was on a warm and cheerful spring day of March 1914 that Natalia returned to her father-in-law's hut. Pantaleimon was mending the broken wattle fence with puffy dove-coloured twigs. The silvery icicles hanging from the roofs were dripping, and the traces of former runnels showed as black scratches on the cornices. The warm sun caressed the melting hills, and the earth was swelling; an early grass showed a green malachite on the chalky headlands that swept in promontories from the Donside hills.

Natalia approached her father-in-law from behind, bending her mutilated, crooked neck.

"Good health, Father!" she said.

"Natiushka! Welcome, my dear, welcome!" Pantaleimon fussed around her. The twigs dropped out of his hand. "Why haven't you been to see us? Come in; Mother will be glad to see you."

"Father, I've come . . ." Natalia stretched out her hand uncertainly and turned away. "If you don't drive me away, I'd like to stay with you always," she added.

"What then, what then, my dear? Are you a stranger to us? Look, Gregor has written about you in his letter. He's told us to ask about you."

They went into the kitchen. Ilinichna wept as she embraced Natalia. Wiping her nose on the end of her kerchief, she whispered:

"You want a child. That would win him. Sit down. I'll get you some pancakes, shall I?"

Dunia, flushed and smiling, came running into the kitchen and embraced Natalia around the knees. "You shameless one! You forgot all about us!" she reproached her.

They all talked together, interrupting one another. Ilinichna, supporting her cheek on her palm, grieved as she looked at Natalia, so changed from what she had been.

"You've come for good?" Dunia asked as she rubbed Natalia's hands.

"Who knows? . . ."

"Why, where else should she live? You'll stay with us," Ilinichna decided, as she pushed a platter of pancakes across the table.

Natalia went to her husband's parents only after long vacillation. At first her father would not let her go. He shouted at her in indignation when she suggested it, and attempted to persuade her against such a step. But it was difficult for her to look her people in the face; she felt that with her own family she was almost a stranger. For his part, after he had seen Gregor off to the army Pantaleimon was continually wheedling her to come, for he was determined to have her back and to reconcile Gregor to her.

From that day of March Natalia lived with the Melekhovs. Piotra was friendly and brotherly; Daria gave little outward sign of her dissatisfaction, and her occasional hostile glances were more than compensated by Dunia's attachment and the parental attitude of the old people.

The very day after Natalia came to them Pantaleimon ordered Dunia to write a letter to Gregor:

Greetings, our own son, Gregor Pantalievich! We send you a deep bow, and from all my fatherly heart, with your mother, Vasilisa Ilinichna, a parental blessing. Your brother, Piotra Pantalievich, and his wife, Daria Matvievna, greet you and wish you health and well-being; also your sister, Dunia, and all at home greet you. We received your letter, sent in February, the fifth day, and heartily thank you for it. And as you wrote that the horse is knocking his legs smear him with some lard, you know how, and don't shoe his hind hoofs so long as there is no slipperiness or bare ice about. Your wife, Natalia Mironovna, is living with us and is well and comfortable. Your mother sends you some dried cherries and a pair of woollen socks, and some dripping and other things. We are all alive and well, but Daria's baby died. The other day I and Piotra roofed the shed, and he orders you to look after the horse and keep it well. The cows have calved, the old mare seems to be in foal, we put a stallion from the district stables to her. We are glad to hear about your service and that your officers are pleased with you. Serve as you should. Service for the Czar will not be in vain. And Natalia will live with us now, and you think that over. And one other trouble, just before Lent an animal killed three sheep. Now keep well, and in God's keeping. Don't forget your wife, that is my order to you. She is a good woman and your legal wife. Don't break the furrow, and listen to your father.

Your father, senior sergeant,
Pantaleimon Melekhov

Gregor's regiment was stationed at a little placed called Radzivillovo, some three miles from the Russo-Austrian frontier. He rarely wrote home. To the letter informing him that Natalia was living with his father he wrote a cautiously worded reply and asked his father to greet her in his name. All his letters were non-committal and obscure in their meaning. Pantaleimon require Dunia or Piotra to read them to him several times, pondering over the thought concealed between the lines. Just before Easter he wrote and asked Gregor definitely whether on his return from the army he would live with his wife or with Aksinia as before.

Gregor delayed with his reply. Only after Trinity Sunday did they receive a brief letter from him. Dunia read it quickly, swallowing the ends of her words, and Pantaleimon had difficulty in grasping the essential thought among the numerous greetings and inquiries. At the end of the letter Gregor dealt with the question of Natalia:

You asked me to say whether I shall live with Natalia or not, but I tell you, Father, you can't stick on again what has been cut off. And how shall I make up to Natalia, when you know yourself that I have a child? And I can't promise anything, it is painful for me to talk about it. The other day a Jew was caught smuggling goods across the frontier and we happened to see him. He said there would be war with the Austrians soon and that their Emperor has come to the frontier to see where to begin the war from and which land to seize for himself. When war begins maybe I shan't be left alive, and nothing can be settled beforehand.

Natalia worked for her foster-parents and lived in continual hope of her husband's return. She never wrote to Gregor, but nobody in the family yearned with more pain and desire to receive a letter from him.

Life in the village continued in its inviolable order; on work-days the grey labour imperceptibly consumed the time, on Sunday mornings the village poured in family droves into the church: the Cossacks in tunics and holiday trousers, the women in long, vari-coloured skirts that swept the dust, and little jackets with puff sleeves. In the square the empty wagon shafts stuck high into the air, the horses whinnied; by the fire-shed the Bulgar settlers traded in fruit set out in long rows; behind them the children ran about in bands, staring at the unharnessed camels superciliously surveying the market square. Everywhere were crowds of men wearing red-banded caps, and women in bright kerchiefs.

In the evening the streets groaned with the tramp of feet, with song, and dancing to the accordions; and only late at night did the last voices die away in the outskirts of the village.

Natalia never went visiting neighbours on Sunday evenings, but sat listening gladly to Dunia's artless stories. Imperceptibly Dunia was growing into a shapely and in her way a beautiful girl. She matured early, like an early apple. This year her elder girl friends forgot that they had reached adolescence before her and took her back into their circle. She was fifteen now, and her figure was still girlish and angular. She was a painful and naïve mixture of childhood and blossoming youth; her little breasts grew and pressed noticeably against her jacket, and in her long, rather slanting eyesockets her black eyes still sparkled bashfully and mischievously. She would come back after an evening out and tell only Natalia her innocent secrets.

"Natalia, I want to tell you something."

"Well, tell on!"

"Yesterday Misha Koshevoi sat the whole evening with me on the stump by the village granaries."

"Why are you blushing?"

"Oh, I'm not!"

"Look in the glass; you're all one great flame."

Dunia rubbed her burning cheeks with her swarthy palms, and her young, artless laugh rang out.

"He said I was like a little azure flower."

"Well, go on!" Natalia encouraged her, rejoicing in another's joy and forgetting her own past and downtrodden happiness.

"And I said: 'Don't tell lies, Misha!' And he swore . . ."

Shaking her head, Natalia sent her laughter pealing through the room. The black, heavy plaits of her hair slipped like newts over her shoulders and back.

"What else did he say?"

"He asked me to give him my handkerchief for a keepsake."

"And did you?"

"No. I said I wouldn't. 'Go and ask your woman,' I told him. He's been seen with Yerofievna's daughter-in-law, and she's a bad woman, she plays about with the men."

"You'd better keep away from him."

"I'm going to!" Dunia continued her story. "And then, as the three of us, two other girls and me, were coming home, drunken old father Mikhy came after us. 'Kiss me, my dears!' he shouted. And Nura hit him on the face with a twig and we ran away."

The summer was dry. By the village the Don grew shallow, and where the surging current had run swiftly, a ford was made, and bullocks could cross to the other bank without wetting their backs. At night a heavy, hot exhalation flowed down from the range of hills into the village, and the wind filled the air with the strong scent of burning grass. The dry growth of the steppe was afire, and a sickly-smelling haze hung over the Donside slopes. At night the clouds deepened over the Don, ominous peals of thunder were to be heard; but no rain came to refresh the parched earth, although the lightning tore the sky into jagged, livid fragments.

Night after night an owl screeched from the belfry. The cries surged terrifyingly over the village, and the owl flew from the belfry to the cemetery and groaned over the brown and grass-grown mounds of the graves.

"There's trouble brewing," the old men prophesied as they listened to the owl screeching from the cemetery.

"There's war coming. An owl called just like that before the Turkish campaign."

"Expect no good when it flies from the church to the dead."

As he talked with the old men in the market-place Pantaleimon solemnly announced:

"Our Gregor writes that the Austrian Czar has come to the frontier and has given orders to collect all his troops in one place and to march on Moscow and Petersburg."

The old men remembered past wars and shared their apprehensions with one another.

"But there won't be any war," one objected. "Look at the harvest."

"The harvest has nothing to do with it. It's the students giving trouble, I expect."

"In any case we shall be the last to hear of it. But who will the war be with?"

"With the Turks across the sea. Depend on it, the water won't keep them apart."

The talk turned to jest, and the old men went about their business.

For two nights Martin Shamil, who lived close to the cemetery, watched by the cemetery palisade for the accursed owl, but the invisible, mysterious bird flew noiselessly over him, alighted on a cross at the other end of the cemetery, and sent its alarming cries over the sleepy village. Martin swore unbecomingly, shot at the black, hanging belly of a cloud, and went home. On his return to the hut his wife, a timorous, ailing woman as fruitful as a doe rabbit, welcomed him with reproaches.

"You're a fool, a hopeless fool!" she declared. "The bird doesn't interfere with you, does it? What if God should punish you? Here am I just up from my bed with my last, and supposing I get pregnant again through you?"

"Shut up, woman!" Martin ordered her. "You'll get pregnant all right, never fear! What is the bird doing here, giving us all the cold shivers? It's calling down woe on us, the devil! If war breaks out they'll take me off, and look at the litter you've got!" He waved at the corner where the children were sleeping.

Guards were set to watch over the meadow hay. The grass beyond the Don was inferior to the hay of the steppe and was sickly and scentless. It was the same earth, yet the grass drank in different juices. In the steppe there was a splendid black soil, so heavy and firm that the herd left no traces where they passed over it. On it grew a strong-scented grass standing as high as a horse's belly. But along the Don banks the soil was damp and rotten, growing a joyless and worthless grass which even the cattle would not always look at.

Haymaking was in full swing when an event occurred which shook the village from one end to the other. The district commissary arrived with an investigator and an officer in a uniform never seen before in the village. They sent for the ataman, collected witnesses, and then went straight to cross-eyed Lukieshka's hut. They walked along the path on the sunny side of the street, the village ataman running ahead like a cockerel. The investigator questioned him:

"Is Stockman at home?"

"Yes, Your Excellency."

"What does he do for a living?"

"He's a master locksmith."

"You haven't noticed anything suspicious about him?"

"Not at all."

"Does he ever have visitors?" the investigator asked, pulling the ataman back.

"Yes; they play cards sometimes."

"But who?"

"Chiefly labourers from the mill."

"But who exactly?"

"The engineer, the scalesman, David, and sometimes some of our Cossacks."

The investigator halted and waited for the officer, who had lagged behind. He said something to him, twisting the button of his tunic with his fingers, then beckoned to the ataman. The ataman ran up on tiptoe, with bated breath.

"Take two militia-men and go and arrest the men you mentioned. Bring them to the administration office and we'll be along in a minute or two. Do you understand?"

The ataman drew himself up and turned back to execute his instructions.

Stockman was sitting in his unbuttoned vest, his back to the door, filing a design on veneer. He glanced round as the officials entered, and bit his lip.

"Please get up; you're under arrest," the investigator ordered.

"What's this for?"

"You occupy two rooms?"

"Yes."

"We shall search them."

The officer walked across to the table and with a frown picked up the first book that came to hand. "I want the key of that trunk," he said.

"To what do I owe this visit?"

"There'll be time to talk to you after."

Stockman's wife looked through the doorway, from the other room and drew back. The investigator's secretary followed her in.

"What is this?" the officer quietly asked Stockman, holding up a book in a yellow cover.

"A book," Stockman replied with a shrug of his shoulder.

"You can keep your witticisms for a more suitable occasion. Answer the question properly."

With a wry smile Stockman leaned his back against the stove. The commissary glanced over the officer's shoulder at the book and then turned to Stockman.

"You're studying?"

"I'm interested in the subject," Stockman dryly replied.

"So!"

The officer glanced through the pages of the book and threw it back on the table. He looked through a second, put it on one side, and having read the cover of the third, turned to Stockman again.

"Where do you keep the rest of this type of literature?"

Stockman screwed up one eye as though taking aim at the officer, and replied.

"You see all that I have."

"You're lying," the officer retorted, waving the book at him.

"I demand—"

"Search the rooms!"

Holding his sabre in his hand, the commissary went across to the trunk, where a pockmarked Cossack militia-man, obviously terrified by the circumstances in which he found himself, had begun to rummage among the clothing and linen. The man turned out everything that it was possible to turn out. The search was conducted in the workshop also. The zealous commissary even knocked on the walls with his knuckles.

When the search was ended Stockman was taken to the administration office. He walked along the middle of the road in front of the militia-men, one arm folded across his old coat, the other waving as though he were shaking mud off it. The others walked along the path by the walls.

Stockman was the last of the prisoners to be examined. Ivan Alexievich, with hands still oily, guiltily smiling David, Valet with his jacket across his shoulders, and Misha Koshevoi were herded together in the anteroom, guarded by militia-men.

Rummaging in his portfolio, the investigator questioned Stockman:

"When I examined you in regard to the murder at the mill why did you conceal the fact that you are a member of the Russian Social-Democratic Labour Party?"

Stockman stared silently over the investigator's head.

"That much is established. You will receive a suitable reward for your work," the investigator shouted, annoyed by the prisoner's silence.

"Please begin your examination," Stockman said in a bored tone, and glancing at a stool, he asked for permission to sit down. The investigator did not reply, but glared as Stockman calmly seated himself.

"When did you come here?" he asked.

"Last year."

"On the instruction of your organization?"

"Without any instructions."

"How long have you been a member of your party?"

"What are you talking about?"

"I ask you how long have you been a member of the Russian Social-Democratic Labour Party?"

"I think that—"

"I don't care what you think. Answer the question. Denial is useless, even dangerous." The investigator drew a document out of his portfolio and pinned it to the table with his forefinger. "I have here a report from Rostov, confirming your membership in the party I mentioned."

Stockman turned his eyes quickly to the document, rested his gaze on it for a moment, and then, stroking his knee, replied firmly:

"Since 1907."

"So! You deny that you have been sent here by your party?"

"Yes."

"In that case why did you come here?"

"They needed a locksmith."

"But why did you choose this particular district?"

"For the same reason."

"Have you now or have you at any time had any contact with your organization during the period of your stay here?"

"No."

"Do they know you have come here?"

"I expect so."

The investigator sharpened his pencil with a pearl-handled penknife and pursed his lips.

"Are you in correspondence with any members of your party?"

"No."

"Then what about the letter which was discovered during the search?"

"That is from a friend who has no connection whatever with any revolutionary organization."

"Have you received any instructions from Rostov?"

"No."

"What did the labourers at the mill gather in your rooms for?"

Stockman shrugged his shoulders as though astonished at the stupidity of the question.

"They used to come in the winter evenings to pass the time away. We played cards. . . ."

"And read books prohibited by law?" the investigator suggested.

"No. Every one of them was almost illiterate."

"None the less the engineer from the mill and the others also do not deny this fact."

"That is untrue."

"It seems to me you haven't the most elementary understanding of—" Stockman smiled at this, and the investigator concluded: "You simply do not possess a sound intelligence. You persist in denials to your own harm. It is quite clear that you have been sent here by your party in order to carry on demoralizing activities among the Cossacks, in order to turn them against the government. I fail to understand why you are playing this game of pretence. It cannot diminish your offence. . . ."

"Those are all guesses on your part. May I smoke? Thank you. And they are guesses entirely without foundation."

"Did you read this book to the workers who visited your rooms?" The investigator put his hand on a small book and covered the title. Above his hand the name Plekhanov was visible.

"We read poetry," Stockman replied, and puffed at his cigarette, gripping the bone holder tightly between his fingers.

The next morning the postal tarantass drove out of the village with Stockman dozing on the back seat, his beard buried in his coat collar. On each side of him a militia-man armed with a drawn sabre was squeezed on the seat. One of them, the pockmarked man who had made the search, gripped Stockman's elbow firmly in his knotty, dirty fingers, casting timorous sidelong glances at him. The tarantass rattled briskly down the street. By the Melekhovs' farmyard a little woman wrapped in a shawl stood waiting for it, her back against the wattle fence. Her grey face was wet with the tears that filled her eyes.

The tarantass sped past, and the woman, pressing her hands to her breast, flung herself after it. "Osip! Osip Davidovich! Oh, how could they—"

Stockman wanted to wave his hand to her, but the pockmarked militia-man jumped up and clutched his arm and in a hoarse, savage voice shouted:

"Sit down or I'll cut you down!"

For the first time in all his simple life he had seen a man who dared to act against the Czar himself.

The long road from Tatarsk to the little town of Radzivillovo lay somewhere behind him in a grey, intangible mist. Gregor tried occasionally to recall the road, but could only dimly remember station buildings, the wagon-wheels clattering beneath the unstable floor, the scent of horses and hay, endless threads of railway line flowing under the wagons, the smoke that billowed in through the open door, and the bearded face of a gendarme on the station platform either at Voronezh or at Kiev, he was not sure which.

At the place where they detrained were crowds of officers and clean-shaven men in grey overcoats, talking a language he could not understand. It took a long time for the horses to be unloaded, but when this had been accomplished the assistant echelon commander led three hundred or more Cossacks to the veterinary hospital. Here followed a long procedure in connection with the examination of the horses. Then allotment to troops. The first troop was formed of light brown horses, the second of bay and dun, the third of dark brown. Gregor was allotted to the fourth, which consisted of plain brown and golden horses. The fifth was composed entirely of sorrel, and the sixth of black horses.

Their road led them along the macadam highway. The Don horses, which had never seen metalled roads before, at first stepped along gingerly, setting their ears back and snorting; but after a while they grew accustomed to the strange feel of the road. The unfamiliar Polish land was crisscrossed with slices of straggling wood. The day was warm and cloudy, and the sun wandered behind a dense curtain of cloud.

The estate of Radzivillovo was some three miles from the station, and they reached it in half an hour. Stroking his horse's neck, Gregor stared at the neatly-built, two-storeyed house, the wooden fence, and the unfamiliar style of the farm buildings. But as they rode past the orchard the bare trees whispered the same language as those in the distant Don country.

Life now showed its tedious, stupefying side to the Cossacks. Torn away from their field labour, they quickly tired at first and spent most of their free time talking. Gregor's troop was quartered in the great tile-roofed wing of the house and slept on pallet beds under the windows. Gregor's bed was by the farthest window. At night the paper pasted over the chinks of the window sounded in the breeze like a distant shepherd's horn, and as he listened to it he was seized with a well-nigh irresistible desire to get up, go to the stables, saddle his horse, and ride and ride until he reached home again.

Reveille was sounded at five o'clock, and the first duty of the day was to clean and groom the horses. During the brief half-hour when the horses were feeding, there was opportunity for desultory conversation.

"This is a hell of a life, boys!"

"I can't stick it!"

"And the sergeant-major! What a swine! He even makes us wash the horses' hoofs!"

"They're cooking pancakes at home now—today is Shrove Tuesday."

"I bet my wife is saying: 'I wonder what my Michael is doing?' "

During exercise the officers stood smoking at the side of the yard, occasionally intervening. As Gregor glanced at the polished, well-groomed officers in their handsome grey cloaks and closely fitting uniforms, he felt that there was an impassable wall between him and them. Their very different, well-ordered, far from Cossack existence flowed on peacefully, untroubled by mud, fleas, or fear of the sergeant-major's fists.

An incident which occurred on the third day after their arrival at Radzivillovo made a painful impression on Gregor, and indeed on all the young Cossacks. They were being instructed in cavalry drill, and Prokhor Zykov's horse happened to kick the sergeant-major's as it passed. The blow was not very hard and it only slightly cut the skin on the horse's left leg. But the sergeant-major struck Prokhor across the face with his whip and, riding right at him, shouted:

"Why the hell don't you look where you're going, you son of a swine? I'll show you. . . . You'll spend the next three days with me!"

The company commander happened to witness the scene, but he turned his back, rubbing the sword-knot of his sabre and yawning boredly. His lips trembling, Prokhor rubbed a streak of blood from his swollen cheek. As Gregor rode past he glanced across at the officers, but they were talking together unconcernedly, as though nothing untoward had happened.

The dreary, monotonous order of existence crushed the life out of the young Cossacks. Until sundown they were kept continuously at foot and horse exercises, and in the evening the horses had to be groomed and fed. Only at ten o'clock, after the roll-call and stationing of guards, were they drawn up for prayers, and the sergeant-major, his eyes wandering over the ranks before him, intoned a "Pater Noster."

In the morning the same routine began again, and the days were as like one another as peas.

In the whole of the estate there were only two women: the old wife of the steward, and the steward's comely young kitchen-maid, Frania. Frania was often to be seen in the kitchen, where the old, browless army cook was in charge. The various troops watched every movement of the young girl's skirt as she ran across the yard. Feeling the gaze of the officers and Cossacks fixed upon her, she bathed in the streams of lasciviousness that came from three hundred pairs of eyes, and swung her hips provokingly as she ran backward and forward between the kitchen and the house, smiling at each troop in turn, but at the officers in particular. Although all fought for her attentions, rumour had it that only the company commander had won them.

One day in early spring Gregor was on duty all day in the great stables. He spent most of his time at one end, where the officers' horses were excited by the presence of a mare. He had just walked past the stall containing the company commander's horse when he heard a sound of struggling and a muffled cry coming from the dark corner at the far end of the stable. A little astonished by the unusual noise, he hurried past the stalls. His eyes were suddenly blinded as someone slammed the stable door and he heard a voice calling in a suppressed shout:

"Hurry up, boys!"

Gregor hastened his steps and called out:

"Who is that?"

The next moment he knocked against one of his company sergeants, who was groping his way to the door. "That you, Melekhov?" the sergeant whispered, putting his hand on Gregor's shoulder.

"Stop! What's up?" Gregor demanded.

The sergeant burst into a guilty snigger and seized Gregor's sleeve. Tearing his arm away, Gregor ran and threw open the door. The light momentarily blinded him; he shaded his eyes with his hand and turned round, hearing an increasing noise in the dark corner of the stable. He went towards the sound and was met by Zharkov buttoning up his trousers.

"What the—what are you doing here?"

"Hurry up!" Zharkov whispered, breathing in Gregor's face. "They've dragged the girl Frania in there . . . undressed her!" His snigger suddenly broke off as Gregor sent him flying against the stable wall. Running to the corner, Gregor found a crowd of Cossacks of the first troop struggling with one another to get to the middle. He silently pushed his way through them and saw Frania lying motionless on the floor, her head wrapped in a horsecloth, her dress torn and pulled back above her breasts, her white legs flung out shamelessly and horribly. A Cossack had just risen from her; holding up his trousers and not looking at his comrades, with a sheepish grin he fell back to make way for the next. Gregor tore his way back through the crowd and ran to the door, shouting for the sergeant-major. But the other Cossacks ran after him and caught him at the door, flinging him back and one putting a hand over his mouth. He sent one man flying and gave another a kick in the stomach, but the others flung a horse-cloth around his head, tied his hands behind him, and threw him into an empty manger. Choking in the stinking horse-cloth, he tried to shout, and kicked lustily at the partition. He heard whispering in the corner and the door creaking as the Cossacks went in and out. He was set free some twenty minutes later. At the door the sergeant-major and two Cossacks from another troop were standing.

"You just keep your mouth shut!" the sergeant-major said to him, winking hard but not looking at him.

The two Cossacks went in and lifted up the motionless bundle that was Frania and, climbing on to a manger, thrust it through a hole left in the wall by a badly-fitting plank. The wall bordered on the orchard. Above each stall was a tiny grimy window. Some of the Cossacks clambered on to the stall partitions to watch what Frania would do, others hastened out of the stables. Gregor also was possessed by a bestial curiosity, and getting on to a partition he drew himself up to one of the windows and looked down. Dozens of eyes were thus staring through the dirty windows at the girl lying under the wall. She lay on her back, her legs crossing and uncrossing like scissor-blades, her fingers scrabbling in the snow by the wall.

She lay there a long time and at last struggled on to her hands and knees. Gregor could clearly see her arms trembling, hardly able to bear her. Swaying, she scrambled to her feet, and dishevelled, unfamiliar, hostile, she passed her eyes in a long, slow stare over the windows.

Then she went, one hand clinging to the woodbine, the other resting and groping along the wall.

Gregor jumped down from the partition and rubbed his throat, feeling that he was about to choke. At the door someone, afterwards he could not even remember who, said to him in distinct and unequivocal tones:

"Breathe a word . . . and, by Christ, we'll kill you!"

On the parade ground the troop commander noticed that a button had been torn from Gregor's greatcoat and asked:

"Who have you been wrestling with? What style do you call this?"

Gregor glanced down at the little round hole left by the missing button; overwhelmed by the memory, for the first time for many a day he felt like crying.

THE LIFE AND WORKS OF MIKHAIL SHOLOKHOV

By GEORGES ALBERT-ROULHAC

MIKHAIL SHOLOKHOV was born on May 24, 1905, in the Cossack village of Kroujiline in the Donets (now the Kamenskaya) Region. His father came from Ryazan; his mother, half-Cossack, half-peasant, was illiterate at the time of Mikhail's birth and learned to read and write only in order to correspond with her son when he went to school. The Soviet author A. S. Serafimovitch, wrote this description of Sholokhov's youth: "From his earliest childhood, little Micha breathed the fresh air of the limitless steppes; he was bronzed by the sun and the hot winds that raise great clouds of dust and dry the lips . . . All his life he was to retain the unforgettable picture of the quiet Don, with the small boats of the Cossack fishermen meandering through the often-flooded fields. The hard work in the fields, the ploughing, sowing, harvesting, gradually formed his character, turning him into an industrious worker—although he was always ready to laugh. The strong, broad-shouldered boy played in the streets with his young Cossack friends and sang with the village girls in the moonlight, playing his full part in that effervescent gaiety that belongs to youth."

Sholokhov was drawn to literature as a boy, and his vocation as an author was revealed early. He wrote plays which were acted in the local youth clubs, and in which he took part himself. When civil war broke out after the Russian Revolution of 1917, he volunteered on the side of the revolutionaries and took part in several actions.

The following year he became a schoolteacher, and in 1923 he went to Moscow, where he worked first as a laborer, then as a clerk. The experience he acquired in these jobs encouraged him to write about what he saw. Finally he offered some of his work for publication in the newspaper of the Young Communists, *The Truth of Youth* and *Komsomolia.* Serafimovitch, who was then the editor of *Komsomolia,* described his first meeting with the young Sholokhov: "One fine April day, a stocky youth wearing a very old Koubanka cap and a well-worn, buttonless overcoat walked into my office. He pulled a manuscript out of his pocket and put it on the table. It was signed with an unknown name, M. Sholokhov. We read it and immediately sent it to the printer. Life in those days was far from easy. I insisted on an advance of royalties from the editor, and was able the next day to make the first payment to the author."

In 1924 Sholokhov returned to his native district. He knew the life of the Don

Cossacks intimately, and his first collection of stories about them, *Donskie rasskazy* (*Tales from the Don*), appeared between 1924 and 1926. Serafimovitch, who had already recognized the talent of the young author, wrote a preface to *Tales from the Don* in which he said, "Sholokhov's tale grows like a flower of the steppes, a living plant. Simply, but with deft and glowing colors, he creates a picture for his readers. His is the language of bright imagery spoken by the Cossacks; terse, intense, animated, it is starkly realistic. He knows his subject well and nothing escapes his prodigious powers of observation. On the other hand, his restraint in dealing with the most pathetic passages only increases the reader's emotional response."

After the Revolution, chaos descended upon the world of the Cossacks and indeed of all Russia. Of these years, Sholokhov once wrote, "It was as if the plough had passed and left a huge furrow separating the earth into two parts." In much of his work, Sholokhov paints a realistic picture of those terrible days, of the merciless struggle between the warring social classes and the disintegration of the social structure. His writings attacked the selfishness of the kulaks, or well-to-do farmers, and praised the growing power and aspirations of the workers and peasants.

In 1928, chapters of his first major work, the novel *Tikhi Don* (*And Quiet Flows the Don*) began to appear in the newspaper *October*. Through this periodical publication, even before the rest of the book was published, Sholokhov immediately sprang to the front rank of Soviet writers. When he first planned the novel, Sholokhov intended to set the story at a time just after the Revolution, when the Cossacks were divided into two camps—one for the Revolution, the other against it. The novel was eventually set in the years 1912–1922, a period of gıeat importance in the history of both Russia as a whole and the Cossacks themselves. On this broad chronological canvas, Sholokhov paints a surprisingly objective picture of the decisive events of the Revolution, neither discounting nor exaggerating them. His characters are depicted as they are, with all their hesitations, doubts, and contradictions. History is related to everyday life, and in the intimate life of Sholokhov's characters the reader sees a reflection of the great global conflicts.

The Russian Revolution convulsed the peoples of the Don basin, putting an end to all illusions about the unity of the various Cosack groups. Henceforth, the class struggle became the principal and universal concern. Cossack kulaks allied themselves with the great landowners and with rich merchants. On the other side of the barricades were landless and moneyless Cossacks, the farm laborers and factory workers. Sholokhov never pretends that most Cossacks adopted revolutionary principles easily and quickly; on the contrary, he insists that only after deep reflection and internal struggles did the Cossacks, with no hope of a return to the status quo, finally associate their future with that of Communist Russia. Aside from these social and political abstractions, the book exhibits Sholokhov's realism at its best. In his panoramic portrait of the brutal customs of prerevolutionary Russia, we see a Cossack mercilessly beating his wife for letting the oxen trample on the hay. Another Cossack publicly whips his young and pretty wife for having cuckolded him. On the other hand, Sholokhov also describes a less harrowing, more peaceful side of Cossack life: the games, feasts, and various ceremonies form an admirable background to our understanding of the historical events that dominate the book.

Despite the tragic quality of the period and the people, Sholokhov avoids deliberate pessimism. *And Quiet Flows the Don* is essentially an optimistic book, with a hidden theme of hope, a theme that promises the renewal of life. The title itself indicates the part played by the landscape and its lyrical overtones. Taken together, the analysis of both history and of individual character, the intensity of the action, the richness and poetry of the setting—all make the novel as broad and majestic as the river it describes. It is a true epic, which has taken a place among the masterpieces of contemporary world literature.

Sholokhov works slowly. He began writing *And Quiet Flows the Don* as early as 1926, and did not finish it until 1940; by the time of the 1953 edition, he had made many alterations. The gestation period of *Podnyataya tselina* (*Virgin Soil Upturned*) (published in 1953 and 1959) was even longer. The theme of this novel is peasant life at another troubled time—the time of the compulsory collectivization of the Russian land and the introduction of the *kolkhozy,* or collective farms, which were fiercely opposed by the kulak element.

This decisive turning point in the economic and social life of his country could not fail to attract Sholokhov's attention, for he was always deeply concerned with contemporary problems. From the first pages of the novel, Sholokhov outlines the conflict that is to be the center of the action—the confrontation of two incompatible social forces, dividing the people of a single village between two utterly different concepts of life, socialism and capitalism. Although most of the poor peasants accept the principle of the *kolkhoz,* others oppose it, openly or clandestinely, and threaten its organizer, Davidor. A schism is thus produced in the population: two factions emerge, those for and those against the rights of private property.

Sholokhov stresses the difficulties of introducing a social change as radical as collectivization to the individualistic mentality of the peasant. But that is not all there is to the book. *Virgin Soil Upturned* describes the total reeducation that a peasant must undergo before he can become a true member of the *kolkhoz.* Some of the peasants work in a half-hearted way, or treat the property of the *kolkhoz* carelessly or negligently. ("It's not mine," they say, "it belongs to the *kolkhoz.*") On the other hand, others take the collective interest to heart, become models of discipline and meet the production norms—the precursors of those who were later known in Soviet Russia as "shock workers."

It is in this book that one of Sholokhov's greatest gifts is most apparent: his language, pithy and full of peasant wit. Old Chtchoukar, for example, is a brilliantly delineated character—a boaster and liar who prides himself on being the most active person in the *kolkhoz,* and tells hilarious stories of buying an air-filled horse from a gypsy and of feeding the workers with frogs. Through him, too, we see how the new life led on the *kolkhozy* contributes to a re-evaluation of people who have previously been misunderstood or even despised. Thus, in scene after scene of *kolkhoz* life, Sholokhov dramatizes fundamental changes in the conscience and behavior of his people.

In 1942, during World War II, Sholokhov wrote a short story, "School of Hate," dealing with the memories of a man who has witnessed Nazi crimes and describing the hatred, engendered by the enemy's behavior, which steels the Soviet people to fight on to victory. It is told in the form of a confession—a confession made by a man completely self-assured but deeply marked by the war, who comes to symbolize justice to the people. Lieutenant Grassimov sums up the main theme of the story: "We have learned to fight well, to hate and to love. The whetstone of war sharpens the feelings admirably."

From May 1943 to February 1944, *Pravda* published excerpts from Sholokhov's new novel *They Fought for Their Country*. It is the story, tersely and simply told, of the campaign on the Don steppes in the summer of 1942. The feats of arms performed by the heroes, Aretov, Lopakhine and Sviagintsev, illustrate the force of Soviet patriotism. Another major character, Nicolai Streltsov, considers his heroic behavior under fire as something quite commonplace, and is impatient to return to the front as soon as possible to rejoin his comrades. "Blood no longer runs out of my ears," he says, "the pains are over. Why should I stay at home when my regiment is in difficulties and its numbers greatly reduced? How could I not return? So here I am! It's easy enough to fight side by side with comrades, even if you're deaf."

Sholokhov's heroes are all industrious men who fight to end the war so that they can return to their normal work. The author depicts each as his calling has formed him, morally and physically. The reader comes to know the agronomist Streltsov, the miner Lopakhine, the farm mechanic Sviagintsev, each with his individual temperament. After the disastrous consequences of the German occupation, these workers feel an implacable hatred toward the invader who prevents the Russian people from living their new life. Loyalty to the fatherland, heroism and scorn of death, the warmth of human relationships, and a sense of solidarity in the struggle—these form the web of the collective conscience of the people. "We have been brothers in life and death," cries one of these heroes. The friendship that links the soldiers is a symbol of the moral and political unity of the people who have given themselves wholeheartedly to the defense of their country.

This war profoundly affected the author of *And Quiet Flows the Don*. In 1957 he published the story "Sudba cheloveka" ("The Fate of a Man"), later made into a successful film. This tale proved to be a new milestone in Sholokhov's career. Once again the emotional strength of the story derives from its perfect simplicity. The hero, André Solokov, is a simple Soviet soldier who has been a prisoner of the Germans and suffered much at their hands. He is a remarkable man, and his strength of character and love of life, his faith in his work and the future ennoble the story and give it a profound significance. Unaffected by the privations of his precarious living, he remains an altruist and adopts a child orphaned by the war. But Sholokhov avoids the obvious happy ending; instead, he forces the reader to meditate on the long, hard journey of life and to feel again the inspiration of love of country and political idealism.

Clearly, Sholokhov is no ivory-tower writer; indeed, he is almost as much a public figure as a creative artist. As a spokesman for the Soviet regime, he writes for the press, gives lectures, takes an active part in writers' conferences; to the public, his opinions are almost law. To understand his attitude toward the Soviet government it is enough to read a sentence taken from one of his public speeches: "Each of us writes according to the dictates of his personal will, but our hearts belong to the Party and to the beloved country which we serve by our art." In him, the man of politics and the man of art are inseparable.

A member of the Communist Party since 1932, and on several occasions a delegate to the Congress of Supreme Soviets, he devotes great energy to his responsibilities. In 1939 he was elected a member of the Soviet Academy of Sciences, only one of many honors and medals for his literary and political work. He was awarded both the Stalin prize and the Lenin prize before the supreme honor of the Nobel Prize for 1965 was bestowed on him by the Swedish Academy. Twenty-two million copies of his works have been printed in the Soviet Union alone, and they have been translated into seventeen languages. These figures are eloquent testimony of how the work of the author of *And Quiet Flows the Don* is regarded in his homeland and all over the world.

Georges Albert-Roulhac is a French literary critic.
Translated by Anthony Rhodes.

THE 1965 PRIZE

By KJELL STRÖMBERG

JEAN PAUL SARTRE justified his refusal of the Nobel Prize in a statement which concluded: "It is regrettable that the Prize should have been given to Pasternak before giving it to Sholokhov, and that the only Soviet work to get an award should be one which is published abroad and banned in his own country. The balance could have been restored by a similar gesture in the other direction . . ."

A year later to the day, the Swedish Academy decided to award the Nobel Prize for Literature to Mikhail Alexandrovich Sholokhov, in particular "for the vigor and the artistic probity with which the author, in his epic work about the Don country, has described an historic phase in the life of the Russian people."

The writer gladly accepted the splendid gift—about $45,000—and also promised to go to Stockholm with all his family to receive it from the hands of the King of Sweden. His answer took several days to arrive because the telegram announcing the good news had come when he was away from his home staying in the vast forests near Uralsk on the Siberian frontier where he was pursuing his favorite sports of hunting and fishing. The award came therefore as a complete surprise, although the world press outside the USSR had been talking of him as the certain winner for several days.

In that year there was a record number of competitors: in fact no fewer than eighty-nine candidates were proposed. In the press forecasts, several writers from Latin America were particularly favored: they were the turbulent Chilean poet Pablo Neruda and his Cuban colleague Nicolás Guillén; the Argentinian novelist Jorge Luis Borges, who had lately visited Sweden; and the Guatemalan Miguel Asturias, who was to win the Prize two years later. There was also talk of two English poets, Robert Graves (who had been a permanent candidate for a quarter of a century) and W. H. Auden, who had recently entered the lists. Also proposed was Alberto Moravia, the brilliant Italian story-teller who was international president of the P.E.N. Club, and three Japanese novelists—Tanizaki, Kawabata, and Yukio Mishima, who was still young, and was supposed to be the Nobel jury's preferred choice.

The award of the Prize to Sholokhov was greeted throughout the world without surprise, as though it corrected an injustice to a first-class writer who was well-known thanks to numerous translations of his novel about the Don River, *And Quiet Flows the Don:* indeed, some astonishment was expressed that he had had to wait such a long time for this prize. This book dated from the thirties and since that time Sholokhov had hardly published anything that came near to competing with this work of his youth. Many critics compared it with Tolstoy's great epic *War and Peace,* and also to Pasternak's *Doctor Zhivago.* Sholokhov was a candidate for the Prize for the first time in 1947, when he had only just become famous, only a year after Pasternak was first proposed.

The same expert was called in to examine the work of these two Soviet candidates, who were proposed almost simultaneously. Professor Anton Karlgren, an eminent expert on Slavic literature, came to the conclusion that Pasternak was the superior, not only in his capacity as a lyric poet but also as a prose narrator. In this domain, because of the subtlety of development of his psychological analysis, he considered Pasternak to be akin to such writers as Marcel Proust. Sholokhov's fresco-like novel, based on the social realism of the nineteenth century, represented a more purely Russian popular tradition influenced by Tolstoy and Turgenev; but too often the great epic flow was weakened by propagandist rhetoric that brought a false note to the account of extraordinary adventures, as well as to the extraordinary characters who appear in it. On the other hand, the writer of the report paid tribute to the spicy humor with which the author surrounds the fabric of events, even horrible ones, and with which the reader is abundantly rewarded. As an impressionist painter, indeed a lyrical one, of nature at all times and in all seasons, Sholokhov had "reached the summit of his art."

The last report on Sholokhov merely notes the characteristic modifications, which were more or less forced on the writer by changes in the political climate, and which he made to the text of subsequent editions of his principal works. The writer of the report also stated that Sholokhov had not published anything after *And Quiet Flows the Don* and *Virgin Soil Upturned* which could influence the Nobel Prize judges. According to persistent rumor, the final scrutiny was far from unanimous; but those are scrupulously kept secrets in the hearts of the Academic jury which, according to its rules, must present a united front to the outside world.

The commentaries in the Soviet press were marked by general satisfaction. The first person to greet the new laureate was Leonid Sobolev, president of the Soviet literary society who, in the past, had joined in the condemnation of the "traitor" Pasternak. Sobolev, writing in *Izvestia,* commented, "To us realistic writers, or rather let us say Socialist realists, the award of the Nobel Prize to Mikhail Sholokhov has a very special meaning. It is a noteworthy fact that this time the Nobel Prize goes to the author of works in which the people, nature, life, and the healthiest optimism all breathe freely to the full extent of their lungs." A few days later he amplified these short, suave words with a long article in the official paper *Literaturnaia Rossia,* in which he insisted on recalling the Pasternak affair in veiled terms. This appears to be the only occasion on which any allusion was made in the Soviet press to that painful business: "Mikhail Sholokhov has been recognized by his people, his epoch, his party and by all our hopes for the future. But the fact that his powerful, shining spirit has received universal recognition in the shape of this great literary Prize—which, alas, not long ago was vilified by being involved in senseless political intrigues which were meant to fan the flames of the Cold War—is not without importance to us. First, it is because justice has at last been done to the work of a great Soviet writer; secondly, because the Nobel Prize itself has been rehabilitated by showing noble and objective recognition of literary talent."

Sholokhov himself, writing in *Pravda*

a few years before on the subject of Pasternak, had accused the Swedish Academy of mixing politics with its literary appreciation, and of not being "objective" in its distribution of rewards. Now Olof Lagercrantz, the literary editor of Stockholm's most widely read newspaper, *Dagens Nyheter,* stated that by awarding the Nobel Prize to Sholokhov the Swedish Academy had committed a political rather than a literary act. He said that the Prize might just as well have been given to the First Secretary of the Communist Party of the USSR. On his fiftieth birthday had not Sholokhov made the following statement: "There are some people who suggest that Soviet writers compose their work at the dictation of the party. The truth is that we write what our hearts dictate. And our hearts belong to the party!" Lagercrantz recalled that Sholokhov had served as a figurehead of the regime as much under Stalin as under Khrushchev, but this did not mean that he had always been accommodating or ready to obey the orders of the regime. "There is no doubt," he concluded, "that from the literary point of view the author of *And Quiet Flows the Don* is a perfectly worthy laureate, in spite of his sour attitude toward persecuted fellow-writers such as Pasternak."

In *Svenska Dagbladet,* another big daily of the Swedish capital, Ake Janzon wrote: "The first Russian Nobel Prize-winner was an exiled poet, Ivan Bunin. The second was a man who had also certainly acquired a big reputation in his own country but who, when the Nobel Prize descended upon him, drew on himself the anathema of the regime and of all right-minded thinkers in political matters. The third is thus Mr. Sholokhov, the darling of those in power and the most famous Soviet writer. No other Russian novelist since the great classic writers and Gorky has had such a universal public as Sholokhov. It is indisputable that he deserves his Prize. . . ."

Elsewhere opinions were not generally very different to those of the Swedish press.

Sholokhov talked candidly to the numerous journalists who came to interview him on his arrival in Stockholm. He had made no secret of his opinion that he had been given the Nobel Prize twenty or thirty years too late. The fact was, he said, that he was the one and only Russian writer who had won the Prize, as Bunin was an expatriate, and Pasternak an "internal exile" whose reputation was mainly based on his gifts as a translator. Sholokhov was almost as proud of a right-and-left shot which brought down two wild geese on the same day that he was told of the award: the Nobel Prize had also dropped out of the sky, he said, since he had long ago given up all thought of expecting it.

Translated by Camilla Sykes.

Henryk Sienkiewicz

1905

"Because of his outstanding merits

as an epic writer"

Illustrated by *CLAUDE TABET*

PRESENTATION ADDRESS

By C. D. AF WIRSÉN

PERMANENT SECRETARY
OF THE SWEDISH ACADEMY

WHEREVER THE LITERATURE of a people is rich and inexhaustible, the existence of that people is assured, for the flower of civilization cannot grow on barren soil. But in every nation there are some rare geniuses who concentrate in themselves the spirit of the nation; they represent the national character to the world. Although they cherish the memories of the past of that people, they do so only to strengthen its hope for the future. Their inspiration is deeply rooted in the past, like the oaktree of Baublis in the desert of Lithuania, but the branches are swayed by the winds of the day. Such a representative of the literature and intellectual culture of a whole people is the man to whom the Swedish Academy has this year awarded the Nobel Prize. He is here and his name is Henryk Sienkiewicz.

He was born in 1846. His youthful work *Szkice weglem* (Charcoal Sketches, 1877) breathes deep and tender sympathy for the oppressed and disinherited of society. Of his other early works one remembers especially the moving story of *Janko muzykant* (*Yanko the Musician,* 1879) and the brilliant portrait of the *Lighthouse-Keeper* (*Latarnik,* 1882). The novella *Niewola tatarska* (Tartar Prison, 1880) gave a foretaste of Henryk Sienkiewicz's future performance in the historical novel, in which he did not show his full ability until the appearance of his famous trilogy. Of the three volumes, *Ogniem i mieczem* (*With Fire and Sword*) appeared in 1884, *Potop* (*The Deluge*) in 1886–1887, and finally *Pan Wolodyjowski* (*Pan Michael*) in 1888–1889. The first volume describes the revolt of the Cossacks supported by the Tartars in 1648–1649; the second deals with the Polish war against Charles Gustave; and the third with the war against the Turks, during which the fortress of Kamieniec was taken after a heroic defense. The climax of *Ogniem i mieczem* is the description of the siege of Sbaraz and of the internal struggle of the inflexible Jeremi Wisniowiecki, debating within himself whether his being indubitably the most resourceful general gives him the right to usurp supreme command. The struggle of conscience ends in the hero's victory over his ambition.

Let us mention in passing that in his trilogy the author has described three sieges, that of Sbaraz, that of Czestochowa, and finally that of Kamieniec, without ever repeating himself in his treatment of the theme. *Potop* contains many excellent tableaux that remain in the reader's memory. There is Kamicia, at the beginning of the novel hardly more than an outlaw induced to fight against his king, who under the influence of his love for a noble woman regains the esteem that he had lost and accomplishes a series of brilliant exploits in the service of the legal order. Olenka, one of Sienkiewicz' many beautiful female characters, is ravishing in her religious faith, her incorruptible rigor, and her devout patriotism. Even the villains in this story are interesting. There is the somber and masterly portrait of Prince Janusz Radziwill, who took up arms against his country, and the description of the banquet at which he tried to inveigle his officers into betraying Poland. Even the traitor has his beauty, and an English critic has drawn attention to the psychological refinement with which Henryk Sienkiewicz shows us the prince debating with his conscience and willfully deluding himself into believing that his rebellion would serve the cause of Poland. Incapable of persisting for long in this voluntary blindness, the prince dies of remorse vainly repressed. Even in the unreliable and libertine Prince Boguslaw there are certain attractive traits of personal courage, of courtly grace and cheerful insouciance. Henryk Sienkiewicz knows people too well to present them uniformly white or black.

Another distinctive trait is Sienkiewicz' habit of never shutting his eyes to the faults of his compatriots; rather he exposes them mercilessly, while he renders justice to the abilities and courage of the enemies of Poland. Like the old prophets of Israel he often tells his people strong truths. Thus in his historical tableaux he blames the excessive Polish desire for individual liberty, which frequently led to a dissipation of energy and made impossible the sacrifice of private interests to the public good. He upbraids the lords for their quarrels and their unwillingness to adapt themselves to the justifiable needs of the state. But Sienkiewicz is always a patriot who certainly puts the brave chivalry of the Polish people in its proper light and who emphasizes the great role effectively played by Poland, formerly the bulwark of Christendom against the Turks and the Tartars. This high objectivity is above all proof of the wisdom of Sienkiewicz' mind and his conception of history. As a good Pole he must disapprove of the attack of Charles Gustave against Poland, but nonetheless he gives brilliant portraits of the personal courage of the king and of the excellent discipline and cohesion of the Swedish troops.

It has often been said that *Pan Wolodyjowski* is the weakest part of the trilogy. We find it hard to subscribe to that opinion. One need only remember the moving account of how the wife of Wolodyjowski escapes from the wily Tartar Azya who combines the qualities of serpent and lion, or the admirable portrait of Basia herself, that beautiful and dauntless soldier wife who combines sweetness with gaiety and courage. The last part of the trilogy is especially rich in gentle and purely human features, as in the beautiful and sublime scene of farewell between Basia and Wolodyjowski, who is about to let himself be blown up with his fort. While the victorious Turks surround the fortress of Kamieniec, when all means of rescue have been exhausted and disaster is imminent, husband and wife are united during an August night in a sort of niche formed by a walled-up gate. He comforts her and reminds her how much happiness they had been granted together and that death is merely a transition. The first to begin the journey to the beyond would only prepare for the coming of the other. The episode is marvelous and enchanting. Although it is not sentimental, it contains such a wealth of pure and true feeling that it is difficult to read it without emotion.

The description of Wolodyjowski's burial is equally grandiose, though in a different manner. At the foot of the coffin, Basia, stretched out on the tiles of the church, is overcome by grief. The chaplain beats the tambourine as if he were giving a signal of alarm and exhorts the dead hero to rise from the catafalque and combat the enemy as before. Then, mastering this outburst of grief, he praises the manly courage and virtues of the dead and prays to God that in this time of extreme danger for the country He may give rise to a liberator. At this moment Sobieski enters the church. All eyes turn toward him. Seized by prophetic enthusiasm, the priest exclaims, "Salvatore" and Sobieski falls to his knees at the side of Wolodyjowski's bier.

All of these descriptions are distinguished by great historical truthfulness. Because of Sienkiewicz' extensive researches and his sense of history, his characters speak and act in the style of the period. It is significant that among the many persons who suggested Henryk Sienkiewicz for the Nobel Prize there were eminent historians.

The trilogy abounds in descriptions of nature admirable in their freshness. Where would one find the equivalent of the very short but unforgettable description in *Ogniem i mieczem* of the steppe as it awakens in the spring, when flowers rise from the soil, insects buzz, wild geese pass over, birds sing, and wild horses with floating manes and dilated nostrils rush away like a whirlwind at the sight of a troop of soldiers?

Another remarkable trait of this grandiose trilogy is its humor. The little knight Wolodyjowski is certainly admirably drawn, but the portrait of the jovial nobleman Zagloba imprints itself perhaps even more firmly in our memory. His vainglory, his girth, and his taste for wine recall Falstaff, but these are their only common traits. Whereas Falstaff is a dissipated and questionable character, Zagloba has a heart of gold; he is faithful to his friends in times of danger. Zagloba himself pretends to be a sober man, made to be a good priest, but in truth he is much addicted to the pleasures of the table. He loves wine and declares that only traitors renounce it because they are afraid to give away their secrets when drunk; what makes him especially abhor the Turks is the fact that they do not drink wine. Zagloba is a terrible gossip—a quality that he considers necessary in winter because otherwise the tongue might freeze and become numb. He flaunts military decorations and boasts of military exploits in which he never took part. In reality his courage—for he has courage—is of another kind. He trembles before every encounter like a coward, but once the battle has begun he is seized by rage against the enemy who will not let him live in peace and he becomes capable of true feats of courage, as when he defeats the terrible Cossack Burlaj.

Moreover, he is wily and resourceful like Odysseus and often finds a way out when the others have come to the end of their tether. He is basically a debonair and emotional man, who sheds tears when some great mishap befalls his friends. He is a good patriot and unlike so many others he does not desert his king. It has been said that the character of Zagloba lacks consistency because in the last volume of the trilogy the grotesque gossip becomes more serious and acquires more social consideration. This opinion is inconsiderate. Sienkiewicz wanted to show us precisely how Zagloba develops and becomes somewhat ennobled while at the same time retaining his old faults. Such a relative improvement is all the more natural as Zagloba, despite all his bizarre faults, is basically as good as a child. Such as he is, Zagloba belongs forever to the gallery of immortal comic characters of world literature, and he is thoroughly original.

The diversity of Henryk Sienkiewicz' talent became apparent when in 1890 he passed from the warrior portraits of his trilogy to a modern psychological novel and published *Bez dogmatu* (*Without Dogma*), which is considered by many critics his main work. The novel is in the form of a journal, but unlike so many other journals, it is never tiresome. With an art hardly surpassed elsewhere it presents to us the type of a worldly man, a religious and moral skeptic, who becomes unproductive because of his morbid need for self-analysis. Through his perpetual indecision, he prevents his own happiness, sacrifices that of others, and finally succumbs. Ploszowski is a highly gifted man, but he lacks moral bones, so to speak: he is without dogma. He is hyper-esthetic and extremely sophisticated, but the sophistication cannot replace his lack of faith and spontaneity. There is the figure of Anielka, delightful in her sad melancholy, who watches the best hopes of her life pass away through the egotism of Ploszowski, yet until the end remains faithful to the laws of duty. The author shows us with insight how in a soul that has once been Christian, like that of Ploszowski, the cult of beauty is insufficient to fill the void left by the loss of religious sentiment. Sienkiewicz has portrayed a type which exists in all countries, a brilliant figure marred by intellectual neurasthenia. *Bez dogmatu* is a profoundly serious book that invites reflection, but at the same time it is an exquisite work of art, delicately chiseled. The inspired account vibrates with controlled melancholy, and if the book appears at times cold, it is the cold of a work of sculpture inherent in many beautiful and noble works of art. We find this frequently, for instance, in the works of Goethe.

Bez dogmatu was followed in 1894 by *Rodzina Polanieckich* (*Children of the Soil*), a work less inspired than *Bez dogmatu* but characterized by great depth in its description of the contrast of a useful country life and hollow cosmopolitanism. Here again we find the figure of a superb woman, the candid, devoted, and tender Marynia. Critics have raised objections to a detail; that is, the sin of passion which Polanieckich commits. Far from defending him, the author has illustrated how a man whose life is neither abnormal nor excessive, let alone perverted, is nonetheless capable of committing a fault, but soon comes to his senses and repents without soft complacency. The ties between Polanieckich and his wife are re-established even more firmly at the end of the book, and the novel is really a glorification of domestic virtues and of sane and salutary social activity. There is much charm in the delicately drawn portrait of the sick child Litka, who sacrifices her child's love for Polanieckich in order to reconcile him with Marynia. The episode is sublime and rich in purity and moving poetry.

The same critics who blamed his trilogy for being too long have caviled at the rapid pace of the short tale *Pojdzmy za nim* (*Let Us Follow Him,* 1892), a simple sketch that paints with great poetic beauty how the countess Antéa, ill and suffering from painful and dangerous hallucinations, is cured by the dying and resurrected Savior. In each case the criticism is irrelevant, for the different subjects demand a different treatment. *Pojdzmy za nim* is admittedly a sketch, but it is a story of deep and moving sensibility. Thus a master's casual chalk sketch because of its intimate characters is often almost equal in value to his more elaborate works. *Pojdzmy za nim* is written with noble piety; it is a modest flower growing at the foot of the cross and enclosing in its blossom a drop of the blood of the Savior.

Religious subjects soon led Sienkiewicz to a vast work that has become universally famous. In 1895–1896 he wrote *Quo Vadis?* This history of the persecutions under Nero had an extraordinary success. The English translation sold 800,000 copies in England and America in one year. Professor Brückner, the historian of Polish literature in Berlin, estimated in 1901 that about two million copies had been sold in these two countries alone.

Quo Vadis? has been translated into more than thirty languages. Although one should not overestimate the importance of such a success—bad books also spread easily provided they are seductive—it still points clearly to the value of a work that never addresses itself to the lower instincts of man but treats an elevated subject in an elevated manner. *Quo Vadis?* excellently describes the contrast between the sophisticated but gangrened paganism with its pride, and humble and confident Christianity, between egotism and love, between the insolent luxury of the imperial palace and the silent concentration of the catacombs. The descriptions of the fire at Rome and the bloody scenes in the amphitheater are without equal. Henryk Sienkiewicz discreetly avoids making Nero a major character, but in a few strokes he has portrayed to us the dilettante crowned with all his vanity and the folly of his grandeur, all his false exaltation, all his cult of superficial art void of moral sense, and all his capricious cruelty.

The portrait of Petronius, drawn in greater detail, is even better. The author was able to rely on the inspired sketch in the two short chapters of the sixteenth book of Tacitus' *Annals.* Starting from these very brief hints Sienkiewicz has constructed a psychological picture that gives a strong appearance of truthfulness and is extremely penetrating. Petronius, the man of sophisticated culture, *arbiter elegantiae,* is a bundle of contradictions. Epicurean and above all skeptic, he considers life a deceptive mirage. Pleasures have made him effeminate, but he still has the courage of a man. While free of prejudices, he is at times superstitious. His sense of good and evil is not strongly developed, but his sense of the beautiful is all the more marked. He is a man of the world and in delicate situations he is capable of acquitting himself with skill and *sang-froid* without compromising his dignity. The skeptic Pyrrhon and the poet of pleasure Anacreon please him more than the uncouth moralists of the Stoa. He despises the Christians, whom he knows little. It seems to him pointless and unworthy of a man to render good for bad according to Christian doctrine. To hope for a life after death, as the Christians do, seems to him as strange as if one were to announce that a new day begins at night. Ruined by the favorite Tigellinus, Petronius dies with the serenity of a death that he had sought himself. The entire description is perfect in its genre.

But *Quo Vadis?* contains many other admirable things. Especially beautiful is the episode, lit by the setting sun, in which the apostle Paul goes to his martyrdom repeating to himself the words that he had once written: "I have fought a good fight, I have finished my course, I have kept the faith" (2 Tim. 4:7).

After this major work Henryk Sienkiewicz returned to the national Polish novel and in 1901 wrote *Krzyzacy* (*The Knights of the Cross*). The task was this time less easy than in the case of the trilogy because there were fewer sources. But Sienkiewicz overcame the difficulties and gave to his version a strong medieval color. The subject of the novel is the fight of the Polish and Lithuanian nations against the Teutonic Knights who, having long ago finished their original mission, had become an oppressive institution more occupied with power and terrestrial gains than with the cross whose insignia the members of the order bore on their coats. It was the Archduke Jagiello, later King of Poland under the name of Wladislaw II, who broke the dominance of the order. He plays a role in the novel, although he is only sketchily drawn according to Sienkiewicz' custom of not giving too much prominence to historical characters. The many characters which are entirely the product of the author's rich fancy attract our attention more strongly and furnish excellent examples of medieval civilization. It was a superstitious epoch and, although the country had been Christianized for a long time, people still put food out at night for vampires and revenants.

Each saint had his particular function. Apollonia was invoked for toothaches, Liberius for stones. It is true that God the Father rules the universe, but this very fact proves that he has no time to look after human affairs of minor importance; consequently he has delegated certain functions to saints. That epoch was indeed superstitious, but it was also full of energy. Huge and solid, the castle of the order stands at Marienburg. The Polish and Lithuanian opponents of the monastic knights do not lack force, either. There is Macko, crude, greedy, bent on the interests of his family, but brave. There is the noble Zbyszko, his mind full of chivalrous adventures. Surpassing all the others, colossal, as if cut in granite, there is the redoubtable Jurand, cruel in his hatred of the Teutonic Order and finally the victim of its terrible revenge. In the hour of his humiliation he is more sublime than ever because of his self-victory and the power of his forgiveness. He is one of the most grandiose of Sienkiewicz' warrior characters. Tableaux of gentleness alternate with those of force. Queen Jadwiga is gentle, but her appearance is elusive. The description of the funeral for the poor, sorely tested Danusia is delicately beautiful like a softly chanted passion service. On the other hand, the fresh and spring-like picture of Jagienka is radiant with exuberant health and liveliness.

All these creations have their individual life. Among the outstanding minor characters are the irascible and bellicose Abbé, unable to brook any contradiction, and Sanders, the seller of indulgences, who sells a hoof of the donkey on which the flight to Egypt took place, a piece of the ladder of Jacob, the tears of the Egyptian Mary, and a little rust from the keys of St. Peter. The closing episode, the battle of Tannenberg in 1410 in which the squadrons of the Teutonic Order were crushed after a heroic battle, is like the finale of a splendid musical drama.

Henryk Sienkiewicz is certainly the first to recognize his debt to old Polish literature. That literature is indeed rich. Adam Mickiewicz is its true Adam, its ancestor by virtue of the full nature of the poetry that distinguishes his great epic. Brilliant as the stars in the sky of Polish literature are the names of Slowacki, a man of fertile imagination, and of the philosopher Krasinski. The epic art has been successfully practiced by men like Korzeniowski, Kraszewski, and Rzewuski. But with Henryk Sienkiewicz that art has reached its full bloom and presents itself in its highest degree of objectivity.

If one surveys Sienkiewicz' achievement it appears gigantic and vast, and at every point noble and controlled. As for his epic style, it is of absolute artistic perfection. That epic style with its powerful overall effect and the relative independence of episodes is distinguished by naive and striking metaphors. In this respect, as Geijer has remarked, Homer is the master because he perceives grandeur in simplicity as, for example, when he compares the warriors to flies that swarm around a pail of milk, or when Patroklos, who all in tears asks Achilles to let him fight against the enemies, is compared to a little girl who weeping clings to the dress of her mother and wants to be taken in her arms.

A Swedish critic has noticed in Sienkiewicz some similes that have the clarity of Homeric images. Thus the retreat of an army is compared to a retreating wave that leaves mussels and shells on the beach, or the beginning of gunfire is compared to the barking of a village dog who is soon joined in chorus by all the other dogs. The examples could be multiplied. The attack on the front and rear of an army surrounded and subject to fire from both sides is compared to a field that is reaped by two groups of mowers who begin their work at opposite sides of the field with the purpose of meeting in the middle. In *Krzyzacy* the Samogites rising from furrows attack the German knights like a swarm of wasps whose nest has been damaged by a careless wanderer. In *Pan Wolodyjowski* we also find admirable images; in order to judge them we should remember that, as often in Homer, the two terms of the comparison converge only in one point, while the rest remains vague. Wolodyjowski with his unique sword kills human lives around him as rapidly as a choir boy after the mass snuffs the candles on the altar one after the other with his long extinguisher. Hussein Pasha, the commander of the Turkish army who vainly tries to leave by the gate that leads to Jassy, returns to the camp to try another exit, just as a poacher who has been tracked in a park tries to escape now on one side and now on the other. The Christian martyrs of *Quo Vadis?* who are prepared for death are already as removed from earthly places as mariners who have pushed off and left the quay. Many more situations equally Homeric and yet equally natural and spontaneous could be cited; thus in *Krzyzacy* Jagienka, at the unexpected sight of Zbyszko, who resembles a young prince, stops short at the gate and nearly drops the jug of wine.

The literary production of Henryk Sienkiewicz is far from over. At the moment he is in the process of publishing a new trilogy entitled *Na polu chwały* (*On the Field of Glory,* 1906) that deals with the time of Sobieski.

His own poetic career has indeed unfolded on the field of glory. He has received valuable tokens of the devotion of his people, all the more precious since, despite his ardent patriotism, he has never flattered his country. On the occasion of his twenty-fifth anniversary as an author a grand national subscription provided the means to buy the castle that had been the original seat of his family and to offer it to him as a present. He was saluted by delegations, congratulatory messages were sent, and the Warsaw theater staged a gala performance in his honor.

An homage from the North has now been added to these proofs of admiration, for the Swedish Academy has decided to award the Nobel Prize for Literature of 1905 to Henryk Sienkiewicz.

ACCEPTANCE SPEECH

By HENRYK SIENKIEWICZ

NATIONS ARE REPRESENTED by their poets and their writers in the open competition for the Nobel Prize. Consequently the award of the Prize by the Academy glorifies not only the author but the people whose son he is, and it bears witness that that nation has a share in the universal achievement, that its efforts are fruitful, and that it has the right to live for the profit of mankind. If this honor is precious to all, it is infinitely more so to Poland. It has been said that Poland is dead, exhausted, enslaved, but here is the proof of her life and triumph. Like Galileo, one is forced to think *"E pur si muove"* when before the eyes of the world homage has been rendered to the importance of Poland's achievement and her genius.

This homage has been rendered not to me—for the Polish soil is fertile and does not lack better writers than me—but to the Polish achievement, the Polish genius. For this I should like to express my most ardent and most sincere gratitude as a Pole to you gentlemen, the members of the Swedish Academy, and I conclude by borrowing the words of Horace: *"Principibus placuisse non ultima laus est."*

QUO VADIS?

By HENRYK SIENKIEWICZ

Translated by C. J. Hogarth

[Excerpt]

XV

Before the Flavians built the Coliseum the majority of the Roman amphitheatres were constructed of wood. Also, nearly all of them had been burnt in the late fire, and therefore in order to give the games which he had promised the people, Nero ordered a number of new amphitheatres to be erected—among them a gigantic Circus for the construction of which huge trunks of trees were brought from the slopes of the Atlas Mountains. Upon this Circus thousands of artisans worked day and night—the plans having been prepared by the celebrated architects Severus and Celer. Indeed, the process of building and fitting was carried on without a break. Wonders were told of the pillars—inlaid with bronze, amber, ivory, mother-of-pearl, and tortoiseshell—which it was to contain. Also, canals filled with ice-cold water from the mountains were to run beneath the benches, for the purpose of maintaining a comfortable temperature throughout the building; while an immense purple velarium, or canopy, was to afford shelter from the sun. Between the rows of benches there were to be placed braziers for the diffusion of Arabic perfumes; and an ingenious device to cause sprinklings of saffron and of verbena to descend upon the heads of the spectators was installed.

On the day when the morning games were to begin throngs of people waited from dawn for the doors of the Circus to open—listening with delight, meanwhile, to the roaring of the lions, the growling of the panthers, and the howling of the dogs. The animals had not been fed for two days, and now bleeding quarters of meat were being dangled before their cages, to excite their fury and hunger. Sometimes, indeed, the storm of howls and roars from the beasts made it impossible for those waiting at the doors of the Circus to hear themselves speak.

At dawn, also, there arose, even in the vicinity of the Circus itself, the deep, calm sound of Christian hymns. Men listened in astonishment, repeating, "It is the Christians, it is the Christians!" The reason was that large numbers of the latter had been transferred to the Circus overnight—persons drawn not from the same prison in each case, as had been the original plan, but from different houses of incarceration. The voices of these men, women, and children, as they sang their morning hymns, were so numerous that people began to declare that the beasts would grow weary and satiated before they could tear such a multitude of victims to pieces; while others asserted that so great a number of victims in the ring would prevent concentration of attention, and permit no one to enjoy the spectacle comfortably. In proportion as the hour for opening the entrance-ways approached, the throng grew merry and more animated, and took to discussing matters of the Circus. Here and there groups would gather together to praise the relative aptness of lions or of tigers for tearing human beings in pieces, and to lay wagers on the same. Also, people talked of the gladiators who were to precede the Christians in the arena. Some lauded the Samnites or the Gauls, while others pinned their faith upon the mirmillones, the Thracians, or the retiarii. As the morning wore on, detachments of these fighters, headed by their trainers, the lanistæ, began to gravitate towards the amphitheatre; but, to avoid tiring themselves before they should be wanted, they marched without arms, and often completely naked, except for garlands of flowers on their heads and green branches in their hands. For the most part young, handsome, and full of life, they looked so splendid in the morning light, with their formidable bodies shining with oil until they almost resembled blocks of granite, that the people, ever prone to admire beauty of form, broke out into frequent applause, and called aloud their names, with which every one was familiar. "Hail, Furnius!" could be heard—"Hail, Leo! Hail, Maximus! Hail, Diomedes!" Young girls threw looks of love at them, and they, in their turn, singled out the fairest of the maidens, and as though they had not a care upon their minds, addressed compliments to these damsels, threw them kisses, and called out, "Take me before death shall do so!" At length the gladiators disappeared within portals whence more than one of their number was never again to issue.

Every moment fresh sights kept attracting the attention of the mob. Behind the gladiators came the mastigophori, whose function it was to lash and urge on the combatants. Next there passed by trains of mules, dragging towards the spoliarium, or place where the dead bodies were to be cast, carts stacked with coffins. The sight of these particularly delighted the people, since from the number of the shells they could form an estimate of the immense proportions of the coming spectacle. The carts of coffins were followed by persons dressed to represent Charon or Mercury, who were charged with the duty of finally dispatching the wounded; by ushers who were to preserve order in the Circus, and to show spectators to their seats; by slaves who were to serve refreshments; and by the detachment of Prætorian Guards which always attended the Imperator in the amphitheatre. Then the doors of public admission were opened, and the people swarmed in. Yet so enormous was the multitude that it took several hours to filter into the building; while, at the sound of the doors being opened, the wild beasts in the vivaria roared more loudly than ever, in excitement at scenting so many human beings massed together. In fact, until the audience had settled into their seats, the roar of the multitude was as the roar of the ocean in a storm.

Presently there arrived also the Prefect of Rome, with his bodyguard, and then litters of Senators, Consuls, Prætors, Ædiles, palace functionaries, officers of the Prætorian Guard, patricians, and fine ladies. The gilding of the litters, the white or coloured robes and ear-rings, jewels and plumes of their occupants, the axes of the lictors—all combined to reflect the sunlight from a myriad glittering points.

From the various parts of the Circus the populace greeted these superior dignitaries with acclamations. Minor detachments of the Prætorians next made their appearance, but the priests of the various pagan sanctuaries arrived later, with, behind them, the sacred Virgins of Vesta, borne aloft in litters, and preceded by lictors.

Nothing more was needed for the spectacle to begin but the presence of Cæsar; and since the latter was anxious not to abuse the people's patience, but, on the contrary, desired to win the public favour by his punctuality, he soon made his appearance in company with Poppæa and the Augustans—the latter including Petronius and Vinicius, who were riding together in the same litter.

The attendants and servants generally of the amphitheatre were all in the pay of Vinicius; and it had been agreed upon that the keepers of the wild beasts should conceal Lygia in an obscure corner of the underground passages until fall of night, when she should be handed over to the young tribune's steward, who would at once start with her for the Alban Hills. Petronius, who was in the secret, had further advised Vinicius to show himself openly in the amphitheatre, and subsequently to escape thence by favour of the military on duty; whereafter he was to make his way into the dungeons, in order that he might prevent any possible mistake by himself pointing out Lygia to the gaolers.

This he succeeded in doing; but, on the gaolers opening the wicket, one of them—a man named Syrus—said to him as he led the way towards the Christians:

"My lord, I know not if you will find her whom you seek; for though we have made inquiries for a young girl named Lygia, no one has answered to the name. However, it is possible that the prisoners do not fully trust us."

So saying, Syrus opened a door, and they entered a vast hall which was not only low, but very dark, since light gained admission merely through barred slits which divided it from the arena. At first Vinicius could distinguish nothing: he could hear only the confused murmur of voices in the hall itself, and the clamour which came from the people in the amphitheatre. After a moment, however, his eyes grew more accustomed to the darkness, and he saw before him groups of weird beings who looked like wolves or bears. These were Christians who had been sewn up in the skins of wild beasts. Some were praying in a standing position; others in a kneeling. Here and there long hair straggling over the fur revealed the fact that the victim was a woman. Mothers, looking like she-wolves, were holding equally hirsute infants in their arms. Yet under the pelts of wild beasts there could be seen clear faces and eyes which shone in the darkness with a sort of feverish joy. It was manifest that the majority of these people were filled with an idea which rendered them insensible to anything that might befall. Some whom Vinicius questioned regarding Lygia made no answer, but looked at him with the eyes of sleepers suddenly awakened. Others smiled at him with a finger to their lips, or pointed to the bars through which faint beams of light were straggling. The only weeping to be heard came from children who were terrified by the din from the wild beasts, and by the beast-like aspect of their parents.

As Vinicius walked beside Syrus he kept examining faces, peering about, and asking questions. At times, also, he stumbled over the bodies of persons who had fainted in the stifling atmosphere. Suddenly he stopped, for he seemed to have caught the sound of a familiar voice. Retracing his steps, and making his way through the crowd, he approached the person who had spoken; and as he did so a beam of light fell upon the head of a man in whom Vinicius recognised, despite the covering of wolf's skin, the attenuated, but implacable, Crispus.

"Repent you of your sins," he was saying; "for the hour is at hand. In truth I say unto you that he who thinks that he will be redeemed by his martyrdom is committing a sin the more, and will be cast into fire everlasting. Every sin which is committed does but renew the agony of the Lord: how, therefore, can you dare to conceive that the agony which is awaiting you can equal that which was endured by the Redeemer? The just and the unjust will die, this day, the same death; but the Lord will recognise His own. Woe unto you, for the teeth of the lions can destroy your flesh, but not your sins, nor yet your account with God. He has shown you sufficient mercy in that He suffered Himself to be nailed to the Cross. Henceforth you will behold Him only as the Great Judge. You, therefore, who think to blot out your iniquities by your agony do blaspheme against the justice of God, and will be cast the more into the abyss. Now that you are about to come face to face with the dread Judge before whom even the righteous will find but sorry grace, repent you of your sins, for Hell is awaiting you."

A shudder passed over Vinicius' form. Though hitherto he had rested all his hopes upon the mercy of Christ, he had just heard it said that even death in the arena would not suffice to gain such mercy! Yet with the swiftness and the brilliancy of lightning there passed through his mind also a thought that it was in very different fashion that the Apostle Peter had spoken to those who were about to die. At the same time, the terrible threats of the fanatical Crispus, added to the darkness of the hall, the imminence of execution, and the aspect of the victims clothed death, filled Vinicius' heart with terror. Together these things seemed to him a thousand times more frightful and more atrocious even than the most sanguinary battle in which he had taken part. Remembering, however, that at any moment the gratings might be opened, he set himself to call for Lygia and Ursus, in the hope that, in default of them, some one would respond who knew him.

And, true enough, a man clad in the skin of a bear plucked him by the toga, and said:

"My lord, they have been left behind in the prison. I was the last to be brought out, and saw the maiden lying sick upon her bed."

"Who are you?" asked Vinicius.

"The quarryman in whose hut you were baptised by the Apostle Peter. I have been in prison three days, and am to die today."

Vinicius drew a deep breath.

"Do you remember, my lord," continued the quarryman, "that it was I who guided you through Cornelius' vineyard, when the Apostle was preaching to us in an out-building?"

"Yes, I remember," replied Vinicius.

"I saw him again later, on the evening of the day before I was thrown into prison. He gave me his blessing, and told me that he would be present in the amphitheatre to bless also those who were to be put to death. That I may behold him at the moment when death comes to me—that I may see him make the sign of the cross—is my constant prayer. It will be easy for me to die then! If, my lord, you know where he is now, I beseech you to tell me!"

Vinicius lowered his voice, and replied:

"He is among Petronius' attendants, disguised as a slave. I know not where they are sitting, but when I regain my own seat I will seek them. Look in my direction when you enter the arena. I will rise and turn my head towards Peter and those who are with him, and then you will be able to find him with your own eyes."

"I thank you, my lord. May peace be with you!"

"And to you may the Saviour be merciful!"

"Amen!"

Vinicius left the dungeon, and returned

to the amphitheatre, where he resumed his place beside Petronius among the Augustans.

"Is she there?" asked Petronius.

"No. She has remained behind in prison."

"Then listen to another idea which has just occurred to me. But as you listen keep glancing in the direction of Nigidia, so that it may be thought that we are discussing her head-dress. Tigellinus and Chilo have their eyes upon us. Well, my idea is this. Have Lygia put into a coffin to-night, and removed for dead. The rest you can guess."

"Yes," was Vinicius' hurried reply.

This conversation was interrupted by Tullius Senecio, who said to them as he leant over in their direction:

"Do you know whether or not weapons are to be allowed the Christians?"

"No, we know not," replied Petronius.

"Well, for my part I should have preferred that to be done," continued Senecio, "since otherwise the arena will come soon to resemble a butcher's slaughter-house. But what a splendid amphitheatre it is!"

And, truly enough, the effect presented was magnificent. The lower benches appeared to be covered with snow, so compact was their white swarm of togas; while above them, on a gilded balcony, Cæsar, with a string of diamonds around his neck and a crown of gold on his head, was seated. Beside him he had Augusta, at once beautiful and menacing; while a little distance away were the Vestal Virgins, high dignitaries, Senators in embroidered mantles, military commanders in brilliant armour, and all the might and magnificence of Rome. Behind, again, sat the knights, while higher up, in every tier, there undulated a sea of dark human heads, backed by lines of masts around which were twined garlands of roses, lilies, creepers, ivy, and vine leaves. Everywhere people were talking loudly, asking questions, singing, applauding clever sallies, bursting into a roar of laughter which rolled from tier to tier, and stamping their feet to hasten the commencement of the spectacle. This stamping of feet resembled distant thunder, and never for a moment ceased. At length the Prefect, after making a tour of the arena with his splendid retinue, gave the signal by dropping a scarf. In answer there came a cry of "Aah!" uttered in unison by thousands of throats from every part of the vast arena.

Usually the spectacle began with the chasing of wild beasts—a sport in which sundry barbarians of the North and South greatly excelled; but this time the opening item was furnished by andabatæ—gladiators who, furnished with helmets lacking eyeholes, fought blindfold. Of these warriors a dozen or so advanced into the arena, and began to cleave the empty air with their swords, while mastigophori urged them towards one another with long forks. This contemptible exhibition the elegant portion of the audience watched with indifference. On the other hand, the populace derived considerable amusement from the gladiators' awkward movements; and whenever two of the combatants met back to back, loud laughter would ring forth, and shouts of "To the right!" or "To the left!"—shouts frequently uttered on purpose to mislead the warriors. A few pairs, however, succeeded in getting to close quarters, and then the struggle became more sanguinary as the more excited of the combatants threw away their shields, and, grasping one another's left hands, began a fight to the death with their right. Those who fell raised their fingers to plead for the audience's pity, but, as a rule, the people demanded the death of such wounded men, especially when they happened to be andabatæ—gladiators, whose faces being covered, had remained unknown to the spectators. Gradually the number of combatants grew smaller, until there survived only two. These were guided in one another's direction, met, fell upon the sand, and mutually stabbed one another to death. Then arena attendants removed the bodies, while Greek youths raked over the arena, in order to cover up the marks of blood. Lastly, saffron leaves were sprinkled over all.

Next followed a graver combat—one which excited the interest of the fashionable throng as much as it did that of the mob. Also, it was one upon which young patricians often wagered or lost their last sestertius. As soon as ever it had begun, tablets were passed round the audience, in order that spectators might inscribe thereon the names of their favourites, and the amount that each man cared to risk upon the gladiator of his choice. Veteran champions who had previously appeared in the arena and won victories gained the greatest number of backers, but certain gamblers staked considerable sums also upon new and unknown gladiators—hoping thereby to make an enormous profit. Cæsar himself laid wagers, and, with him, priests, Vestal Virgins, Senators, knights, and the people generally. Not infrequently the latter, after losing their all, would stake, in addition, their personal freedom.

As the strident tones of the trumpets rang out, a tense and profound silence fell upon the assemblage, and thousands of eyes fixed themselves upon an enormous door which a man dressed as Charon approached and, amid a profound stillness, struck three times with a hammer, as though to summon to death the men who were concealed behind it. The two leaves of the door opened slowly, and from the recesses of a darkened space within there streamed forth into the brilliantly lighted arena a swarm of gladiators.

Thracian gladiators, mirmillones, Samnites, and Gauls—all of them marched in separate groups of twenty-five, heavily armed. Next came retiarii, holding a net in one hand and a trident in the other. At once from some of the benches there arose a fusillade of clapping, which presently swelled into a vast and continuous roar of applause. From top to bottom of every tier there could be seen only inflamed faces, gesticulating hands, and widely opened mouths. The gladiators made a tour of the arena with a regular, elastic tread and much glittering of weapons and rich cuirasses, and then halted before the Imperial balcony—a cohort proud, calm, and splendid. Next, the penetrating sound of a horn stilled the uproar, and, raising heads and eyes, and extending their right hands towards Cæsar, the warriors chanted in a drawling monotone:

"Ave, Cæsar Imperator!
Morituri te salutant!" [1]

Then in a twinkling they separated, and stationed themselves at the margin of the arena. They were to attack one another in detachments, but before they did so the most famous of the fencers had the right to engage in a series of single combats—a form of fighting which afforded greater opportunities of displaying individual courage and address. From the Gallic detachment there issued Lanio, a champion well known to habitués of the amphitheatre as the victor in many previous encounters. With his huge helmet and the cuirass which encircled his formidable torso, he looked, in the sunshine which was flooding the sand of the arena, like an immense glittering beetle. To meet him there advanced the no less famous retiarius Calendio.

Among the spectators wagers began to circulate:

"Five hundred sestertii upon the Gaul!"

"Five hundred upon Calendio!"

---

[1] "Hail, Cæsar Imperator!
We, about to die, salute thee!"

"By Hercules, a thousand!"

"Two thousand!"

On reaching the centre of the arena, the Gaul fell back, with his sword in line and his head lowered to observe his adversary through the eyelets of his visor; while Calendio—light, statuesque, and stark naked save for a loin-cloth—began to revolve around his massive antagonist, making graceful passes with his net as he did so, raising and lowering his trident, and singing his habitual chant of

> "Non te peto; piscem peto.
> Quid me fugis, Galle?" [1]

The Gaul, however, so far from fleeing, held his ground, and set himself to change his position in such a way that he always had his enemy in front of him. In his body and monstrous head there now seemed to be a suggestion of the terrible—a suggestion of the fact that that mighty bulk, enclosed in steel, was engendering the attack of a thunderbolt.

Ever the retiarius kept approaching or retiring by sudden leaps, as well as causing his trident to flutter so rapidly that the eye could scarcely follow its movements. Several times the teeth of the trident rang upon the shield, but the Gaul never flinched—thus giving proof of his gigantic strength. His whole attention seemed to be concentrated, not upon the trident, but upon the net, which kept fluttering around his head like a bird of ill-omen. With bated breath the audience followed the splendid fencing of these gladiators; until at length Lanio chose a moment to rush in upon his adversary, who, leaping aside under the levelled sword, turned, straightened his arms, and again launched his net. The Gaul faced about, caught the net on his shield, and, like his adversary, leapt backwards. The audience roared applause, and new wagers were laid. Cæsar himself, who had been talking to Rubria and paying small attention to the spectacle, now turned his head in the direction of the arena.

Again the gladiators engaged in combat, but with such dexterity, such precision of movement, that at times it might have been thought that for them it was not a question of life or death, but a mere opportunity of displaying their address. Twice Lanio evaded the net; after which he began to give ground in the direction of the edge of the arena. Thereupon those who had staked wagers upon him cried out (since they did not wish to see him rest), "To the attack!" The gladiator obeyed them by again assuming the offensive. Suddenly the retiarius' arm spouted blood, and his net fell. Lanio collected himself on his haunches, and sprang forward to administer the final stroke; but at the same moment Calendio, who had feigned to be unable to continue wielding his net, leant sideways, evaded the point of the sword, and, slipping his trident between the knees of his adversary, brought him to the ground. The other tried to rise, but instantly became enmeshed in the fatal net, in which his every movement served the more to entangle his hands and feet. Finally a stab from the trident nailed him to the earth.

With a supreme effort the fallen man raised himself upon one arm, wriggled round, and tried to rise. It was in vain. Again he raised to his head the failing hand from which the sword had fallen. Then he rolled over on his face. With the prongs of the trident Calendio pinned the man's neck to the ground, and, leaning with both hands upon the shaft of his weapon, turned towards Cæsar's balcony.

The entire Circus was rocking with the roar of human voices. For those who had staked wagers upon Calendio the latter was, at that moment, even greater than Cæsar; which fact itself caused all ani-

---

[1] "I seek not thee; I seek a fish.
Why fleest thou me, O Gaul?"

mosity against Lanio to vanish from their bosoms, seeing that, at the price of his blood, he had filled their purses. As for the mob in general, its wishes in the matter were mixed. On every tier as many signals for mercy could be seen as signals for death. The retiarius, however, looked only towards the balcony on which Cæsar and the Vestals were seated as he awaited their decision.

Unfortunately for Lanio, Nero did not like him, for the reason that of late—that is to say, before the fire—he had wagered against the defeated gladiator, and had lost considerable sums to Licinius. Consequently he now extended his hand from the edge of the balcony—thumb turned downwards. Instantly the Vestals imitated his example. Calendio knelt with one knee upon the breast of the Gaul, drew from its sheath a dagger, and, opening his adversary's armour up to the height of the neck, plunged into Lanio's throat his triangular-bladed weapon. It entered to the hilt; and as it did so a few voices cried out: "Peractum est!" With a convulsion or two like those of a bullock which is being slaughtered Lanio drummed the sand with his heels, rolled over, and lay motionless. There remained no need for the official who was dressed as Mercury to ascertain, by the test of the hot iron, whether he still lived.

At once the corpse was removed, and other pairs of gladiators made their appearance; after which there came a battle between whole detachments of these men. In the battle the mob took part with heart and soul and voice. It shouted, it roared, it whistled, it clapped its hands, it laughed, it egged on the combatants, it went delirious with joy, while all the time the gladiators, divided into two parties, struggled with one another in mad abandon, with thorax pressed to thorax, bodies entangled in a mortal embrace, tremendous limbs cracking at the joints, swords wallowing in breasts and bellies, and blanched lips vomiting torrents of blood. Towards the close of the combat some of the novices became seized with a panic so unbearable that, breaking away from the *mêlée,* they fled in disorder; whereupon mastigophori met them with loaded scourges, and drove them back into the thick of the fighting. Soon the sand became strewn with corpses as at every moment fresh bodies—naked or clad in steel—augmented the lines of dead warriors which radiated outwards like a sheaf. Over these bodies there fought the living as they charged against weapons and steel bucklers, cut their feet upon broken swords, and fell to the ground. The mob grew mad and drunken with the orgy of death. It breathed it in, it sated its eyes with it, it gladly sucked into its lungs the exhalations from the slaughter.

At length the vanquished had, almost to a man, been slain. Only a few wounded combatants were kneeling or staggering about in the centre of the arena, and stretching out hands for mercy to the audience. To the successful warriors garlands and boughs of olive were distributed as prizes. That done, there ensued a brief interval which, by orders of the all-powerful Cæsar, was converted into a public banquet. Braziers charged with perfumes were lighted, men with syringes sprinkled the crowd with a fine mixture of saffron and violet-powder, and a general distribution was made of roast meats, sweet cakes, olives, and other fruits. The people ate, chattered, and applauded Cæser, as an inducement to him to be even more liberal in the future. And, true enough, the desired result followed; for, as soon as hunger and thirst had been satisfied, hundreds of slaves made their appearance with baskets of gifts. Into these baskets Greek youths dressed as Cupids plunged their hands, and scattered articles of every sort among the spectators; and when lottery tickets also were distributed there began a riot in which men crowded and trampled one another, called for help, sprang over the rows of seats, and got stifled in the terrible crush. The reason of this was that whoever drew a lucky number became the potential winner of a house and garden, or of a slave, or of a splendid costume, or of a wild beast (which he or she would be able to re-sell to the amphitheatre). The disorder grew until the Prætorian Guards were forced to interfere; for after every distribution of tickets people began to be carried out with broken arms or legs, while some were trampled to death in the rush.

The wealthy, however, took no part in this scramble for lottery tickets—the Augustans, in particular, finding a superior diversion in the spectacle presented by Chilo's useless efforts to prove to the public that he could equal any man in his ability to view unmoved the sight of fighting and of shedding of blood. In vain did the unfortunate man frown, in vain did he bite his lips and clench his fists until the nails bit into the palms. His Hellenic temperament, added to his personal cowardice, could not stomach such spectacles calmly. His face had turned white, his forehead had broken out in beads of sweat. At length, with eyes turned inwards, chattering teeth, and lips which were perfectly livid, he sank back in his seat—his form twitching with spasmodic convulsions.

The first part of the spectacle having come to an end, the people began to leave their places, in order to stretch their legs in the corridors and converse.

"Well, Greek?" said Vatinius to Chilo as he plucked the old man by the beard. "Is the sight of a torn skin so unbearable to you?"

Chilo smiled a wry smile which disclosed the only two yellow teeth which now remained to him.

"My father was not a cobbler," he retorted. *"I* had no one to teach me how to repair leather."

"Macte! Habet!" [1] cried several voices. Nevertheless, others joined in the raillery.

"It is not his fault that he has a cheese for a heart," cried Senecio.

"Nor is it your fault that you have a pig's bladder for a head," retorted Chilo.

"Perhaps you will yet become a gladiator, Chilo. You would do well in the arena if you were armed with, say, a net."

"Were I to catch *you* in my net, I should have caught a stinking brute indeed!"

"And what of the Christians?" asked Festus of Liguria. "Should you not like to be a hound and worry them?"

"I would rather be that than your brother!"

"Away with you, Mæotian leper!"

"Away with *you,* Ligurian mule!"

"Evidently your skin is itching. Pray do not ask me to scratch it."

"Scratch your own skin! Yet, were you to rid it of its ringworm, you would have rid it of what is best in you."

Thus the bantering went on—Chilo, amid general laughter, returning abuse for abuse, while Cæsar, at intervals, clapped his hands, shouted "Macte!" and incited the banterers to further efforts. At length Petronius approached the Greek, and, tapping him on the shoulder with his light cane of carved ivory, said coldly:

"Very good, philosopher. But you have made a great mistake. The gods created you to slit purses; whereas you have cast yourself for the part of a demon. That is why you will never play the part to the end."

The old man looked at him with his yellow eyes, but could not, at the moment, find a retort come ready to the tip of his tongue. At length with a sort of effort he ejaculated:

"Yes, I *shall* play the part to the end."

[1] "Good! He has scored there!"

At this moment a fanfare of trumpets announced the close of the interval. A general movement followed, as well as the usual series of altercations as to ownership of seats previously occupied by Senators and patricians. Gradually, however, the noise subsided, until perfect silence reigned in the theatre. Meanwhile a number of attendants had entered the arena, and smoothed with rakes the piles of clotted blood and sand which had become formed during the previous item.

It was now to be the turn of the Christians. This "turn" represented a new form of amusement for the populace, and no one knew how the victims would bear themselves. Possibly it would give rise to scenes altogether out of the common. Everywhere on the faces of the audience there was stamped an expression of hostility, since the victims who were to provide the spectacle were the people who had burnt Rome and its ancient treasures, who had drunk the blood of infants, who had poisoned fountains, who had cursed the human race, who had perpetrated nameless crimes. The popular hatred was such that even the most terrible punishments seemed likely to prove inadequate. The only fear was lest the pain inflicted should not correspond to the past misdeeds of the condemned miscreants.

The sun had now mounted high in the heavens, and its rays, filtering through the purple velarium, were flooding the amphitheatre with blood-coloured light, and causing the sand to glow fiercely. In that light, in those faces, in that expanse of arena which was soon to be filled with human torture and animal fury, there was something appalling. The atmosphere of the scene seemed to be charged with terror and death. The crowd, usually jovial, was growing moody under the influence of the hate-charged silence. On every face could be discerned a complete absence of pity.

The Prefect made a sign; whereupon the old man who represented Charon entered the arena, crossed it slowly, and, amid the brooding stillness, knocked thrice at the great door with his hammer.

Then in the amphitheatre there arose a murmur of "The Christians, the Christians!" The iron hinges creaked, from the underground passages within there came the usual cry of the mastigophori, "Ad arenam!" and in a twinkling the great open space had become peopled with, as it were, a throng of woodland satyrs. All ran forward with a feverish swiftness, and, on reaching the centre of the arena, knelt down behind one another, raising their hands to heaven.

The populace, thinking from this that the victims were imploring mercy, became seized with rage at the sight of such cowardice, and stamped, whistled, threw empty bottles and gnawed bones into the arena, and shouted, "The wild beasts! Let loose the wild beasts!"

But suddenly an unexpected thing happened. From the centre of that throng of skin-clad beings there arose the sound of singing, and for the first time in a Roman amphitheatre there was heard the hymn, "Christus regnat!"

The people stared at one another as the victims sang with eyes uplifted to the velarium. The faces of the victims were pale, but visibly inspired. At length even the mob began to understand that the Christians were not asking for mercy, but saw before them neither the Circus nor the audience nor the Senate nor Cæsar. Louder and louder rose the "Christus regnat"; until, from the top to bottom, and from end to end, of the countless tiers of spectators, persons began to ask one another, "Who is he, this Christus, who reigns in the mouths of folk who are about to die?"

Then another grating was opened, and into the arena there rushed, with savage bounds, whole packs of dogs—gigantic yellow Molossian hounds from the Peloponnesus, pied hounds from the Pyrenees, and wolf-like hounds from Hibernia—all purposely half-starved, with lank sides and bloodshot eyes. The entire amphitheatre resounded with the barkings and growlings of these beasts. The Christians had finished their hymn, and, kneeling as motionless as though they had been turned to stone, were chanting in unison, "Pro Christo, pro Christo!"

Scenting human beings within the skins of the animals, and taken aback by the absolute calm of the victims, the hounds dared not at first attack them. Some even tried to leap the barriers, while others rushed barking round the arena, as though they were pursuing some invisible quarry. At length the audience grew tired of this. Thousands of throats rang out—some imitating the roaring of wild beasts, others baying like hounds themselves, and others rating the animals in every imaginable tongue. The amphitheatre rocked with the din. At length the maddened hounds rushed towards the kneeling Christians—then drew back with a snapping of their jaws; until finally a large Molossian hound drove his fangs into a woman's shoulder, and bore her to earth with his weight. That done, some scores of hounds bounded into the centre of the group, as though they were entering a breach in a wall; whereupon the audience ceased to shout, and fixed its attention more attentively upon the spectacle. Yet still above the snarls and the growlings of the beasts there rose the plaintive voices of men and women chanting "Pro Christo, pro Christo!" even though the arena was now full of writhing, convulsive heaps of dogs and human beings. Blood came flowing in streams from torn bodies as the hounds wrenched limb from limb. Indeed, the Arabic perfumes with which the amphitheatre had been sweetened were overpowered by the penetrating odour of gory flesh and entrails.

At last only here and there was there to be seen a kneeling figure; and presently even these few became centres of snarling masses of hounds.

At the moment when the Christians entered the arena Vinicius fulfilled his promise to the quarryman by rising and turning his head towards the spot where the Apostle was concealed among Petronius' attendants. Then he reseated himself, and remained gazing at the frightful spectacle without moving, with glassy eyes, with the face of a dead man. At first the thought that the quarryman might have been mistaken, and that Lygia too might be with those poor victims, completely paralysed him; but when he heard the voices chanting "Pro Christo!" when he beheld innumerable victims confessing their faith and glorifying God in the very act of death, another sensation came over him—a sensation which, though torturing like the most terrible pain, could not be stifled. The idea had just occurred to him that since Christ Himself had been put to death, and thousands were now perishing in His name, so that blood flowed like water—well, a drop or two more could signify nothing, nothing, and to ask for mercy would be an actual sin. The thought reached his brain from the arena, pervaded him with the death-rattle of every victim, and took final possession of him as he caught the scent of the carnage. Yet still he prayed—prayed with dry lips —"Christ! Christ! Thy Apostle also is praying for her!" At length he lost consciousness, and became oblivious of all around him. In that condition he seemed to see blood mounting like an incoming tide, and surrounding the Circus, and overwhelming the whole of Rome. No longer could he hear the baying of the hounds, nor the clamour of the mob, nor the voices of Augustans crying out, "Chilo has fainted!"

"Chilo has fainted," repeated Petronius, turning towards the Greek. True enough, the latter, white as a sheet, was sitting with his head thrown backwards and his mouth open, so that he looked like a corpse.

At that moment some new batches of victims, dressed, like the first, in the skins of wild beasts, were being driven into the arena. Like their predecessors, they knelt down. Nevertheless the hounds, which had now reached the end of their strength, refused to rend these new victims. Except for those which sprang upon victims who happened to be nearest them, the pack lay down, raised their bloodstained jowls, and remained panting heavily, with heaving flanks.

Upon this the mob, thoroughly roused, drunk with carnage, and beside itself with delirium, raised strident shouts of "The lions, the lions! Let loose the lions!"

The lions had been reserved for the morrow; but at these spectacles in amphitheatres the mob imposed its will upon every one, including even Cæsar. Caligula alone—a man as insolent as he had been versatile in his whims—had dared to contradict the populace, and even to have it cudgelled; but more often than not even *he* had yielded. As for Nero, applause was more precious to him than all the world besides. Consequently he never thwarted the people, and this time in particular was doing all he could to appease a nation exasperated by the burning of its capital. For that purpose was it that he had attacked the Christians, and laid upon them the blame for the disaster.

That being so, he made a sign for the lions' den to be opened; upon seeing which, the mob at once grew calmer. Harshly did the gratings creak behind which the lions were confined, and at the sight of the great beasts the hounds gave vent to stifled whines, and rushed to the other side of the arena as, one by one, the objects of their terror—huge tawny brutes with ponderous, shaggy heads—entered. Cæsar himself turned his weary face in their direction, and raised his emerald monocle to his eye, in order the better to see them. As for the Augustans, they received the lions with applause, while the populace in general counted them on its fingers, and watched eagerly, to note the impression which they were producing upon the kneeling Christians. The latter were still repeating their "Pro Christo, pro Christo!"—a formula incomprehensible to many among the audience, and annoying to all.

In spite of the process of starvation to which they had been subjected, the lions did not hasten to attack the victims. Apparently the red glare in which the sand was bathed troubled their sight, for they blinked their eyes as though dazzled. Some even stretched their tawny limbs in lazy fashion, while others opened their jaws in yawns, as though on purpose to show their fangs. Gradually, however, the odour of blood from the torn bodies which still littered the arena exercised its effect upon them. Their movements became nervous, their manes began to bristle, and their nostrils emitted loud sniffs. Suddenly one of their number sprang upon the corpse of a woman who had had her face bitten away, and, planting its fore-paws upon the body, began to lick the congealed blood with its spiny tongue. At the same moment another of them approached a Christian who was holding in his arms an infant wrapped in the skin of a fawn. The infant, sobbing and crying, clung convulsively to its father, who, wishing to preserve its life, if only for an instant, forced himself to untwine its arms from his neck, in order that he might pass the little one to his companions behind. But the child's cries and struggles had irritated the lion. It uttered a short, sharp roar, crushed the child to death with a blow of its paw, and, seizing the head of the father in its gigantic jaws, proceeded to gnaw it to pieces.

Upon that the lions in general rushed upon the knots of Christians. Some of the women could not refrain from uttering cries of terror, though these were soon drowned by the roar of applause, and the roar of applause, in its turn, by the sound of the spectators rising to get a better view. And in truth there were terrible things to be seen—heads completely disappearing within gaping jaws, breasts torn open with a single bite, and hearts and lungs exposed. Everywhere, too, there was to be heard the sound of bones being crunched by massive fangs. Some of the lions, seizing their victims by the sides or the back, went leaping madly around the arena, as though seeking a quiet spot in which to devour their prey; while others fought with one another—rearing on their hind legs, struggling like wrestlers, and filling the amphitheatre with thunder. Rising, the spectators left their seats, and gravitated towards the lower tiers, in order to get the best possible view; with the result that many of them were crushed to death, and for a time it looked as though the furious mob would overflow into the arena, and rend the Christians in company with the lions. At one moment there could be heard cries scarcely human, at another applause, at another roars, snarls, the cracking of bones, and the whining of dogs. Then again the only sound to be heard was the sound of groaning.

Cæsar, holding his emerald to his eye, regarded the scene attentively, but the face of Petronius expressed only disgust and contempt. As for Chilo, he had long since been carried out of the amphitheatre. Again and again the dungeons vomited up new victims for slaughter. From above, from the topmost tier of the building, the Apostle Peter looked down upon them. No one saw him, for every head was turned towards the arena. At length, he rose to his feet; and just as once before, in Cornelius' vineyard, he had blessed to death and to eternity those who were about to be imprisoned, so now he blessed with the sign of the cross those who were enduring agony in the jaws of wild beasts. He blessed their blood and their sufferings; he blessed the corpses which had become changed into shapeless heaps, and the souls which had fled from the blood-stained arena. And as he did so certain persons raised to him their eyes; and as they did so their faces became radiant—they smiled on seeing, high over their heads, the sign of the cross. But Peter's heart was breaking.

"O Lord," he prayed, "may Thy will be done! It is for Thy glory, and as a testimony to the Truth, that my sheep are perishing. Thou didst say unto me, 'Feed My sheep,' and behold, Lord, I do commit them unto Thee again. Take them unto Thyself, make them Thine own, heal their wounds, abate their sufferings, and grant them on high an even greater measure of happiness than the pain which they have endured on earth!"

Suddenly Cæsar seemed to be seized with a fit of frenzy or with a desire to outshine anything that had ever been seen in Rome before. At all events he whispered a few words in the ear of the Prefect, who thereupon left the balcony, and hastened to the prisoners' dungeons. Even the mob was stupefied when it saw the gratings once more open, and beasts of the most various kinds possible released—tigers from the Euphrates, panthers from Numidia, bears, wolves, hyænas, and jackals. In fact, the whole arena became a moving mass of striped and spotted, yellow, brown, and fawn-coloured bodies, which formed a vast and frightful whirlpool of animal life. The spectacle was unreal. The thing had been overdone. Amid the roars, howls, and snarls of the beasts there could be heard the strident, hysterical laughter of frightened women (among the audience) whose nerves had at last given way. Every one was growing alarmed. Faces were beginning to darken, and numerous voices to cry out, "Enough, enough!"

Yet it had been easier to let loose the beasts than it now proved easy to expel them from the arena. However, Cæsar had devised a means for clearing the scene which would at the same time provide a new amusement for the people. In every passage-way, between the tiers of seats, there now appeared, bow in hand, bands of Numidian Negroes, with plumes in their hair and ear-rings in their ears. At once the mob divined what was to follow, and greeted them with shouts of approbation. The Numidians approached the barriers, and, fitting arrows to their stretched bow-strings, began to let fly among the swarm beasts. Truly it was an unprecented spectacle, this of these ebony warriors, with their supple forms bent backwards as they loosed a hail of darts from their ceaselessly twanging bows. With the whizzing of the strings and the whistling of the feathered bolts were mingled howls of the beasts and cries of admiration from the spectators. Wolves, panthers, bears, and the few human beings who had remained alive in the arena fell side by side with one another. Here and there a lion, on feeling the bite of an arrow in his flank, would turn round his foam-flecked jaws to seize and gnaw the shaft of the missile. From every side came yelps of agony. As for the lesser beasts, they started to run blindly round the arena, in an access of panic, or else to charge the barriers with their muzzles. Without a moment's cessation, however, the arrows increased in number, until everything in the arena which had been alive was now stretched in the final throes of death.

Then into the arena there rushed hundreds of slaves, armed with spades, shovels, brooms, handcarts, baskets for collecting and carrying away entrails, and sacks full of sand. Soon the entire expanse was swarming with busy workers, and in a twinkling the corpses had been removed, the blood and excrement dug in, or raked away, or covered with sand, and the arena sprinkled with a new and thick layer of the same material. That done, there entered Cupids, who sprinkled everywhere petals of roses and lilies. Lastly, the perfume-braziers were lighted afresh, and the folds of the velarium drawn back, since the sun had now sunk low in the heavens.

Upon this the crowd gazed at one another in astonishment—asking themselves what new spectacle was awaiting them that day. In truth there was awaiting them a spectacle for which no one had come prepared. Cæsar, who, a little while ago, had left the Imperial balcony, now suddenly reappeared in the flower-strewn arena—clothed in purple and crowned with gold. Behind him walked twelve choristers, furnished with lutes. With a silver lute in his hand, Nero advanced solemnly to the centre of the great space, bowed several times to the audience, and cast his eyes heavenwards. For a moment he stood thus, as though awaiting inspiration, and then, striking the strings of the lute, began:

"O son of Latona,[1] O radiant god,
Who of Tenedos, Chrysos, and Chios art king,
Art thou he who, though having in his care
The city, thrice sacred, of Ilion,
Didst yield it to th' assault of the Argive hosts,
And suffer the holy sanctuaries
Which blazed in thy honour without cease
To be stained with the blood of Trojan men?
Greybeards raised their hands to thee,
O thou of the puissant silver bow.
Mothers from secret, stricken breasts
Besought thine ear with cries of pain
As they prayed thee to 'fend their children's lives.
Yet, though those cries might have rent a stone,
To the suffering of this thy people's heart

[1] The god Apollo.

Thou didst prove, O Smintheus, more hard
than stone."

Then the song passed gradually into an elegy—into a dirge that was plaintive and full of pain. Complete silence reigned in the amphitheatre. After a while Cæsar, himself affected, sang on:

"With the dulcet sound of thy heavenly lyre
Thou yet canst drown the wails of grief;
E'en though the sadness of thy song
Doth fill the eye, like a flower, with dew.
But who shall blot out the day of woe,
Of fire and ruin, of ashes and dust?
O Smintheus, when all things were failing us,
Where, thou radiant god, wert thou?"

Here Cæsar's voice quivered, and his eyes grew moist, while the Vestal Virgins also were seen to be weeping. For a moment the people remained silent. Then there burst forth a long, continuous storm of applause. Through it, at intervals, came the sound of creaking vehicles as the bloodstained remains of Christian men, women, and children were conveyed from the vomitoria to the pits of interment, known as puticuli.

Meanwhile the Apostle Peter, his aged, tremulous head buried in his hands, was crying aloud in spirit:

"O Lord, O Lord, to whom, then, hast Thou given the dominion of the world? When wilt Thou establish in this city Thy capital?"

XVI

The sun had set in the west, and left behind it only the glow of evening, when the spectacle in the amphitheatre came to an end. The crowd poured out of the entrance-ways into the city streets. The Augustans alone delayed their departure until this human flood should have, to a certain extent, cleared away. Then in a group they left their seats, and gathered around the Imperial balcony, to which Cæsar had returned for the purpose of receiving the customary meed of praise. Nevertheless, although the audience had not been sparing of its applause, Nero was in a dissatisfied mood, since he had hoped for an enthusiasm absolutely unprecedented—for a furore akin to madness. In vain did the Augustans loudly belaud him, in vain did the Vestal Virgins kiss his divine hands, in vain did Rubria droop her golden head until it almost touched his breast. No, he was not satisfied. In particular did the silence preserved by Petronius annoy him. A single word—that is to say, a single *eulogistic* word, a word that might have thrown into relief the merits of the hymn—would, at that moment, have done Nero a world of good. At length, unable to contain himself, he signed to Petronius to ascend the dais.

"Why do you not speak?" he inquired.

"Because I cannot find words to do so," replied Petronius coldly. "You have surpassed yourself."

"That is my opinion also; yet this mob—"

"How can you expect such a mongrel rabble to be a judge of poetry?"

"Then you too noticed that I did not receive the applause which I ought to have done?"

"The moment was not well chosen."

"And wherefore?"

"For the reason that when one is suffocated with the odour of blood one cannot make the best use of one's ears."

Nero clenched his fists, and exclaimed:

"Oh, those Christians! They have burnt Rome, and wish also to attack myself! What further tortures can I invent for them?"

Petronius perceived that he had adopted the wrong line; so, leaning forward, he murmured:

"Your hymn is miraculously beautiful.

Yet permit me to make one observation. In the fourth line of the third strophe the rhythm halts a little."

Nero, as though detected in a crime of the utmost infamy, turned purple with shame, threw a look of terror around him, and replied in a whisper:

"You—you notice everything! Yes, I know what you mean, and I *will* change the line. But do you think that any one else has noticed it? Are you *sure* that no one else has done so? In any case I adjure you by all the gods not to mention it to a soul—no, not if you value your life!"

Petronius frowned, and said, as though giving free rein to his weariness and lack of interest:

"Divine one, if I displease you, you are at liberty to condemn me to death; but do not, I pray you, keep threatening me with death, since for such threats I care nothing." And he looked Nero full in the face.

"Do not trouble yourself," at length said Cæsar. "You know that I love you."

"That is a bad sign," was Petronius' inward comment.

"Also," continued Cæsar. "I should have liked to have invited you to a banquet to-day, but would rather shut myself up, and recast that cursed line in the verses. If I did not do so, others than yourself might notice the fault—Seneca, perhaps, or Secundus Carinas, although I hope soon to be rid of both of them."

With that he summoned Seneca to his side, and informed him that he was about to send him, together with Acratus and Secundus Carinas, to tour the provinces and elsewhere, with the aim of collecting money from the various towns, villages, and more famous temples. Seneca, however, understanding that this would be a mission of wholesale robbery, sacrilege, and outrage, returned a blank refusal.

"Nay, my lord," he said. "I must go into the country to await death, for I am old, and my nerves are ailing."

Yet it was not so much his Iberian nerves that were at fault (since they had a greater resisting power than Chilo's), but his general health, which had worn him to a shadow, and turned his head completely white.

Nero glanced at him, and reflected that in any case he would not be troubled with him much longer.

"Very well," he said. "Of course I do not wish to expose you to the risks of a journey when you are ill. Rather, in view of the affection which I feel for you, I wish to have you always by my side. That being so, you will shut yourself up in your house, and not leave it again."

Then he burst out laughing as he added:

"If I were to send Acratus and Carinas alone, it would be as though I sent a couple of wolves to get me some sheep. Whom can I set in authority over them?"

"Myself, my lord," said Domitius Afer.

"No," retorted Cæsar. "I do not mean to draw upon Rome the wrath of Mercury—which would certainly be the result of your vexing him with your knavery. I want, rather, a Stoic of some kind, like Seneca, or like my new friend, the philosopher Chilo."

With this he turned round, and inquired:

"What has become of that Chilo?"

The latter, having recovered himself under the influence of the fresh air, had returned to the amphitheatre in time to hear the hymn to Apollo. He now approached Cæsar, and said:

"Behold, I am here, O radiant offspring of the sun and of the moon. Though ill, I have been restored to health by your singing."

"Then I will send *you* to the Achæans," said Cæsar. "Probably you know, to a sestertius, what the resources of their every temple are?"

"You may do as you suggest, O Zeus," replied Chilo; "and you will find that the gods will render you such a monetary tribute as they have never yet rendered to a mortal man."

"Very good. Yet I should be loath to deprive you of the sight of the games."

"O Baal," began Chilo; but the rest of his sentence was drowned in the laughter of the Augustans, who were delighted to see the Imperial good humour restored.

"No, my lord," said they. "Do not deny this fearless Greek the sight of the games."

"My lord," retorted Chilo, "at least deny me the sight of these rascals, of these geese of the Capitol, whose brains put together would scarce fill an acorn-cup. O first-born of Phœbus, I feel disposed to compose a Greek hymn in your honour; and for that purpose would I fain spend a few days in the temple of the Muses, in order that I may implore their inspiration."

"No, no!" cried Cæsar. "That is a mere subterfuge to escape the rest of the games. No, no, Chilo!"

"My lord, I swear to you that I would fain write a hymn."

"Then you shall write it by night, and seek inspiration, rather, of Diana, who is Phœbus' sister."

Chilo bowed, but at the same time cast a look of fury at the laughing Augustans. The Emperor now turned to Senecio and Sullius Nerulinus, and said:

"Do you reckon that, of the Christians set aside for to-day's spectacle, even one half have yet been dealt with?"

Old Aquilus Regulus, who was an expert in matters of the Circus, reflected a moment and replied:

"Spectacles in which there figure unarmed and unskilled actors last a long time, and are less interesting than are the other sort."

"Then," said Cæsar, "in future I will provide these people with weapons."

Upon this the superstitious Vestinus suddenly awoke from a reverie, and asked with an air of mystery:

"Have you noticed that, when at the point of death, these Christians seem to have a vision? They look up to the skies, and, apparently, die without pain. I feel sure that they can see something as they do so."

As he spoke he raised his own eyes to the opening above the amphitheatre—to the opening over which night had begun to throw its own velarium of countless stars. His companions, however, answered with laughter, and with ribald suggestions as to what the nature of the Christians' vision might be. Presently Cæsar signed to the slaves who were holding the torches, and left the Circus, followed by Vestal Virgins, Senators, Augustans, and officials at large.

The night was clear and mild. Outside the Circus a crowd had lingered to see Cæsar depart, but its aspect was silent and moody, and the scanty applause which it raised soon died away. From the spoliarium there was still issuing an endless train of carts, laden with the blood-stained remnants of Christians.

Petronius and Vinicius made the journey home in silence. Only when they were approaching the villa did Petronius at length inquire:

"Have you thought over what I said to you?"

"Yes," replied Vinicius.

"Do you understand that for me also it is now a matter of life and death to rescue Lygia, despite Cæsar and Tigellinus? I think that in the struggle I shall come out the victor—that in the game I shall win, even though it be at the cost of my life. To-day's work has confirmed me in my purpose."

"May Christ prosper you!"

"Well, you shall see."

While they were talking the litter came to a halt at the villa, and they descended.

As they did so a dark figure approached them.

"Is that the noble Vinicius?" it asked.

"Yes," replied the tribune. "What do you want?"

"I am Nazarus, the son of Miriam. I come from the prison with news of Lygia."

Vinicius leant heavily forward upon the youth's arm, and stared at him in the light of the torches without being able to utter a single word. Nevertheless Nazarus divined the question which was fluttering on the tribune's lips.

"Yes, she is alive," he said. "Ursus has sent me to tell you that often in her delirium she mentions your name in her prayers to God."

"Glory be to Christ!" exclaimed Vinicius. "He alone can restore her to me."

Then he led Nazarus into the library, where presently they were joined by Petronius.

"The illness saved her from outrage," continued Nazarus; "for it made the villains afraid of catching the infection. Also, Ursus and Glaucus the physician watch over her day and night."

"And are the gaolers the same as before?"

"Yes, my lord; and she still occupies their room. As for the brethren who were in the underground dungeons, they are all dead of fever or suffocation."

"Who are you?" put in Petronius at this point.

"One whom the noble Vinicius well knows," replied the youth. "I am the son of a widow with whom Lygia used to lodge."

"And you are a Christian?"

The youth glanced shyly in Vinicius' direction, but, perceiving that he was engaged in prayer, raised his head, and replied:

"Yes."

"Then how did you contrive to gain entry to the prison?"

"By having myself engaged to remove the corpses. I did so in the hope of assisting my brethren, and of procuring some news concerning them."

Petronius looked keenly at the youth's handsome face, blue eyes, and thick, dark hair. Then he asked:

"From what country come you, my friend?"

"I am a Galilean, my lord."

"Would you like to see Lygia again free?"

"Yes, even if it were to cost me my life!"

"Then," put in Vinicius, "tell the gaolers to lay her in a coffin as though she were dead, and do you yourself find some men to help you to carry her away by night. Near the Burial Pits you will find other men waiting with a litter, to whom you will deliver the coffin. Finally, you will promise to each gaoler, on my behalf, as much gold as he can carry away in his pockets."

While speaking thus, Vinicius had quite lost the expression of torpor which, of late, had become habitual with him. In him there had revived the soldier, and hope was restoring his former energy once more.

Nazarus raised his hands, crying:

"May Christ restore her to health, for freed she shall be!"

"Will the gaolers prove complacent?" asked Petronius.

"Yes," was Vinicius' reply. "Already they have consented to let her escape; and the fact that she is to be taken away as a corpse will make their task the easier."

"True, there is a man whose duty it is to test the bodies with a hot iron, to ascertain if they are really dead," said Nazarus; "but a few sestertii will suffice to induce him not to touch the face with his iron, while a piece of gold will cause him to touch only the winding-sheet, not the body."

"Tell him," said Vinicius, "that he shall have a purse full of such pieces. But do you think you can obtain reliable men for the rest of the scheme?"

"Yes. I can obtain men ready even to sell their wives and children. Once corrupted, the gaolers will allow any one we like to enter."

"In that case you could include myself among your men?" said Vinicius.

But Petronius opposed this, on the ground that Vinicius might be recognised by the Prætorians; which mishap would ruin all.

"You must not approach either the prison or the Burial Pits," he said. "Every one—including, most of all, Cæsar and Tigellinus—must be led to think that she is dead. Otherwise they will at once revive the hue and cry for her. The only way in which we can avert suspicion is to have her removed to the Alban Hills while we ourselves remain in Rome. In a week or two, however, you will fall ill, and send for Nero's physician, who will order you also to the Hills. There you will rejoin her, and then—"

Here Petronius reflected for a moment; after which, with an evasive gesture, he concluded:

"Well, *then,* perhaps, the times will have changed."

"May Christ have pity upon her!" exclaimed Vinicius. "She is ill, and may die during the removal."

"In the first instance we will hide her somewhere close at hand; and, afterwards, the fresh air will cure her. Have you not in the Alban Hills some tenant-farmer whom you could trust?"

"Yes, I *have* such a one," replied Vinicius. "Near Coriola, in the Hills, I know of a man who carried me in his arms when I was a child, and who is devoted to me."

Petronius tendered him a set of tablets.

"Write to this man," he said, "and tell him to come hither to-morrow. I will send a courier with the letter."

Within a few minutes a courier was galloping for Coriola.

Before departing, Nazarus took Vinicius aside, and said to him under his breath:

"My lord, I intend to tell no one of our plans—not even my mother; but the Apostle Peter is to come to us after leaving the amphitheatre, and I should like to confide to him all that we are intending."

"You can speak aloud in safety," replied Vinicius. "The Apostle was seated among Petronius' servants at the amphitheatre. For the rest, I myself will come with you."

He called for a cloak, and they set out.

Petronius, left behind, drew a deep breath.

"Ah, Ahenobarbus!" he said to himself. "You wish to feast your eyes upon a lover's agony, do you? And you, Augusta, you began by being jealous of this girl's beauty, and now you have a mind to eat her raw because your Rufius is dead? And you, Tigellinus, you wish to destroy her in order to do me a bad turn? —Ah well, I may inform you, and, indeed, every one else, that she is *not* going to appear in the arena. I am going to snatch her out of your hands so neatly that all your plans will end in smoke. And, later on, I shall say to you, each time that you happen to greet my eyes: 'Good day to you, O set of fools whom Petronius has fooled!' "

Entirely satisfied with himself, he passed into the triclinium, and sat down to supper with Eunice. During the meal the lector, or reader, recited to them the Idylls of Theocrites. Outside, the wind was bringing clouds from the heights of Soractum, and gathering them into a storm which was to trouble that summer night. At intervals the rolling of thunder could be heard among the seven hills.

Within, Petronius and Eunice reclined side by side as they listened to the loves of shepherds, told in the musical dialect of the Dorians. At length, calmed in spirit, they rose, and prepared themselves for a night's rest. Presently a slave announced that Vinicius had returned, and Petronius hastened to meet him.

"Well?" he said. "Has any new development occurred? Has Nazarus gone to the prison?"

"Yes," replied Vinicius, passing his hand over his damp hair. "He has gone thither to confer with the gaolers, while I myself have seen Peter, who has recommended me to pray, and to believe that all will yet turn out well."

"Good! If our scheme turns out as we are hoping, we shall be able to remove her to-morrow night."

"Yes. The farmer, with his men, will be here at daybreak."

"Then go you and take some rest."

Nevertheless Vinicius, on reaching his cubiculum, knelt down, and engaged in prayer.

At dawn Niger, the farmer, arrived from Coriola. For precaution's sake he had left his four slaves—trusty men from Britain—in a tavern in the Suburra, together with mules and a litter.

At the sight of his young master the farmer was greatly moved, and said as he kissed his hands and eyes:

"Are you not well, dear master? Or is it that grief has removed the colour from your face? At first sight I could scarcely recognise you."

Leading the man aside into the inner colonnade, Vinicius there confided to him his secret.

"So she is a Christian!" cried Niger with a keen glance at Vinicius.

"Yes," replied the tribute. "And I myself am a Christian."

Glittering tears of joy sprang to Niger's eyes.

"I thank Thee, O Christ!" he exclaimed. "I thank Thee for having caused the scales to fall from the eyes which, beyond all others in the world, I love!"

Presently Petronius entered, bringing Nazarus with him.

"I have good news for you!" he cried to Vinicius from a distance. And, true enough, the news was good. In the first place, the physician Glaucus had given his word that Lygia would live, although the gaol fever from which she was suffering was the disease of which hundreds of other prisoners were dying, both in the tullianum and elsewhere; while, in the second place, both the gaolers and the tester of corpses had been bought over, as well as an assistant named Attys.

"Also, we have pierced some holes in the coffin," said Nazarus. "The only danger is lest she should utter a groan or make some exclamation as we are passing through the ranks of the Prætorians. However, Glaucus is going to administer to her a narcotic. The lid of the coffin will not be nailed down, so that it will be easy for you to lift it and transfer Lygia to your litter while we replace her, in the coffin, with a sack of sand."

"Are any other bodies to be removed from the prison?" asked Petronius.

"Yes," replied Nazarus. "A score or so of people have died during the night; and by this evening more will have passed away. Though we shall be forced to follow in the train of their coffins, we intend so to linger as to get left behind. That is to say, as soon as ever we reach the street corner my companion will begin to walk lame to such an extent that we shall soon be outdistanced. Meanwhile you will be awaiting us near the small temple of Libitina. May God send that the night be dark!"

"God will guide us," said Niger. "Last night was clear, yet suddenly a storm broke; and though the sky to-night is equally cloudless, the air is stifling. In fact, every night at present is likely to be rainy and dark."

"And you will be marching without torches, I presume?" put in Vinicius.

"Only those who march at the head of these processions carry torches. In any case, station yourselves near the temple of Libitina as soon as ever it grows dark, although ordinarily we do not remove the corpses until shortly before midnight."

For a moment nothing more was said, and only the hurried breathing of Vinicius broke the silence.

At length Petronius turned to him, and said:

"Yesterday I was of opinion that it would be best for both of us to remain at home; but now I see that that would be impossible."

"Yes, yes!" replied Vinicius. "I at least must be there. No one but myself must take her from the coffin."

"And once she has reached my house at Coriola, *I* will continue to be answerable for her," added Niger.

Here the conversation came to an end. Niger returned to his men at the tavern, and Nazarus to the prison, with a bag of gold under his tunic. For Vinicius there began a day of feverish waiting.

"The affair is bound to prove successful," Petronius told him. "It could not have been better conceived. True, for a while you will have to feign mourning, and to go about in a black cloak; but that need not entail your absenting yourself from the Circus. No; let yourself be seen there. Everything has turned out so well that a miscarriage is impossible. Meanwhile, are you perfectly sure of your farmer?"

"He is a Christian," was Vinicius' reply.

Petronius looked at him in astonishment—then shrugged his shoulders, and said, as though speaking to himself:

"By Pollux, how the sect grows in spite of everything! And what a root it takes in men's minds! If a similar reign of terror were to threaten other folk, they would at once renounce their gods—Roman, Greek, and Egyptian alike. It is wonderful! By Pollux, but if I thought that anything in the world could still lie at the disposal of our deities I would promise each one of them six white bulls, and a dozen to Jupiter Capitolinus! However, do you be equally unsparing of promises with that Christ of yours."

"I have not only promised, but have given, Him my soul," replied Vinicius.

With this Petronius re-entered his cubiculum, while Vinicius repaired to the slope of the Vatican Hill, to the quarryman's hut in which he had received baptism at the hands of the Apostle. Somehow he had a fancy that Christ would be more ready to listen to his prayers in this cabin than anywhere else. Throwing himself upon the floor of the hut, he surrendered his aching soul to supplication, and in the effort became so entirely absorbed as to forget where he was, and to take no notice of what was passing around him. Only when afternoon was come was he aroused by the trumpets of Nero's Circus; whereupon he rose to his feet, and left the hut. The heat was intense, and the silence, though periodically broken by the sound of the brazen instruments, had running through it also the restful bourdon of grasshoppers. Above the city the sky was still blue; but low on the horizon, in the direction of the Sabine Hills, dark clouds were beginning to mass themselves.

On arriving home, Vinicius found Petronius awaiting him in the atrium.

"I have just been to the Palatine," said the elder man. "I had a purpose in showing myself there, and even took part in a game of dice. To-night Anicius is to give a banquet, and I let it be known that, though we shall be present thereat, we shall not arrive until after midnight, owing to the fact that I must first take some sleep. True enough, I *shall* attend the festival, and should advise you to do the same."

"Is there no news of Niger or of Nazarus?" asked Vinicius.

"No. We shall not see them till midnight. To-morrow there is to be an exhibition of crucified Christians, but perhaps the rain will put a stop to the spectacle."

Here he touched Vinicius' arm.

"You shall see her," he added, "not on the cross, but at Coriola. By Castor, but from the moment when we rescue her I would not again surrender her for all the jewels in Rome!"

At nightfall there fell a heavy shower, which steamed on the sun-baked pavements and filled the streets with mist; and it was followed alternately by intervals of fair weather and further spurts of rain.

"Let us make haste," at length said Vinicius. "It is possible that the storm may lead them to remove the bodies earlier."

"Yes; it is time we were moving," assented Petronius.

Donning Gallic cloaks with hoods, while Petronius also armed himself with a poniard, they left the villa by the garden gate. The storm had emptied the streets, and from time to time a flash of lightning would throw into crude relief houses newly built or houses still in course of construction. At length they saw before them the mound on which stood the diminutive temple of the goddess Libitina, with, at its foot, a group of mules and horses.

"Niger!" called Vinicius in a low voice.

"I am here, my lord," replied an answering voice from the mist of rain.

"Is everything ready?"

"Yes, beloved master. But do you take shelter under the mound, or the rain will soak you to the skin. What a storm it is! I think that hail will follow."

True enough, hailstones had begun to fall, and the temperature of the air was rapidly falling. The men conversed in muffled tones.

"Even should we be seen," said Niger, "no one will suspect us, for we shall be taken for persons sheltering from the storm. Yet I am afraid that the removal of corpses may be put off until to-morrow."

"No, the hail will not continue long," said Petronius. "Besides, we can remain here till daybreak if necessary."

So they waited with strained ears. Presently the hail ceased, but was followed by a smart shower of rain. Now and then the wind rose, and brought with it the fearful stench of corpses decaying in the Burial Pits, where they lay covered only with a sprinkling of earth.

Suddenly Niger exclaimed:

"I can see a light through the mist! Yes, and another, and another! They must be torches."

Then, turning to his men, he added:

"Give a look to your mules, and stand ready."

"Yes, they are coming," said Petronius.

The lights grew gradually more distinct, until it became possible to distinguish the flames of torches flickering in the wind. Niger made the sign of the cross, and breathed a prayer.

The mournful cortège halted when it drew level with the temple. Petronius, Vinicius, and the farmer pressed themselves into the shadow of the mound, but the bearers had halted but to swathe their mouths and faces in linen, as a precaution against the stench which, in the immediate neighbourhood of the Pits, was abominable. Soon they again lifted the stretchers, and resumed their way. One coffin alone remained stationary before the little temple.

Vinicius darted forward, followed by Petronius, Niger, and the four British slaves with the litter. Alas! Nazarus' sad voice greeted them from the darkness with the words:

"My lord, she and Ursus have been transferred to the Esquiline prison, and it is another body that we are carrying. She was taken away from the Mamertine before midnight."

As they re-entered the villa Petronius' face looked dark as night, and he made no attempt to console Vinicius, since he knew that to effect a rescue from the Esquiline dungeons was an impossibility. The reason for the transfer, he divined, was that Lygia might not die of the fever, but be reserved for her fate. From the bottom of his heart he felt sorry for her and for Vinicius. Also, he reflected that this was the first time that ever in his life he had failed in an enterprise which he had undertaken.

"Fortuna has deserted me!" he said to himself. Then he glanced at Vinicius, who was gazing at him with dilated pupils.

"What is the matter with you?" asked the elder man. "Have you caught the fever?"

Vinicius replied in a strange voice:

"I still believe that *He* can restore her to me."

Over the city the storm was beginning to die away.

XVII

A three days' rain—an exceptional phenomenon in Rome during the summer time—added to storms of hail which, contrary to the natural order of things, beat upon the city by night as well as by day, interrupted the progress of the games. The people grew alarmed, and took to predicting a sorry vintage harvest; until finally, when a thunderbolt had reduced the statue of Ceres to a mere ingot of bronze, sacrifices were ordered to be offered in the temple of Jupiter Capitolinus. In response the priests of Ceres had it put about that the wrath of the gods had fallen upon the city in revenge for the tardiness displayed in the punishing of the Christians; whereupon the populace demanded, and obtained, an edict that, regardless of the elements, the games should resume their course. Simultaneously fine weather returned, and the Circus speedily filled with thousands of spectators. Cæsar also arrived early, accompanied by the Vestals and his Court.

The spectacle was to begin with a fight between Christians and Christians; to which end the latter had been clothed as gladiators, and furnished with weapons both of offence and of defence, like professional combatants. But a miscalculation had been made. The Christians threw down upon the sand their nets, tridents, spears, and swords, and rushed into one another's arms with mutual exhortations to accept their fate resignedly. Upon this the spectators became seized with a resentment and fury that knew no bounds. Some rated the Christians as cowards, while others declared that they had maliciously declined to fight out of sheer hatred for the people, and in order that the latter might be cheated of the pleasure which a display of courage always gave. Finally Cæsar issued orders for genuine gladiators to be loosed upon the victims, who in a twinkling were massacred where they knelt in the arena.

As soon as the bodies had been cleared away there followed a series of mythological tableaux invented by Cæsar himself, including a spectacle of Hercules dying on Mount Œta amid a circle of genuine flame. At the thought that perhaps the rôle of Hercules had been assigned to Ursus Vinicius shuddered; but the turn of Lygia's faithful servitor had not yet come—it being another Christian who was consumed at the stake. Next, Chilo, who had failed to obtain Cæsar's absolution from the duty of being present at the games, had the pleasure of beholding a tableau in which there figured persons whom he himself had known. The tableau represented the deaths of Dædalus and Icarus—the part of the former being allotted to the aged Euricius who had once shown Chilo the sign of the fish, and the part of Icarus to Euricius' son, Quartus. By means of special machinery both were hoisted to an immense height, and then let fall. Quartus alighted so near to the Imperial balcony that his blood bespattered the carving with which its exterior was adorned, and even the border of the purple awning. The actual fall Chilo did not see, for he had closed his eyes; but as soon as he heard the dull thud made by the body, and perceived blood to be at his very side, he came very near to fainting. Tableau succeeded tableau. In particular did the infamous tortures of virgins who were outraged by gladiators clad in the skins of wild beasts delight the mob. In this exhibition Christian maidens figured as priestesses of Cybele and Ceres, as the daughters of Danais, and as Dirce and Pasiphaë. Finally, a number of girls of tender age were torn asunder by wild horses. These new inventions of Cæsar's met with loud applause from the populace; and, proud of such recognition, and glorying in his work, he never once removed the emerald monocle from his eye.

Next there came tableaux derived from the annals of Rome. First of all a sickening odour of roast flesh filled the amphitheatre. This was Mucius Scævola with his hand in the brazier. The Christian victim who played the part uttered not a groan, but stood with his eyes turned heavenwards and his blackening lips murmuring a prayer. As soon as he had received the *coup-de-grâce,* and his dead body had been removed to the spoliarium, the usual midday interval was announced.

Accompanied by the Vestals and the Augustans, Cæsar left the amphitheatre, and repaired to an immense scarlet pavilion in which there had been prepared for him and his guests an abundant repast. The majority of the audience followed Cæsar's example, and flocked outside to stretch their cramped limbs and attack the viands which, by Cæsar's orders, slaves offered to all and sundry. Around the Imperial pavilion picturesque groups soon formed, but others of the spectators descended into the arena, on quitting their seats, and, fingering the blood-clotted sand, fell to discoursing knowingly on the preceding spectacle, and on those which were to come. In time, however, these knowing ones gravitated, like their fellows, to the banquet, and there remained in the arena only a few who were held there, not by curiosity, but by compassion for the coming victims—although this fact they concealed when they returned to the corridors.

Next, the arena was raked over, and a number of holes dug in the sand—the outermost line of these holes extending to within a few paces of the Imperial balcony. From without came the cries and clatter and applause of the populace, while within the building men worked feverishly to set the stage for a new spectacle of torture. Suddenly the gates of the cuniculi, or dungeons, opened, and from every outlet there streamed into the arena swarms of Christians entirely naked, and carrying crosses on their shoulders.

Every inch of the sand now became crowded. Old men and women advanced at a run—their backs bending beneath the weight of their wooden burdens; while beside them came men in the prime of life, women with flowing hair with which they strove to veil their nakedness, youths, and even young children. For the most part, victims and crosses were alike garlanded with flowers; while with blows and lashes the attendants of the arena forced the condemned to fit their crosses into the holes which had been dug, and to hold them in position there. The persons thus brought forth to die were those whom it had not been possible to throw to the lions and other ferocious beasts.

Presently black slaves seized the victims, and laid them upon the crosses; after which, with all possible speed, they nailed the victims' hands to the cross-pieces, since it was necessary that everything should be in readiness by the time the spectators had regained their seats. Consequently the amphitheatre resounded with the blows of hammers; and these, re-echoing from the furthermost lines of crosses, penetrated even to the tent where Cæsar was entertaining the Vestals and his friends. In that tent wine was being drunk, raillery directed at Chilo, and doubtful badinage whispered in the ears of the Vestals. In the arena nails were being driven into the hands and feet of Christians, shovels were rattling, and earth was being heaped into the cavities into which the crosses had been fitted.

Among the victims was Crispus, whom the lions had not had time to rend. Always prepared for death, he was rejoicing to think that his hour had come. Except for his loins, which were girt about with a garland of ivy, as well as for his head, which was crowned with roses, his emaciated body was stark naked. Yet his eyes never ceased to flash with inextinguishable energy, nor his face to evince implacable fanaticism. Nor had his heart changed. Just as, in the dungeon, he had threatened his brethren (sewn in the skins of wild beasts) with the divine wrath, so now, instead of consoling his companions, he thundered out the words:

"Thank you the Saviour, in that He is permitting you to die the death which He himself died! Peradventure, for that death, a portion of your sins will be forgiven you! Yet tremble you before Him, inasmuch as justice will be done, and the unjust will be set apart from the just!"

Thus he spoke to the accompaniment of the clattering of hammers. Ever the arena was growing more and more studded with crosses. Turning to those of the victims who were still standing beside the instruments prepared for their torture, Crispus continued:

"I see the heavens opened, but I also see Hell gaping. Do I myself know how I am to account to the Saviour for my life?—yes, even though I have in me faith, and abhor evil? Yet it is not death that I fear, but resurrection—not punishment, but judgment. For the day of wrath is come."

Suddenly from one of the benches near the arena there arose a calm, solemn voice which said:

"Not the day of wrath, but the day of mercy, of salvation, and of joy. I say unto you that Christ will gather you unto Himself, and console you, and bid you sit down at His right hand. Have ye faith, for the heavens are indeed opening before you!"

At these words every eye turned in the direction of the voice. Even those who were already hanging on crosses raised their pale, tortured faces to gaze at the man who had thus spoken. He, approaching the barrier which bounded the arena, blessed those within it with the sign of the cross. For a moment Crispus flung out an arm at the speaker, as though to annihilate him with a look. Then, recognising him whom he threatened, he let the arm fall to his side as with bent knees and in a hushed voice he murmured:

"The Apostle Paul!"

Then, to the utter astonishment of the arena attendants, all who had not yet been nailed to their crosses knelt down. Paul turned to Crispus, and said:

"Do not threaten them, Crispus, for today they will be with you in Paradise. You think that they are about to be condemned: but who is going to condemn them? Will He condemn them who, for their redemption, gave His only Son? Will Christ condemn them who, for their redemption, died even as they, for His doctrine, are about to die? Will He condemn them who love them? And who else shall bring an accusation against the Lord's elect?—who shall say of their blood, 'It is accursed'?"

"Nay, but I hate evil," said the old man.

"Over hatred of evil has Christ set the love of one's neighbour. For His religion is love, not hatred."

"I have sinned in the very hour of death!" exclaimed Crispus, striking his breast.

At this moment a soldier approached the Apostle, and asked of him:

"Who are you that are speaking to the condemned?"

"A Roman citizen," replied Paul calmly. Then, turning to Crispus again, he continued:

"Fear not, for to-day is the day of mercy. Die, therefore, in peace, O faithful servant of God."

Here two Negroes approached Crispus to nail him to the cross.

"Pray for me, my brethren!" was his final cry. No longer did his face look stern: on his statuesque features there lingered only an expression of gentleness and peace. Voluntarily he assisted the executioners in their task by extending his arms along the cross-pieces; after which he looked up to heaven, and resigned himself to ardent prayer. Nothing did he seem to feel. Even when the nails pierced his hands he did not shrink, nor did a spasm of pain cross his countenance; and all the time that his feet were being nailed to the cross, and the cross being raised, and the earth being stamped down around its foot, he continued praying, ever praying. Only when the crowd began, with ribald shouts and laughter, to re-enter the building did the old man frown, as though indignant that the impious mob should trouble the peace, the calm, the sweetness of his death.

The Circus now seemed to have been planted with a forest in which there was suspended to each tree a human being. The cross-pieces of the trees and the heads of the crucified were gilded with sunlight, while the floor of the arena was studded with golden lozenges of the same, dancing amid a sea of dark shadows. The pleasure of the spectacle lay in watching the slow agony of the victims. So dense was the forest of crosses that the attendants could scarcely pass between the trees—the outer rings being garnished principally with women, and Crispus, as the most important victim, being placed almost exactly opposite the Imperial balcony, on a huge cross of which the base was festooned with hawthorn.

None of the martyrs had, as yet, expired, but some of those who had been the first to be suspended had fainted. Yet not a groan was there to be heard, not a single cry for pity. Some had their heads leaning upon one shoulder, or drooping upon their breast, as though they had been overcome with sleep; others seemed to be meditating; others, with their eyes turned heavenwards, were feebly moving their lips. In the presence of that awful forest of crosses, of those outstretched bodies, of that deathlike silence, the joyous clamour of the people suddenly hushed. Even the nudity of those stiffened, contracted female forms no longer excited the lust of the mob. No wagers were laid as to which victim would die before which, as had hitherto been the custom. Even Cæsar seemed weary of it all as indolently he twisted the necklace which encircled the huge neck beneath his gigantic head.

Suddenly Crispus opened his eyes, and caught sight of Nero. Instantly his face resumed an expression so implacable, his

eyes began to blaze with such a terrible light, that the Augustans fell to whispering among themselves, and to point him out with their fingers. Finally Cæsar's own attention became attracted, and slowly he raised the monocle to his eye. Thus, in absolute silence, all sat staring at Crispus, who was vainly endeavouring to detach his right hand from the cross.

At length, with breast inflated and straining sides, he cried:

"Woe unto you, matricide!"

This insult, offered to him in the very presence of his people, caused Cæsar to frown, and to let fall the emerald. Once more Crispus' voice, growing ever more and more menacing, resounded through the amphitheatre:

"Woe unto you, slayer of your mother and of your brother! Woe unto you, Anti-Christ! The abyss is opening beneath your feet, death is stretching out its arms to seize you, the tomb is yawning to receive your body! Woe unto you, O living corpse, for you shall die in fear and be damned for all eternity!"

His limbs horribly extended, so that he looked like a living skeleton, the old man shook his white beard over the Imperial balcony, and, in doing so, bestrewed the balcony with petals from the rose-garland with which he had been crowned.

"Woe unto you, murderer!" he exclaimed a third time. "For your hour is at hand!"

With that he made a last desperate effort to release his right hand from the cross, in order that he might shake it at Cæsar; and for a moment or two it seemed that he would succeed. Suddenly, however, his arms stretched themselves out, his body sank down, his head fell forward upon his breast, and his spirit passed away.

In that forest of crosses the weaker of the martyrs were now sleeping the eternal sleep.

XVIII

"My lord," said Chilo, "the sea is like olive-oil, and the waves seem to have sunk to rest. Let us set out for Hellas. In Hellas the glory of an Apollo awaits you. In Hellas crowns and triumphal progresses will be offered you. In Hellas men will greet you as a god, and the gods themselves accept you as their guest and their equal. On the other hand, *here,* my lord—!"

He said no more, for his lower lip had started so violently to tremble that his words died away into inarticulate sounds.

"Yes, we will set out as soon as ever the games are over," replied Nero. "But already there are people who are beginning to say that the Christians were innocent; and if I were to set out now, every one would soon be repeating that statement. But what is frightening you so much, you rotten old mushroom?"

Light though his tone was, the attention with which he scrutinised the Greek betrayed his anxiety. As a matter of fact he had been greatly alarmed by Crispus' words. Even after he had returned to the palace, rage, shame, and fear banished sleep from his eyes.

The superstitious Vestinus glanced around him, and said in a mysterious voice:

"Did you hear the old man, my lord? There is something strange about these Christians. In any case their deity seems to grant them an easy death. Is there not some risk of that deity avenging them?"

"*I* am not to blame," said Cæsar quickly. "Tigellinus it was who organised the games."

"Yes, it *was* I," assented Tigellinus: "nor do I care a fig for all the Christians in the world. Vestinus is a mere bag of superstition, while this lion-hearted Greek of yours would die at the sight of a hen ruffing her feathers to defend her young."

"Very good," said Nero; "but in future you will either have these Christians' tongues cut out or gags stuffed into their mouths."

"Yes, I will have them gagged with fire, my lord."

"Woe is me!" groaned Chilo.

Cæsar, however, reassured by Tigellinus' boast, burst out laughing, and said as he pointed to the old Greek:

"Behold the bearing of the descendant of Achilles!"

And, indeed, Chilo's appearance was most woe-begone. His few remaining hairs had turned completely white, and his face become stamped with an expression of ever-growing anxiety. There were even moments when his haggard bearing might have conveyed the impression that he had lost his senses. Occasionally he would fail to answer questions put to him, while at other times he would be seized with fits of fury, and grow so scrurrilous in his replies that the Augustans would change their minds about angering him further.

One of these fits had just seized him.

"You can do what you like with me," he cried, "but to the games I will *not* go!" And he snapped his fingers defiantly.

Nero looked at him for a moment; then said as he turned to Tigellinus:

"See to it that in the Gardens Chilo walks by my side. I desire to observe how our torches will impress him."

The menace in Cæsar's tone made Chilo tremble.

"My lord," he said, "even if I go with you, I shall see nothing. My sight is always bad at night time."

"Oh, it will be light enough on *that* occasion," replied Cæsar with an ominous smile, "—as light as day itself."

Then he turned to the Augustans, and fell to discussing with them the chariot races which were to conclude the games.

Petronius approached Chilo, and said as he touched his arm:

"I was right when I told you that you would never play the part to the end."

To which the other replied:

"To do so I shall need to get drunk."

With that he stretched a trembling hand towards a jar of wine, but lacked the strength to fit it to his lips. Vestinus took from him the vessel, and, leaning over him with a countenance full at once of curiosity and of alarm, inquired:

"Are the Furies pursuing you?"

The old man looked at the speaker with mouth open, as though he had failed to understand the question. Then he fell to blinking his eyes.

Vestinus repeated the question.

"No," replied Chilo; "but all is gone dark before my eyes."

"Dark, do you say? May the gods have mercy upon you! What do you mean? Dark?"

"Yes, with a darkness that is terrible and unfathomable. And out of that darkness something is advancing towards me —something of which, for some reason or other, I am afraid."

"I have always thought that sorcerers exist. Do you have bad dreams at present?"

"No, for I cannot sleep at all. The thought of the torturing of these people has prevented me from so doing."

"Then you are sorry for them?"

"No; but why should so much blood have been shed? You heard what that man on the cross said? Evil is awaiting us."

"Yes, I *did* hear what that man said," muttered Vestinus in a lower voice. "But those people were incendiaries."

"No, that is untrue."

"And enemies of the human race."

"That also is untrue."

"And poisoners of fountains."

"Untrue, untrue!"

"And devourers of children."

"Untrue, untrue, I tell you!"

"What?" asked Vestinus in astonishment. "Do you yourself, who betrayed them to Tigellinus, say that?"

"Yes, for I am wrapped in darkness, and death is advancing towards me. Sometimes I seem to be dead already, and you yourselves to be dead also."

"No, it is the Christians who are dead. *We* are alive. But tell me: what is it that these people see as they are dying?"

"They see Christ."

"Their God, you mean? Is he a powerful God?"

Chilo answered with a counter-question:

"What sort of torches are they going to burn in the Gardens? Did you hear what Cæsar said?"

"Yes, I heard, and I know. The torches are to be what are known as sarmentitii and semaxii. That is to say, the Christians are to be wrapped in the condemned shift, tied to stakes, soaked in oil, and set on fire. May their God not send fresh disasters upon the city in revenge! Semaxii—it is a most terrible form of torture!"

"Nevertheless I would rather witness it than the other forms, for it causes no blood to flow. . . . Pray bid a slave raise this cup to my lips, for I am thirsty, and my hand so shakes with old age that I spill the wine."

Chilo's companions also were discussing the Christians.

Old Domitius Afer had not a single good word for them.

"They had become so numerous," he said, "that they might have fomented a civil war. Yet, would you believe it?—they actually declined to accept weapons in the arena to defend themselves with! Moreover, they are people who die like sheep."

"Let them try to do otherwise!" said Tigellinus menacingly.

"You are wrong," put in Petronius. "They *do* arm themselves."

"With what, pray?"

"With fortitude."

"It is a new weapon indeed!"

"Possibly. But can you say that they die like ordinary criminals? No. They die as though the criminals in the matter were the men who condemn them to death. I refer to ourselves and to the Roman people generally."

"What rubbish!" cried Tigellinus.

"What a prince of fools!" retorted Petronius.

Some of those present, struck with the justice of what Petronious had said, looked at one another in astonishment, and repeated:

"It is true. There *is* something out of the common in the manner in which these Christians meet death."

"And I, for my part, assert that, in dying, they behold their deity," added Vestinus.

Upon this some of the Augustans turned to Chilo.

"Hi, old man!" they cried. "Do you who know them so well tell us what it is they behold."

The Greek gave a gulp, spat out upon his tunic the wine which he had just drunk, and replied:

"They behold the Resurrection!"

And with that he became seized with such violent shudderings that those who were seated near him burst into roars of laughter.

XIX

For some time past Vinicius had been spending his nights away from home. Petronius told himself that possibly his nephew had on foot some new scheme for rescuing Lygia from the Esquiline prison, but forbore to question him, lest he should bring misfortune upon the supposed enterprise. Ever since he had failed to deliver Lygia from the Mamertine goal he had lost faith in his lucky star.

Nor did he now count upon the successful issue of Vinicius' attempts. Though the Esquiline prison, which had been hastily constructed by connecting together the cellars of various houses which had been demolished in order to isolate the flames, was not as terrible a place as was the old tullianum of the Capitol, it was a hundred times more strictly guarded, and Petronius had not the slightest doubt that the reason why Lygia had been transferred thither was that she might not die of fever, and so escape death in the arena.

"One thing is certain," he said to himself: "and that is that Cæsar and Tigellinus are reserving her for a special spectacle that shall be more atrocious than all the rest. Vinicius will ruin himself to no purpose."

Vinicius too had lost faith in his own initiative. Only Christ could save her. The one thing left to the young man was to devise a means of seeing her in prison. He knew that, in spite of all obstacles, Nazarus had succeeded in gaining access to the place, as a remover of corpses; and the thought haunted him until eventually he decided to try a similar resource. In return for an immense sum the superintendent of the Burial Pits added him to the staff which was nightly dispatched to the various prisons to inquire for bodies of the dead. That done, he knew that the darkness of the night, his slave's costume, the rags, soaked with terebinthine, in which his head would be wrapped, and the miserable lighting of the prisons would help to conceal his identity. Besides, who would ever have dreamt that a patrician, the son and the grandson of consuls, would be figuring in the habiliments worn by grave-diggers, who were exposed to the infectious emanations of the gaols and of the Burial Pits? Who would ever have dreamt that such a man could adopt a pursuit to which only the blackest of destitution or the condition of slavery was capable of reducing a human being?

When the centurion had examined the corpse-removers' badges the great iron gate of the prison was opened, and Vinicius saw before him a huge vault whence access could be obtained to a number of smaller cellars. A few lanterns shed a dim light over the scene, which was swarming with prisoners. Some of the latter, stretched along the walls, were asleep; others were sitting with their elbows on their knees, and their faces buried in their hands. Here and there an infant was lying pressed to its mother's bosom, and from every side came the sound of coughs, sobs, muttered prayers, hymns intoned under the breath, and blasphemous exclamations of gaolers.

Everywhere there reigned an odour of corpses and human sweat. In dark corners there crouched dim figures whose features were indistinguishable, while under the flickering lanterns there could be discerned white faces with hollow cheeks, eyes strained or feverish-looking, and bluish lips—the whole surmounted with hair that was plastered to the forehead with perspiration. Some of these ailing folk were uttering cries in their delirium, while others were calling for water, or begging to be put to death.

Vinicius' knees tottered under him as he gazed at these things. The mere thought that Lygia was in this Gehenna caused his hair to bristle and his throat to contract. The amphiheatre, the fangs of wild beasts, the cross—anything would be better than these frightful dungeons, which were full of putrescent corpses!

"How many have died to-day?" asked the superintendent of the Burial Pits.

"About a dozen," replied the governor of the prison. "By to-morrow morning there will be more, for some of those along the wall are already at their last gasp."

With that he fell to railing against

women who concealed their dead children in order to keep them the longer. Such corpses, it appeared, could be traced only by the smell.

"I would rather be a slave serving a sentence in a country prison," he concluded, "than have to watch over dogs who rot even before they are dead."

The superintendent of the Burial Pits consoled him by saying that his (the superintendent's) lot was equally unenviable.

Meanwhile Vinicius had been fruitlessly searching for Lygia, until at length he had been forced to suppose that never again should he see her alive. The number of cellars which were connected with one another by passages freshly hewn in the walls was about a dozen, and the grave-diggers entered only those of them which they knew to contain corpses. Consequently it was a terrible thing for him to have to think that what had cost him so much labour to achieve was destined to go for nothing.

Fortunately the keeper of the Burial Pits came to his assistance.

"The corpses must be removed at once," he said, "if you gaolers are not to die as well as the prisoners."

"There are only ten of us for all the dungeons," replied the head gaoler; "and even of those a few must sleep."

"Then I will leave you four of my men, and they shall make a tour of the cellars, to see if there are any more corpses."

"If you will do that, I will take care that you have something to drink to-morrow. But, first of all, each body must be taken to the office, for orders have been given that the throat of every corpse is to be cut before being removed to the Burial Pits."

"Good! Then you shall send me some wine."

The superintendent of the Burial Pits detailed the four men in question—one of them being Vinicius—and set them to collect the dead on stretchers.

Vinicius breathed afresh. Now at least he would find Lygia again. He explored the first of the cellars in detail, but found nothing; nor in the second and third cellars did his search meet with better results. It was now growing late, and the corpses had been removed, while the gaolers had stretched themselves out in the passages separating the cellars, and gone to sleep. Even the children had worn themselves out with weeping, and fallen to silence. Nowhere was a sound to be heard save the laboured breathing of overcharged bosoms and, here and there, the muttering of a prayer.

Suddenly, as Vinicius entered a fourth cellar that was smaller than the preceding ones, and raised his lantern, he gave a start. Beneath the bars of a ventilator he seemed to have caught sight of the gigantic outlines of Ursus. Hastily blowing out his lantern, he approached the Lygian.

"Is that you, Ursus?" he inquired.

The giant raised his head.

"Who are you?" he demanded.

"Do you not recognise me?"

"How can I recognise you when you have blown out the lantern?"

But Vinicius had caught sight also of Lygia, stretched out upon a cloak beside the wall; and without a further word he knelt down by her side. Then Ursus recognised him, and said:

"Blessed be Christ! Yet do not wake her, my lord."

Vinicius looked at her through his tears. In spite of the darkness, he could see that her face was pale as marble, and that her shoulders were wasted. The sight filled him with a yearning love that was almost an agony of pain—with a love that was full of pity, of veneration, and of respect. He fell with his face to the earth, and pressed his lips to the hem of the cloak on which the young girl was lying.

For a long time Ursus looked at him in silence. Then, plucking his tunic, he said:

"My lord, how did you obtain admittance? Have you come to save her?"

Vinicius rose to his feet.

"Show me how to do that!" he exclaimed.

"I was hoping that you had already found a means, my lord. The only means of which I can think is—" And he glanced towards the bars of the ventilator. Then, as though answering himself, he added:

"Yes; but behind those bars are soldiers."

"A hundred Prætorians," assented Vinicius.

"Could we not make our way through them?"

"No."

The Lygian rubbed his brows, and again put the question:

"How did you obtain admittance?"

"Through a badge, as a remover of corpses." Then like lightning an idea flashed through his brain.

"By the Saviour's Passion," he went on, "but I could do this. I could remain here, and let Lygia take this badge, wrap her head in this linen, throw this cloak around her, and leave the prison in my stead. There are several young men among the superintendent's staff, so that the Prætorians would not recognise her; and, once she had gained Petronius' house, she would be safe."

With lowered head the Lygian replied:

"She would never consent to the plan, for she loves you. Moreover, she is ill, and unable to stand upright. If Petronius and yourself, my lord, have failed to rescue her, who else shall do it?"

"Christ—and Christ alone."

For a while the pair remained silent. Deep down in his simple heart the Lygian was thinking: "Yes, Christ could save us all; so, if He has not done so, it means that the hour of punishment and of death has arrived." Death for himself he feared not, but from the bottom of his soul he grieved for the child who had grown up in his arms, and whom he loved better than his own life.

Suddenly Lygia opened her eyes, and laid her burning hands upon those of Vinicius.

"Ah, I can see you!" she exclaimed. "I *knew* that you would come!"

"Yes, I am come, my beloved! May Christ take you under His protection, and save you, my darling Lygia!"

More he could not say, lest he should betray his grief in her presence.

"I am ill, Marcus," she went on, "and whether it be here or in the arena, I must die. But in my prayers I asked to see you before I departed, and Christ has heard me, for you are come!"

Still he could not speak—still he could only clasp her to his breast. So she continued:

"Yes, I knew that you would come, and that to-day the Saviour would permit us to say farewell to one another. Though I am soon going to Him, I love you, Marcus, and shall always love you."

Vinicius mastered himself, choked down his grief, and said in a voice which he forced to calmness:

"My beloved, you shall not die. The Apostle bid me have faith, since he also would pray for you. He himself has known Christ; and Christ, who loved him, can refuse him nothing. Had you been ordained to die, Peter would never have bidden me have faith. Yet he said to me, 'Only have faith.' No, Lygia; Christ will show us His compassion—He will not let you die, He will not suffer such a thing to come about. By the name of the Saviour I swear to you that Peter also is offering up prayer on your behalf."

The solitary lantern which was suspended over the door had gone out, but a stream of moonlight was entering through the ventilator. In the opposite corner a child gave a wail, then hushed again. From without came the voices of Prætorians who, having been relieved from guard, were playing at scriptæ duodecim under the prison wall.

At length Lygia replied:

"Marcus, Christ Himself once cried, 'My Father, if it be Thy will, suffer this cup to pass from Me!' Yet He drank that cup to the dregs, and died upon the Cross. Thousands also are perishing for His sake. Why, therefore, should I alone be spared? Who am I, Marcus? Have I not heard Peter say that he too will suffer martyrdom? What am I as compared with him? When the Prætorians first came to seek us I felt afraid of death and torture; but now I no longer fear them. See what a terrible place this prison is: why, therefore, should I not rejoice to leave it for Heaven? Remember that here below there is Cæsar, but that in Heaven there is the Saviour, who is kind and pitiful. There death does not exist at all. Do you who love me think how happy I shall be with Him! Do you who love me remember that one day you will rejoin me on high."

For a moment she paused to recover her breath; then she took Vinicius by the hand, and said as she raised it to her lips:

"Marcus."

"Yes, beloved?"

"You must not weep for me. Remember always that soon you will be at my side again in Heaven. My life will not have been a very long one, but God has given me your soul for a precious possession, and I shall be able to tell Christ, when I meet Him, that, though I am dead, and you have seen me die, and you are left desolate here on earth, you did not oppose His will. *He* will reunite us, and I shall always love you and be with you."

Again breath failed her, and she concluded in scarcely audible accents:

"Promise me this, Marcus."

"Yes, by the sacred Head of God, I promise it!"

Then through the darkness he saw Lygia's face grow radiant. Once again she raised his hand to her lips as she murmured:

"Your wife—at last I am your wife!"

On the other side of the prison walls the Prætorians who had been playing at scriptæ duodecim had begun to quarrel; but within those walls there were souls who had forgotten gaol, gaolers, and the world alike, and who, communing together, could seek refuge in prayer to God.

XX

For three days—or, rather, for three nights—nothing disturbed their happiness. As soon as the task of separating the living from the dead had been performed, the weary gaolers would stretch themselves out in the corridors, and permit of Vinicius entering Lygia's cell, and not leaving it until the bars of the ventilator had begun to show forth the light of dawn. Lygia would lie with her head upon Vinicius' breast, and together they would talk of love and of death. In these interviews—indeed, in their every thought and desire and hope—they grew to detach themselves more and more from life. They resembled navigators who, having left the land far behind them, can no longer discern the immensity of the ocean and the sky, but go sailing slowly onwards into the infinite. Whenever, in the morning, Vinicius left the prison he saw the world and the city and his friends and the ordinary objects of life as in a dream. All seemed strange and distant; all seemed empty and ephemeral. Even the imminence of death by torture had ceased to intimidate him, for he felt that it was possible to pass through martyrdom in a state of absorption, with the sufferer's eyes fixed elsewhere. As he and Lygia confided their love to one another they would tell themselves how great their mutual affection would be, and how they would live together, not upon earth, but in the world beyond the grave. And if at times their thoughts turned to things of earth they spoke as travellers who, before departing on a far journey, discuss the preparations necessary for the same. Otherwise they remained wrapped in the peace which envelops two solitary, disregarded monoliths. Their one desire was that Christ would not separate them; and the ever-growing conviction that He would grant them their desire caused them to love Him as the binding force which would for ever unite them in infinite love and boundless peace. The dust of earth they had already shaken off, and their souls were being purified to the clarity of a tear. Though under the shadow of death, and surrounded by suffering and misery, and stretched upon a prison pallet, they yet felt that they had entered Heaven. Taking Vinicius by the hand, Lygia, saved and sanctified, was leading her lover towards the inexhaustible source of life.

Petronius could not understand why Vinicius' face had come to be charged with a deeper restfulness than it had ever before manifested. At times he began to think that his nephew must have devised a new scheme of rescue, and felt hurt that it should not have been confided to him at once. At length he could not forbear saying:

"You seem altogether changed now. I pray you, do not treat me as a stranger, since I both wish and have the power to be useful to you. Have you come across anything fresh?"

"Yes," replied Vinicius; "and it is something wherein you could not help me. After she is dead I intend to confess my faith openly, and to follow her."

"Then you have abandoned all hope?"

"Christ will restore her to me, and we shall never again be separated."

"You need not look to your Christ for that: Thanatos could render you the same service."

"No, my friend. You cannot understand what I mean."

"No, I cannot, and do not wish to, understand. This is not the moment for discussing the point, but do you remember what you said to me the night when we failed to rescue Lygia from the tullianum? *I* had lost all hope, but *you* remarked as we re-entered the villa: 'In spite of everything, I believe that Christ can restore her to me.' Restore her to you, indeed! If I were to throw a goblet into the sea, none of our ancient gods could recover that goblet; and if your deity does not go to any greater trouble than that to please you, I cannot see why I should pay him a whit more honour than I do to the older deities."

"Not only that, but He will restore me to *her,*" said Vinicius.

Petronius shrugged his shoulders.

"Are you aware," he remarked, "that to-morrow the Gardens of Cæsar are going to be illuminated with living torches, in the shape of Christians?"

"To-morrow?" re-echoed Vinicius.

With a heart quivering with distress and terror he hastened to the superintendent of the Burial Pits, in order to obtain from that functionary his badge; but a new disappointment awaited him, for the superintendent declined to hand over the tessera.

"Pardon me, my lord," he said. "I have done all that I could for you, but I dare not risk my life. To-night the Christians are to be removed to Cæsar's Gardens, and the prison will be full of soldiers and officials. Should you be recognised, I should be lost, and my children with me."

Vinicius understood that it would be useless to insist further. Nevertheless there remained to him a ray of hope in the thought that perhaps some of the soldiers who had seen him before would allow him to pass without a badge. When night came he, as usual, donned a ragged tunic, swathed his face in linen, and repaired to the prison.

Unfortunately, that night the badges were scrutinised more carefully than usual; and, to complete the catastrophe, the centurion Scævinus—a soldier strict in general, and devoted, body and soul, to Cæser in particular—recognised Vinicius.

Yet even within that mail-clad breast there lurked a spark of pity for unfortunate humanity. Instead of giving the alarm by striking the point of his spear against his buckler, the centurion took Vinicius aside, and said:

"Return home, my lord. I have recognised you, but have no wish to ruin you by speaking out. At the same time I cannot grant you admittance, so I would pray you to depart, in the hope that the gods may send you consolation."

"Yes, I understand that you cannot grant me admittance," replied Vinicius; "but suffer me to remain here, and to watch the departure of those about to be removed."

"That at least will not be contrary to my orders."

So Vinicius took up a position before the main gate, to wait till the condemned should issue thence. At length, towards midnight, the gate opened to vomit forth a crowd of men, women, and children, surrounded by a detachment of Prætorians. The night was clear, for the moon was shining brightly, and it was an easy matter to distinguish the prisoners' features. The Christians walked two and two in a long, mournful procession—the silence broken only by the clanking of the soldiers' accoutrements. So numerous were the prisoners that it would appear as though every dungeon must now be empty. Among them Vinicius distinctly recognised Glaucus the physician; but he also perceived that neither Lygia nor Ursus was among the throng of those brought forth to die.

XXI

Darkness had not completely set in when the populace began to direct its steps towards the Gardens of Cæsar. Dressed in holiday attire, and crowned with flowers, the people marched, singing gaily, to witness a new and splendid spectacle. Almost every man was drunk, and the cries of "The semaxii, the sarmentitii!" resounded throughout the whole of that quarter of Rome. Once before the city had been regaled with the spectacle of persons being burnt alive at the stake; but never before had the number of condemned approached its present proportions. Wishing to make a comprehensive clearance of the Christians, as well as to arrest the progress of the gaol fever which was spreading from the prisons to the city at large, Cæsar and Tigellinus had completely emptied the dungeons, until there remained in them only a few score persons who were to be reserved for the close of the games. The result was that, on passing the entrance-gates of the Gardens, the crowd halted in stupefaction: for every avenue—both those which led to the thickets and those which traversed the meadows—as well as every clump of trees, the banks of every pond, and the borders of every parterre of flowers, stood picked out with resin-soaked stakes to which Christians had been bound!

From the summits of the knolls, whence the view was not obscured by the curtain of trees, there could be seen long lines of bodies adorned with flowers, ivy, and myrtle-leaves. Topping the heights, and descending into the hollows, they extended such distances that the nearest stakes looked like ships' masts, and the furthest like a multi-coloured jumble of flower-bedecked thyrsi.

Soon darkness fell, and the first stars began to shine forth. By the side of every condemned person slaves armed with torches stationed themselves; and as soon as a trumpet sounded, as a signal for the spectacle to commence, each slave applied his torch to the base of the stake beside which he was standing.

Upon this the straw, saturated with oil, which was concealed beneath the garlands blazed up into a flame which, ever increasing, soon caused the wreaths of ivy to unroll, until the fire had begun to lick the feet of the victims. The spectators remained silent, but from the Gardens there went up one gigantic groan, compounded of thousands of wails of agony. Nevertheless many of the victims, with eyes raised to the star-bespangled heavens, started to sing hymns to the glory of Christ; and as the people listened, the hearts of even the most hardened among them contracted for a moment as from the summits of the smaller stakes there came the piteous voices of children crying, "Mother, mother!" while ruffians in the most advanced stage of intoxication could not repress a shudder at the sight of innocent, childish faces contracted with torture or half-veiled by the smoke which was already suffocating some of the victims. Still the flames mounted upwards as, one by one, they consumed the garlands of ivy and roses. Both the principal avenues and those which ran crosswise were now a sea of fire; and every clump of trees, every lawn, and every flower-bed was brilliantly illuminated with a light which awoke countless reflections in the ponds and basons, and tinted the trembling leaves with rose-colour. The place seemed to be plunged in daylight. Everywhere throughout the Gardens there hung the smell of roasting flesh, even though from time to time slaves stationed beside braziers which had been set between the stakes heaped those vessels with fresh myrrh and aloes. Here and there among the crowd there would arise cries of pity in addition to the shouts of joyous intoxication; and these cries kept growing louder in proportion as the fire increased —in proportion as it enveloped stakes, crept upwards towards breasts, twisted hair with its burning breath, threw a veil over blackened faces, and then rose yet higher, as though to proclaim the triumph and the victory of the force which had been unchained.

As soon as the spectacle had begun Cæsar appeared among his people in a splendid quadriga drawn by four white racing stallions. Clad in a chariot-driver's costume which was designed to include the colours of the Greens (those of his own and the Court party in general), he was followed by a number of other chariots, full of splendidly dressed courtiers, of Senators, of priests, of naked, rose-garlanded bacchantes who, drunk, and holding cups of wine in their hands, kept uttering wild cries, and of musicians who, costumed to represent fauns or satyrs, were playing harps, lutes, fifes, and horns. In other chariots there rode matrons and virgins of Roman families—all equally drunken and half-naked; while on either side of these chariots walked Greek youths, brandishing thyrsi adorned with ribands, or playing on tambourines, or strewing flowers in front of the horses' hoofs. Thus amid smoke and the lines of human torches the procession made its way to the prinicpal avenue—there to be greeted with shouts of "Evohe, evohe!" Cæsar, who had at his side Tigellinus and Chilo (the nervous terror of the latter greatly amused him), drove his horses at a foot's pace, the better to view the flaming bodies, and to listen to the acclamation of his people; and as he advanced, his monstrous arms, stretched lengthwise by the reins, seemed to be making a gesture of benediction over the mob, while his face and half-closed eyes were smiling, and his garlanded head seemed to be shining above his people like the head of a god, or even like the sun itself.

Every now and then he would halt before some virgin whose breast was beginning to crackle in the flame, or before some child whose face was contracted with agony. Then he would continue his progress, with, behind him, his train of drunken, straggling, uproarious attendants. At intervals he would salute the people, or, leaning back, and supported by the gilded reins, engage in conversation with Tigellinus. At length, arrived at a great fountain where two avenues crossed one another, he descended from his chariot, signed to his companions, and plunged into the crowd.

There he was received with renewed cries and applause. Bacchantes, nymphs, Augustans, priests, fauns, satyrs, and soldiers surrounded him in a frenzied ring, while around the edge of the fountain a hundred fresh torches blazed forth, of which Cæsar made a tour—stopping every now and then to make a remark on the victims, or to rally Chilo, whose face was full of unutterable despair.

At length the party arrived at an exceptionally tall stake that was ornamented with myrtle and festooned with ivy. The ruddy flames were licking the knees of the victim, but his face was indistinguishable, owing to smoke thrown off by the green branches as they caught fire. Suddenly the night wind blew aside the smoke, and exposed the head of an old, grey-bearded man. At the sight Chilo shrank back like a wounded serpent, and uttered a cry which resembled the croak of a raven rather than the sound of a human voice.

"Glaucus! Glaucus!" he shrieked.

From the summit of the blazing stake Glaucus the physician looked down upon him. With his sad face bent forward, he gazed at the man who had betrayed him, who had robbed him of wife and children, who had inveigled him into a den of villains, and who, after all had been forgiven him in the name of Christ, had once more delivered his benefactor to the executioners. Glaucus' eyes were riveted to the face of the Greek. Every now and then smoke would veil those eyes, but each stirring of the breeze caused Chilo once more to see them piercing his very soul. He tried to turn and flee, but could not. As though petrified, he remained standing where he was. His one sensation was that something in him had broken, and had shattered everything—that the end was come, that Cæsar and Cæsar's Court and the crowd were growing dim before his sight, and that around him there was only a terrible limitless, lightless void in which, like two points of fire, the eyes of a martyr were summoning him before his Judge. The other, ever drooping his head, continued to gaze at him. All who were near felt conscious that something was passing between these two men. Yet laughter died on every lip, for Chilo's face had grown terrible to look upon—it was as though it was *his* body that the tongues of fire were licking. Suddenly he staggered, threw up his arms, and cried in a voice at once horrible and heartrending:

"Glaucus! In the name of Christ! Forgive me!"

All around them ceased speaking, and a shudder ran through the crowd as every eye raised itself to the stake.

The martyr's head nodded gently, and from the summit of the stake there came, in a stifled voice that was half a groan, the words:

"I forgive you."

With a cry like that of a wild beast Chilo fell forward upon his face, and, digging his hands into the ground, scattered earth upon his head. Suddenly the flames spurted forth, enveloped Glaucus' breast and face, unrolled the crown of myrtle from his head, and devoured the ribands which had adorned the shaft of the stake—the latter now flaming up into a column of dazzling brilliancy.

When Chilo arose his countenance was so transformed that the Augustans seemed to see before them another man. His eyes were shining with an extraordinary brightness, and his wrinkled forehead seemed so to diffuse ecstasy that he who but a moment before had been a feeble old coward now seemed to have become a priest inspired of God to reveal the eternal verities.

"What has happened to him? He is mad!" murmured several voices.

As they did so he turned towards the crowd, raised his right hand, and said—or, rather, cried—in a voice so piercing that not only the Augustans, but also the populace at large, caught the words:

"Roman people, on my life do I swear that innocent persons are perishing! *He, he* is the incendiary!"—and he pointed his finger at Nero.

For a moment there was silence. The courtiers stood petrified. Still Chilo kept pointing his trembling hand, with its accusing finger, at Cæsar. Then a tumult broke forth. Like the billows of the sea when suddenly unchained by a squall, the people rushed towards the old man, to get a better view of him. Some voices cried out, "Hold him!" and others, "Alas, alas, we have been betrayed!" Every moment the uproar was increasing, and the bacchantes, uttering piercing screams, began to run towards the chariots amid a perfect storm of hoots, whistles, and shouts of "Ahenobarbus! Matricide! Incendiary!" Suddenly some stakes which had become burnt through fell amid a shower of sparks, and a blind stampede of the surrounding spectators carried Chilo away towards the other end of the Gardens.

Everywhere charred stakes were beginning to fall across the paths, and to fill the avenues wth smoke, sparks, the smell of burnt wood, and the odour of human grease. Also, the lanterns had become extinguished, and the Gardens were plunged in darkness. Terrified, anxious, and menacing, the people crowded towards the gates, while ever the news of what had happened kept passing from mouth to mouth, changing form as it did so, and growing in proportion. Some said that Cæsar had fainted; others that he had confessed to having originated the fire; others that he had been seized with a dangerous illness, and been taken away for dead on his chariot. Here and there, also, words of pity for the Christians made themselves heard. "If it was not they who burnt Rome, why should there have been this shedding of blood and unjust torturing? Will not the gods wreak vengeance for the death of these innocents, and what expiatory offerings can avail to avert the divine wrath?"

The words "these innocents" began to be repeated with increasing insistence. Women wept aloud with pity for the many children who had been thrown to the wild beasts, or nailed to crosses, or burnt alive in those accursed Gardens. And by degrees that pity gave place to curses upon the heads of Cæsar and Tigellinus. Suddenly a group of people halted, and exclaimed: "Who is the deity which could give these victims such fortitude in the face of torture and death?" Then they entered their houses, absorbed in thought.

Meanwhile Chilo was wandering about the Gardens, unconscious of which direction he was taking. Every now and then he brushed against half-charred corpses, or clutched at smouldering remains which covered him with showers of angry sparks. Then he would seat himself, and gaze around him with unseeing eyes. The Gardens were almost wholly wrapped in darkness, but between the trees a few straggling beams of moonlight sufficed to throw an uncertain glow over the avenues, over the charred stakes which had fallen across them, and over human trunks which had become transformed to shapeless blocks. Ever amid the moonbeams the old Greek seemed to discern the face of Glaucus, with its flashing eyes; and as often as he did so he would rise and flee from the light. At length, emerging out of a dark shadow, he found that some irresistible force had led him back to the fountain where Glaucus had yielded up his life.

At this moment a hand touched his shoulder.

The old man turned, and, seeing before him an unknown man, cried:

"What is it? Who are you?"

"I am an Apostle—Paul of Tarsus."

"And I am a man accursed. What is it you desire?"

"I desire to save you."

Chilo staggered against a tree.

"For me no salvation is possible," he said dully.

"Then do you not know that Christ pardoned the thief upon the cross?"

"And do *you* not know what I—yes, what *I*—have done?"

"Yes; but also I have seen your sorrow, and have heard you testify to the truth."

"O my lord, my lord!"

"And if that servant of Christ could forgive you in the hour of agony and of death, will not Christ Himself forgive you?"

Chilo seized his head in his two hands, as though he could feel himself going mad.

"Forgiveness?" he said. "Forgiveness—for *me?"*

"Yes," replied Paul; "for our God is a God of mercy."

"For me?" groaned Chilo again.

"Lean upon my arm," said the Apostle, "and come with me."

They moved away towards the junction of the two main avenues—guided thither by the plashing sound of the fountain, which, in the night stillness, seemed to be weeping over the bodies of the martyrs.

"Yes, our God is a God of mercy," repeated the Apostle. "With how many pebbles, cast into the waters, could you hope to fill up the abyss of the sea? And the mercy of Christ is as the abyss of the sea; and in it all the sins and the faults of men are swallowed up as are the pebbles in the belly of the ocean. The mercy of Christ is like also unto the heavens which cover the mountains, the earth, and the sea; for everywhere it is present, and to it are there set no bounds. You suffered in soul before the stake whereon Glaucus was hanging, and Christ saw your suffering. You cried aloud, without a thought of what may befall you on the morrow, '*He, he* is the incendiary!' and Christ will not forget your words. Yes, your unworthiness and your deceitfulness have come to an end, and in your heart there remains only a boundless repentance. Come, therefore, to me, and listen. I too once hated Him. I too once persecuted His elect. I too once yearned not for Him, nor believed in Him. Then one day He appeared unto me, and called me: and since that day I have loved none but Him. Listen, therefore. He has sent you this remorse and this fear and this sorrow that He may call you to Himself. Though you hated Him, He has always loved you. Though you have delivered over His children unto torture, He wishes to pardon you, and to save you."

Paul had captivated his hearer, had conquered him, was leading him away as a soldier escorts a prisoner.

"Come with me," he went on, "and I will bring you to His presence. Why have I sought you out? Because He has bidden me gather in souls through the power of His love, and I must accomplish His will. You have said to me, 'I am a man accursed'; but *I* say to *you,* 'Only have faith, and you will be saved. You have said to me, 'I am a man beyond redemption'; but *I* say to *you,* 'He loves you.' Look at me. In the days when I hated Him, only hatred dwelt in my heart; but now that I no longer hate Him, the love of Him has taken the place of love of father and mother, has cast out the thought of riches and pomp. In Him alone is there salvation, in Him alone is there the power to take your repentance into account. He shall look upon your misery, He shall remove from you all fear, He shall raise you up, and seat you beside Himself!"

The spray of the fountain was gleaming silver in the rays of the moon. All around was calm and in solitude, for in this quarter of the Gardens slaves had cleared away the charred stakes, together with the bodies of the martyrs.

Chilo fell upon his knees, buried his face in his hands, and remained thus without speaking. Paul raised his eyes to the stars, and prayed:

"O Lord, look down upon this sinner—upon his repentance, upon his tears, upon his agony! O God of mercy who hast given Thy blood for our sins, I beseech Thee by Thy Passion, by Thy Death, and by Thy Resurrection to pardon this soul!"

Then for a long while the Apostle prayed in silence, still gazing at the stars. Suddenly from Chilo, crouching at his feet, there came a groan. "O Christ, O Christ, pardon me!" he cried.

Paul approached the fountain, took thence some water in the palms of his hands, and returned to the kneeling wretch.

"Chilo," he said, "I baptise thee in the name of the Father, and of the Son, and of the Holy Ghost! Amen!"

Chilo raised his head, and stretched out his arms. As he did so the moon shed a tender glow over his white hair and fixed, pale features. Gradually the night was gliding by. From the great aviaries of the Gardens there came to them the sound of a cock saluting the dawn. Yet still Chilo knelt where he was, a statue of sorrow.

At length he asked:

"What more ought I to do before death shall come to me?"

Paul awoke from his meditations on the measureless power to which even souls like that of this Greek were fain to submit themselves, and replied:

"Have faith, and testify to the truth."

Then they departed together. At the gates of the Gardens the Apostle blessed the old man once more, and they took leave of one another. Chilo had demanded this to be done, since he foresaw that Cæsar and Tigellinus would have him pursued.

Nor was he mistaken. On reaching home, he found the house surrounded by Prætorians, who straightway seized him, and led him away to the Palatine.

Cæsar had retired to rest, but Tigellinus was still on duty. He greeted the Greek with a calm, but menacing, face.

"You have committed the crime of offering an insult to the Sovereign," he said; "nor shall you escape the punishment for that crime. Yet if to-morrow, from the centre of the arena, you will declare that you were drunk and had not your wits about you, as well as that the Christians were the true originators of the fire, your chastisement shall be limited to stripes and exile."

"I cannot, my lord," said Chilo gently.

Tigellinus approached him with long strides, and said in a muffled, but terrible voice:

"What? You cannot, you dog of a Greek? You were *not* drunk? Then, if you do not yet understand what is awaiting you, look there!"

He pointed to a corner of the atrium in which, beside a large wooden bench, four Thracian slaves were standing, armed with cords and pincers.

Chilo repeated:

"I cannot, my lord."

Fury was boiling in Tigellinus' heart, but still he kept a rein over himself.

"You have seen the Christians die," he said. "Do *you* wish to die as they did?"

The old man raised his white face, and for a moment his lips moved in silence. Then he said:

"I also believe in Christ."

Tigellinus looked at him in amazement.

"You dog!" he shouted. "Without a doubt you have gone mad!"

Leaping upon Chilo, he seized him by the beard, brought him to the ground, and stamped upon him again and again, his lips foaming.

"You shall retract!" he kept shouting. "You shall retract, you shall retract!"

"I cannot," groaned the Greek once more under Tigellinus' heels.

"Then away with the fellow to the torture!"

The Thracians seized the old man, threw him down upon the bench, tied him with cords, and began to crush his lean calves between their pincers. Yet all the while that they were binding him the old man even kissed their hands! Then he closed his eyes, and remained motionless, as though dead.

Yet he was still alive, for when Tigellinus bent over him, and once more put the question, "Will you retract?" Chilo's white lips moved feebly, and there escaped from them, in a scarcely audible whisper, the words:

"I—can—not."

Tigellinus signed for the torture to cease, and fell to pacing the atrium. At length a new idea seemed to strike him. Turning to the Thracians, he said:

"Tear out his tongue!"

XXII

In order to give a representation of the drama "Aureolus," the theatres and amphitheatres of Rome were accustomed so to arrange their stages as to permit of the latter being opened out to form two separate scenes. However, after the spectacle in Cæsar's Gardens the ordinary arrangements were dispensed with, since it was designed that all the spectators should witness the death of the crucified slave who, in the play, is devoured by a bear. Usually the part of the latter was taken by an actor clothed in a bearskin, but on this occasion the representation of it was to be "natural"—an invention of Tigellinus' own. At first Cæsar declared that he would not attend the performance; but, later, acting on his favourite's advice, he changed his mind. That is to say, Tigellinus explained to him that, after what had happened in the Gardens, it was more than ever necessary that he, Cæsar, should show himself in public. At the same time, he assured his master that the crucified slave should not insult him as Crispus had done. Lastly, to attract the people—now surfeited with such things—to the spectacle, promises were made of renewed largesses, and of a banquet in the brilliantly lighted amphitheatre.

At dusk the Circus was full to the roof. Also, the whole body of Augustans, with Tigellinus at their head, were present—though less for the purpose of enjoying the spectacle than for that of evincing their loyalty to Cæsar after the late incident, and of entertaining themselves with Chilo, of whom the whole city was talking. Only a few patricians, moved by feelings of humanity, begged Tigellinus to renounce these pursuits.

"Look where they are leading you," said Barcus Soranus. "Although your aim was to satisfy the populace's desire for vengeance, and to make the nation believe that justice was being meted out to the true culprits, you have attained an absolutely opposite result."

"Yes, that is true," added Antistius Verus. "Every one is now whispering that the Christians were innocent. If *that* is what you call cleverness, then Chilo was right when he said that your brains would not fill the cup of an acorn."

Tigellinus turned upon them.

"It is whispered," he snarled, "that your daughter, Barcus Soranus, and your wife, Antistius Verus, have shielded their Christian slaves from the justice of Cæsar."

"It is not true!" cried Barcus anxiously.

"No, indeed!" added Antistius Verus with equal disquietude in his tones. "The truth is that your divorced wives are jealous of the virtue of mine, and wish to ruin her."

Others also were speaking of Chilo.

"What can have come to him?" said Eprius Marcellus. "He himself betrayed the Christians to Tigellinus. From a beggar he suddenly became rich, and might have ended his days in peace, and had a splendid funeral, and been awarded a monument on his tomb. Truly the man must have gone mad!"

"No, he has not gone mad; he has become a Christian," said Tigellinus.

"Impossible!" cried Vitellius.

"Was I not right?" put in Vestinus. "Did I not tell you that, though you might cut the throats of these Christians, it was ill making war upon their god? Never should such a one be made light of. Look at what has happened! For my own part, though I have not burnt Rome, I would, if Cæsar should permit me, lose not a moment in offering a hecatomb to the Christian deity. And it would be well if all of you were to follow my example."

"Tigellinus laughed when I said that the Christians were arming themselves," said Petronius. "Well, to that I would add that the Christians are winning victory after victory."

"How so, how so?" asked a score of voices.

"In this way. If a man like Chilo cannot resist them, who is to do so? And if you imagine that after each spectacle the number of Christians does not increase, you had better become menders of pans or shavers of chins, in order the better to learn what the people really think, and what is passing in the city."

"By the sacred peplum of Diana, but that is no more than the truth!" cried Vestinus.

Barcus turned to Petronius.

"What is it you actually mean?" he inquired.

"I am merely ending what you have begun. I say that enough blood has been shed."

Tigellinus smiled ironically.

"And *I* say," he remarked, "that a little more—just a little more—must be shed."

"Well," commented Petronius, "if the head which you have on your shoulders is not enough for you, you have another and a wooden one on the top of your staff."

The conversation was interrupted by Cæsar entering the balcony in company with Pythagoras. At once the drama of "Aureolus" began, although but little attention was bestowed upon it, owing to the fact that the thoughts of every one were occupied with the Greek. The mob also had had such a surfeit of tortures and blood that it grew weary, whistled, hurled impertinent cries at the Court, and noisily demanded that the bear scene should be hurried on, since that was all that interested it. Had it not been for this desire to see the condemned man, as well as for the expectation of largesses, the spectacle would not have held the people at all.

At length the expected moment arrived. First of all, some Circus attendants brought in a wooden cross, made low, so that when the bear rose on its hind legs it would be able to reach the victim's breast. Next, two men led in—or, rather, dragged in—Chilo, who, his legs having been broken, was unable to walk. With such expedition was he nailed to the cross that the Augustans were disappointed of being able to observe him at their leisure; and it was only after the cross had been raised to an upright position that every eye obtained a view of him. Yet few of those who beheld the spectacle were able to recognise in this old and naked man the Chilo of recent days. After the tortures inflicted by Tigellinus his face had become perfectly bloodless, except that on his beard, white with the burden of years, a red stain showed where his tongue had been torn out. So transparent was his skin that every bone could be distinguished; yet, full of sorrow though his face was, it was also as quiet and restful as that of a man asleep. Perhaps he was thinking of the thief on the cross whom Christ pardoned. Perhaps in his soul he was saying to the God of mercy: "O Lord, though I have been a venomous wretch, Thou Thyself knowest that I have been starved with hunger, and trampled under foot, and beaten and derided, all my life. Yes, I have been poor, O Lord, and very unhappy, and now they have tortured me, and nailed me to the cross. O God of pity, Thou wilt not reject me in the hour of death?" Peace seemed to have sunk deep, with repentance, into that mortified soul.

No one raised a shout of merriment, for in that old man there was something so peaceful, so frail, so defenceless, so weak that each man found himself wondering why a human being who was already at the point of death need have been further tortured and crucified. Among the Augustans Vestinus kept fidgeting about, and whispering in awestruck accents:

"See how these Christians die!"

The others, however, were looking anxiously for the appearance of the bear, while also secretly wishing that the spectacle would come to an end. At length the bear lurched heavily into the arena—turning from side to side its massive head, and always looking at the ground. It seemed to be wondering what was next to be done. Presently, on catching sight of the cross and the naked form, it approached them, and, raising itself upon its haunches, sniffed at the victim. After a moment, however, it lowered its forepaws again, seated itself at the foot of the cross, and remained there, growling gently, as though its beast's heart were sorry for the human wreck above it.

Upon this the Circus attendants tried to rouse the bear with cries, while the people still sat silent. Presently Chilo raised his head slowly, and let his eyes wander over the spectators. At some point among the topmost benches his gaze halted. As it did so his breast began to heave, and, to the amazement of the audience, his face lightened to a smile, his forehead grew radiant, his eyes turned heavenwards, and from under his heavy eyelids two tears slowly welled, and as slowly coursed over his cheeks.

Then he died.

Suddenly, from on high, near the velarium, a deep voice cried:

"Peace to the martyr!"

Lower down, in the amphitheatre, there hung only a brooding silence.

XXIII

The spectacle in the Gardens of Cæsar had considerably deplenished the prisons; and though people suspected of having yielded to "the Oriental superstition" continued to be arrested and thrown into gaol, the man-hunt, becoming less and less fruitful of results, had much ado to provide the number of victims necessary for the few remaining spectacles. The people, gorged with blood, had begun to evince an increasing weariness of such entertainments, as well as an increasing uneasiness, due to the extraordinary conduct of the condemned. In fact, the apprehensions of the superstitious Vestinus had seized upon every mind, and among the populace the wildest tales were in circulation as to the reprisals which the Christian deity was likely to exact. This uneasiness was added to by the fact that the typhoid fever which had ravaged the gaols had now spread to the city at large; with the result that burials had enormously augmented in frequency, and men kept for ever repeating that fresh propitiatory offerings were necessary to appease the unknown god. In the temples sacrifice was being made to Jupiter and to Libitina; but in spite of all —in spite of the best efforts of Tigellinus and his myrmidons—the rumour that the city had been fired by Cæsar's orders, and that the Christians were innocent, was gaining ground from day to day.

For this very reason Cæsar and Tigellinus were averse to calling a halt in their system of persecution. To calm the people new edicts were issued for further distributions of grain, wine, and olive-oil, and clauses added thereto which should facilitate the re-construction of the ruined mansions of the Quirites. Other regulations prescribed the width to be given to the new streets, and the kind of materials to be employed as a precaution against the occurrence of a second conflagration. Cæsar himself attended the sittings of the Senate, and consulted the Conscript Fathers with regard to the welfare of the people and of the city. Yet no quarter was allowed to the condemned, since, above all things, the "Lord of the World" wished to convince the mob that such an unprecedented system of repression could only be employed against genuine criminals. Not a voice in their favour was raised in the Senate, since no one cared to draw down upon himself the anger of Cæsar; and, moreover, those skilled in political matters declared that, put into practice, the new doctrine would shatter the bases of the Roman dominion.

Vinicius had now abandoned all hope of saving Lygia; and since he had taken leave of life he had concentrated his thoughts upon Christ, and looked to meet Lygia again only in eternity. He divined that she too was preparing herself for death, and that their souls, despite the walls which separated them, were advancing hand in hand: and as he looked forward to the future, he smiled, as though a great happiness were awaiting them both.

The same irrepressible torrent of faith as had detached so many thousands of converts from earth, and borne them beyond the tomb, had seized also upon Ursus. Once upon a time he had been unable to bear the thought of Lygia's death; but, since then, echoes had reached him of what was passing in the amphitheatres and in the Gardens of Cæsar, and death had come to seem to him a blessing far superior to any of which the mortal mind could conceive. Consequently he no longer had the courage to implore Christ to deprive Lygia of that blessing. In his simple soul the fact that he had heard that all people were equal in the sight of God did not debar him from imagining that a daughter of the Lygian kings must necessarily enjoy an exceptionally large share of the divine happiness that was promised, and that, in the eternal glory, a place by the very side of the Lamb would be assigned to his queen. Also, he felt sure that Christ would permit him, Ursus, to continue in her service. His secret desire was that he should suffer death on the cross, even as the Lamb of God had done; but since that seemed to him a happiness not to be looked for, he scarcely dared, for all that he knew that Rome meted out crucifixion only to the worst of criminals, to pray for such an end. Probably, he thought, he would be thrown to the wild beasts; and the expectation of this greatly vexed and disturbed him. From boyhood upwards he had dwelt in forests, and, thanks to his superhuman strength, had not attained man's estate before he had become famous among the Lygian people. The hunting of wild animals had been his favourite occupation, and even to-day the sight of such brutes in the vivaria or in the amphitheatres was able to awake in him a desire to wrestle with and to rend them. Consequently he feared lest, on the day when he should be forced to meet them in the arena, he might find himself assailed by thoughts unworthy of a Christian.

He spent his days in praying, in rendering his fellow prisoners various services, in helping the gaolers, and in comforting his young princess, who often confided to him her regret that during her brief life she had not succeeded in accomplishing as many good works as had been performed by Saint Thabita (whose life had been related to her by the Apostle Peter). The gaolers, who, at first, had been smitten with respect for the giant's frightful strength, ended by loving him for his gentleness. Often, amazed at his peaceful bearing, they asked him the cause of it; whereupon he would speak to them of the life which was to follow death, and with such unassailable conviction that they became lost in astonishment. How could these dens which the sun never visited be visited by such happiness? More than one gaoler told himself that his avocation was the avocation of a slave, and his life a life of misery. More than one of them began to think that only death could put an end to his misfortunes. Unfortunately death filled them with new fears, since they had nothing to hope for beyond it; whereas this giant and this virgin who, like a flower, could blossom even in a dungeon were going to their death as though they were approaching a gate which was to open up to them a realm of infinite bliss.

XXIV

One evening Petronius received a visit from the Senator Scævinus, who launched out into a long conversation on the subject of the terrible times in which they were living. Also, he spoke of Cæsar, and so openly that Petronius, for all his relations of friendship with the Senator, resolved to be on his guard. The other, however, continued his complaints; saying that the world was turning upside down, that men had gone mad, and that things would end in a disaster still more terrible than the burning of Rome. Likewise he declared that the Augustans themselves were discontented; that Fenius Rufus, second in command of the Prætorians, strongly opposed the odious authority of Tigellinus; and that the whole family of Seneca were angry over Nero's conduct with regard to his old tutor and to Lucan. Finally, the Senator made a passing allusion to the irritation in general felt by the people, as also by the Prætorians, who were mostly on the side of Fenius Rufus.

"But why do you tell me all this?" asked Petronius.

"Because of my anxiety for Cæsar," replied Scævinus. "I have a distant relative of the same name as myself, who is a Prætorian: from him I learn what is passing in the Prætorian camp, where, as elsewhere, discontent is on the increase. Caligula too went mad, and the result of it we know—namely, that he fell by the hand of Cassius Chærea. Of course that was a terrible crime to commit, and there is not a man among us who would approve of it; yet certain it is that Chærea ridded the world of a monster."

"In other words," rejoined Petronius, "you reason as follows: 'I do not approve of Chærea, but he was the instrument of fate. May the gods send others like him!' "

Scævinus changed the subject to a eulogy of Piso. He spoke highly of Piso's birth, of his greatness of soul, of his affection for his wife, of his wisdom, of his self-possession, and of his rare gift of attracting and influencing his fellow men.

"Cæsar has no children," added Scævinus, "and therefore all men see in Piso his successor. Incontestably he will not want for assistance in establishing himself on the throne. Fenius Rufus is in his favour, and the Annæus family are devoted to him. As for Plautius Lateranus and Tullius Senecio, they would lay down their lives on his behalf, as also would Natalis, Subrius Flavus, Sulpicius Asper, Afranius Quinetianus and Vestinus."

"The latter would be of little use to him," remarked Petronius. "Vestinus is afraid of his own shadow."

"True, he is nervous on the subject of dreams and phantoms; but he is also a brave man who might well be created a Consul. Nor ought the fact that he secretly disapproves of this persecution of the Christians to be disagreeable to you, seeing that you are interested in having an end put to such atrocities."

"Any interest that I may have in the matter is confined to Vinicius, for whose sake I should be glad to save a certain maiden; but since I am in disgrace at Court, I am not likely to achieve my desire."

"What? Do you not perceive that Cæsar is again trying to make terms with you? He has need of you for his expedition to Achæa."

"Lucan could take my place."

"Ahenobarbus detests him, and has practically decided upon his death. As usual, all that Nero lacks is a pretext. Lucan fully understands that he must hasten."

"By Castor, but that may be true. For myself, I could find a very simple means of regaining the Imperial favour."

"What means?"

"That of repeating to Ahenobarbus all that you have just said."

"But I have said nothing whatever!" cried Scævinus anxiously.

Petronius laid his hand upon the Senator's shoulder.

"No," he remarked. "You have merely expressed an opinion that Cæsar is mad; you have merely named Piso as his probable successor; and you have merely added that 'Lucan fully understands that he must hasten.' Hasten to do what?"

Their eyes met.

"You will not repeat what I have said?" said Scævinus again.

"By the hips of Cypris, do you not *yet* know me? No, I shall *not* repeat your words, for I did not hear them, nor did I wish to do so. Life is too short to take note of everything that happens to cross one's path. All I ask is that you shall at once pay Tigellinus a visit, and talk to him for just such a space of time as you have devoted to myself. What you may talk of during that visit I care not."

"But why should I do this?"

"Why? For the following reason. If, at any moment, Tigellinus should come to me and say, 'Scævinus has been to see you,' it is necessary that I should be able to reply, 'Yes; and he has been to see you too.' "

Scævinus broke his ivory cane in half, crying:

"May the breaking of this cane avert the Furies! Yes, I *will* pay Tigellinus a visit, and also Nerva, who is giving a banquet to-night. Shall you yourself be there? In any case we shall meet in two days' time, at the amphitheatre, on the occasion of the concluding spectacle of Christians. Until then farewell."

"Yes, in two days' time," repeated Petronius to himself after Scævinus' departure. "Well, there is not a moment to be lost. Ahenobarbus has need of my company in Achæa, so perhaps he is going to make the first advance."

Upon that Petronius decided to employ an extreme measure.

At Nerva's banquet Cæsar himself ordered that his late favourite should be his *vis-à-vis* at table; and when they had taken their seats he remarked:

"I feel as though I had never lived in

Rome at all—as though Greece must have been my birthplace."

"At all events it is in Greece that you will reap yet added glory," replied Petronius.

"Indeed, I hope so, and that Apollo will evince no jealousy. Should I garner fresh laurels, I will offer him a hecatomb that will be for ever remembered."

Upon this Scævinus cited Horace's lines:

> "Sic te diva potens Cypri,
> Sic fratres Helenæ, lucida sidera,
> Ventorumque regat Pater." [1]

"The ship is waiting for me at Neapolis," said Nero, "and I must depart—yes, depart to-morrow."

Petronius looked him full in the eyes.

"Should you do so, my lord," he inquired, "may I first offer you a nuptial banquet to which I should like specially to invite you?"

"A *nuptial* banquet? On the occasion of whose nuptials?"

"On the occasion of those of Vinicius and the Lygian King's daughter. True, at this moment the latter is in prison; but in her capacity of a hostage she cannot lawfully be detained a prisoner. Moreover, you yourself have sanctioned the marriage; and inasmuch as your decrees resemble those of Zeus in that they allow of no appeal, I know that you will set her at liberty, in order that I may hand her over to her betrothed."

The cool indifference and assurance of Petronius' words dumfounded Nero, who all his life had experienced a difficulty in answering a direct question.

"Yes, I know," at length he replied with a look of confusion. "It was of her I was thinking, as well as of the giant who strangled Croto."

"Then both are reprieved," said Petronius calmly.

Here Tigellinus came to his master's assistance.

"It is by the will of Cæsar that the maiden is in prison," said he; "and you yourself, Petronius, have just said that the decrees of Cæsar allow of no appeal."

All present knew the history of Vinicius and Lygia, but nothing was said, for all were curious to see the issue of the conflict.

"If she is in prison," said Petronius distinctly, "it is owing to your ignorance of the law of nations, and *against* the will of Cæsar. Fool though you are, Tigellinus, you will scarcely be fool enough to tell me that it was she who fired Rome. Even were you to do so, Cæsar would not believe you."

By this time Nero had recovered his presence of mind, and had begun to blink his short-sighted eyes with a sinister expression.

"Petronius is right," he remarked.

Tigellinus stared at him in amazement.

"Yes, Petronius is right," repeated Nero. "To-morrow the prison gates shall be opened to the pair; and of the nuptial ceremony we will speak again on the following day, in the amphitheatre."

"Again I have lost!" thought Petronius.

So convinced did he feel that Lygia's hour was come that on the morrow he dispatched a trusty freedman to the superintendent of the spoliarium, with orders to treat with that functionary for the purchase of the corpse, in order that, after the execution, the remains might be sent to Vinicius, if the latter should desire to have them.

XXV

It was in Nero's day that Rome first conceived a taste for evening performances

---

[1] "May the potent goddess of Cyprus,
And Helen's brethren, the twinkling stars,
And the Father of the Winds go with you!"

in circuses and amphitheatres; and especially was this taste fostered by the Augustans, in that such performances were usually a prelude to a banquet and other orgies which lasted far into the night. Sated though the populace was with blood, the news that the end of the games was approaching, and that the last of the Christians were to die at an evening spectacle, brought a vast crowd to witness the entertainment. In particular, the Augustans, to a man, attended, since they guessed that Cæsar's intention was to divert himself with the contemplation of Vinicius' agony; and though Tigellinus had said nothing as to the species of punishment reserved for the young tribune's betrothed, the very silence of the Prefect had served to whet the general curiosity. Those who, in former days, had seen Lygia at Plautius' house had marvellous tales to relate concerning her beauty; while some there were whose exclusive pre-occupation it was to wager whether or no she would actually appear in the arena—the cause of their doubt being the fact that the guests at Nerva's banquet had given differing versions of Nero's reply to Petronius. Some persons even alleged that Nero would restore her, or had already restored her, to her lover, and cited as their reason for so supposing the circumstance that she was a hostage, and therefore possessed, under the law of nations, of a right to worship what deity she pleased, and in no case to be punished for so doing.

Indeed, upon the spectators also had this uncertainty, this curiosity, this expectation taken a hold. Cæsar arrived later than had been his wont. With him, in addition to Tigellinus and Vatinius, came Cassius—a centurion of prodigious stature and enormous strength. Also, the Prætorians were present in greater numbers than usual, and were commanded, not by a centurion, but by the tribune Subrius Flavus, who was known to all for his blind attachment to the Imperial person. Clearly Cæsar wished, should any untoward incident arise, to be safeguarded against any desperate attempt on the part of Vinicius. The public curiosity rose to fever pitch, and every eye kept turning greedily to the seat occupied by the unfortunate tribune. His face was deadly pale, and on his forehead there were standing great drops of sweat.

Petronius, still uncertain as to what was about to happen, had done no more than ask his nephew if he was ready for the ordeal, and if he intended to be present at the spectacle. To both questions Vinicius had returned an answer in the affirmative, but a shudder had shaken him from head to foot, since he suspected that Petronius had reason for his inquiries. For a long time past the young man had been half-alive. Already he had entered the portals of death, as well as accepted the fact that Lygia was about to do the same, since for both the act of death would mean at once deliverance and re-union. This alone had enabled him to contemplate the fatal moment with calmness. But now the blow had fallen—now, under his very eyes, there was to take place the martyrdom of the being who was dearer to him than life itself! Once more the despair which he had conquered began to rage in his soul; once more the desire to rescue Lygia at all costs took possession of him. Since dawn he had been trying to obtain admittance to the arena dungeons, in order to ascertain if she were really there; but Prætorians had been on guard at every entrance, and they had been armed with such strict orders that even those of their number who knew him had not dared to yield either to his prayers or to his gold. Indeed, he felt as though the uncertainty would kill him even before he came to behold the spectacle itself. Yet still at the bottom of his heart there lurked a last remnant of hope. Perhaps Lygia was *not* among the number of the condemned? Perhaps all his terrors were in vain? At intervals he would grapple this idea to his soul with his whole imagination. Yet when, on being repulsed from the gate of the cuniculum, he returned to his seat in the amphitheatre, and realised from the curious glances directed at him from every quarter that even the most frightful suppositions were admissible—well, then there was nothing left for him to do but to implore Christ with passionate, even menacing, vehemence. "Thou, and only Thou, canst save her!" he kept repeating as he twisted his hands convulsively. "Thou, and only Thou, hast the power!" Never had he foreseen how unspeakably terrible the moment would be. He felt that, should he be forced to witness Lygia's agony, his love for Christ would turn to hatred, and his faith to despair. Yet still he dreaded to offend the Christ whom he was imploring; wherefore he did not pray that Lygia might be spared, but only that she might die before she had been dragged into the arena. From the fathomless depths of his pain there rose to Heaven, again and yet again, the cry: "Do not refuse me that! Nothing do I ask but that! O Christ, grant it me, and I will love Thee even a thousand times more than I have hitherto done!" In short, his thoughts were all at sea, and he had quite lost his desire for blood and vengeance. True, at times he felt a yearning to rush upon Cæsar, and to strangle him where he sat; but the next moment he would remember that that yearning was contrary to Christ's wishes and commandments. Next, a few rays of hope would shoot through his brain—he would begin to believe that all these things which were so terrifying his soul would be averted by an omnipotent and merciful hand; but almost at once that optimistic feeling would give place to one of boundless desolation, as though He who by a word could have overthrown the building and rescued Lygia had abandoned her, even though she adored Him with the whole strength of her pure spirit. He kept thinking of the fact that she was there, in that dark cuniculum—a defenceless prey to the bestiality of the gaolers, the while, sad and weak and at her last gasp, she awaited death in that foul arena, without even knowing what punishment had been invented for her. At length, like a man who, rolling towards the edge of a precipice, clutches at anything which may break his fall, Vinicius fastened upon the idea that by faith he still could save her. Faith was all that remained to him: and had not Peter said that faith could shake the world to its foundations?

Absorbed in this hope, he put away all doubt from his mind, and threw his whole being into the words, "I have faith." Surely a miracle would come of them.

Yet, even as excessive tension bursts a cord, so the efforts put forth by Vinicius broke his spirit. A deathlike pallor overspread his countenance; gradually a cold torpor crept through his body. Under the belief that his prayer had been granted, he imagined himself to be at the point of death. Also, it seemed to him that Lygia must be already dead, and that Christ was taking them to Himself. Suddenly the arena, the gleam of the countless white togas, the light of thousands upon thousands of lanterns and torches alike vanished from before his eyes.

Yet the fainting fit was of short duration, for soon the impatient shouts of the crowd recalled him to himself.

"You are ill," whispered Petronius in his ear. "Have yourself taken home." And, without paying further attention to what Cæsar was saying, he rose to support the young tribune towards the entrance. Pity was surging in his heart, and he felt infuriated to see Nero, with his emerald at his eye, calmly watching Vinicius' agony—doubtless in order, at some future date, to describe it in mock-pathetic stanzas, and so to win applause from the mob!

Vinicius shook his head. He might die in that amphitheatre, but he would never leave it.

Just at that moment the Prefect threw down upon the sand a red scarf; and as he did so the gate facing the Imperial balcony grated upon its hinges, and from the dark opening behind it there emerged into the brilliantly lighted arena the figure of the Lygian, Ursus. At first he blinked his eyelids, as though dazzled; then he advanced to the centre of the circle, and looked around him to discern what it was he had to meet. The Augustans and most of the populace knew that this was the man who had strangled Croto; and from tier to tier the murmurs rose. Gladiators of exceptional physique were not lacking in Rome, but never had the eyes of the citizens seen a giant like this. Senators, Vestals, Cæsar, Augustans, and the mob alike gazed with the admiration of connoisseurs at those formidable thighs, at that breast which resembled a pair of shields draw together, and at those Herculean arms.

He remained perfectly motionless in the centre of the arena—looking, as he stood there in his nudity, like a colossus of granite which had in its barbaric countenance a tinge of sadness mingled with vigilance. At length, perceiving the arena to be empty, he turned his blue, childlike eyes in turn upon the spectators, upon Cæsar, and upon the gratings of the cuniculi whence he expected executioners to issue.

At the moment of entering the arena his heart had for a second quivered with the hope that he was about to die upon the cross; but, on perceiving neither cross nor socket-hole, he conceived that he had been adjudged unworthy of such a favour, and was to meet his end in some other fashion—probably under the fangs of wild beasts. He was unarmed, and had resolved to die patiently, even as the Lamb would have had him do; but since he wished to address one more prayer to the Redeemer, he knelt down, joined his hands together, and raised his eyes to the stars which were glittering through the aperture in the velarium.

This posture displeased the mob, which had grown tired of seeing human beings die like sheep. If the giant refused to defend himself the spectacle would prove a fiasco. Here and there a whistle shrilled forth, while other voices called loudly for the mastigophori and their scourges; but gradually silence fell, since no one knew what was able to face the giant, nor whether at the decisive moment he would decline to fight.

The mob had not long to wait. Suddenly there resounded a deafening clatter of iron bars, and from out of the grating opposite to the Imperial balcony there rushed, amid the yells of the beast-keepers, one of the monstrous aurochs of Germany, with, bound upon its head, a naked woman.

"Lygia! Lygia!" shouted Vinicius as, seizing his hair in both hands, he writhed like a man who feels the point of a spear penetrating his entrails. Again and again he gasped in a hoarse, inhuman voice.

"I have faith! I have faith! O Christ, work a miracle!"

Indeed, he did not feel Petronius throw a toga over his head as he uttered the words. He only felt that either death or agony had darkened all before his eyes. He could look at nothing, he could see nothing when he did so. The sensation of this wrapped him in a sort of horrible darkness, with no idea left to him but to keep his lips deliriously repeating:

"I have faith! I have faith! I have faith!"

The amphitheatre had suddenly become absolutely still. Only the Augustans had risen *en masse* in their places. In the arena there was passing an unprecedented scene. At the sight of his princess bound upon the horns of the savage bull, the

Lygian, hitherto humble and prepared for death, had sprung forward like a man scorched with living fire, and, with back bent, was creeping, zigzag fashion, towards the maddened beast.

Then from every throat there issued a short, a tremulous cry of amazement, followed by a profound silence. For with a single bound the Lygian had reached the beast and gripped its horns!

"Look!" cried Petronius as he snatched away the toga from Vinicius' head. The other rose, lifted a face of a deadly whiteness, and stared with wild, fixed eyes at the arena. Not a man present could breathe. A fly might have been heard winging its way through the arena. Never since Rome had been Rome had such a sight been seen.

The man was holding the beast by the horns. Up to the ankles his feet were planted in the sand; his back was bent like the arch of a drawn bow; his head had disappeared between his shoulders; the muscles of his arms had emerged in such relief that the skin seemed as though it must crack under the strain of their enlargement. Yet he had stopped the bull full in its career, and now was fixed with it in such absolute immobility that the spectators saw before them, as it were, a statuesque representation of the feats of Theseus or of Hercules. Nevertheless this apparent immobility was the result of the unseen tension of two furious forces. The aurochs also had its feet planted in the sand, while the dark, shaggy bulk of its body had curled together like a gigantic ball. Which of the two adversaries would first become exhausted, which of the two adversaries would first fall—that, for the entranced spectators of the struggle, meant, at that moment, more than their own fortunes, more than the fate of Rome, more than the worldwide dominion of the Roman Empire. This Lygian had suddenly become a demi-god. Cæsar himself had risen to his feet to view the spectacle, which Tigellinus, knowing the man's strength, had purposely organised with the ironical words, "Let the conqueror of Croto overthrow the bull that *we* will loose against him!"

And now every one was contemplating with stupefaction the picture presented—incapable of believing that it was real. Some people had raised their arms, and were standing fixed in that posture; others had their foreheads running with sweat, as though it was they themselves who were struggling with the bull. In all that vast circle there was to be heard only the singing sound of the lantern-flames and the cracking of brackets under their weight of torches. Speech had died on every lip, and hearts were beating as though they would burst the breasts which contained them. For every spectator the struggle seemed to be lasting for centuries.

And all this while the man and the beast remained fixed in their frightful effort—remained chained, as it were, to the ground.

Suddenly a deep, groaning bellow mounted from the arena. Every throat let forth a shout. Then again there was absolute silence. Men believed themselves to be dreaming. *For under the iron arms of the barbarian the monstrous head of the aurochs was slowly turning round!*

The Lygian's face, neck, and arms had become purple, and the arch of his back had bent yet more. It was clear that he was rallying the remainder of his superhuman strength, and that soon the latter would be exhausted.

Always growing more and more stifled and hoarse and painful, the aurochs' bellowing mingled with the strident breathing of the Lygian. Gradually the animal's head was turning more and more to one side; until suddenly there escaped from its gullet a huge slobbering tongue. An instant later the ears of the spectators who were nearest to the arena caught the dull sound of bones breaking. Then, with its withers twisted under it, the beast collapsed in a heap—dead!

In a twinkling the giant had released the horns, and taken the girl into his arms. Then he fell to panting vehemently. His face was pale, his hair was plastered with sweat, and his shoulders and arms were dripping. For a moment or two he stood motionless, as though dazed; then he raised his eyes, and looked at the spectators.

The audience had gone mad. The walls of the immense building were quivering with the clamour of tens of thousands of throats. The spectators on the upper tiers had left their places, flowed downwards towards the arena, and crammed themselves into the passage-ways, the better to view the Hercules. From every quarter came voices demanding his pardon—passionate, insistent voices which soon combined into an immense outcry. To a mob which, above all things, admired physical strength the giant had become an idol—he had become the first personage in Rome.

For his own part, he understood that the people were demanding for him his life and liberty; but it was not of those boons that he was thinking. For a moment or two he cast his eyes around him; then he approached the Imperial balcony—balancing the form of the young girl in his outstretched arms as he raised suppliant eyes which said: "It is *her* pardon that I ask for; it is *she* who must be saved; it is for *her* that I have done this."

At once the spectators divined his desire. At the sight of the unconscious maiden, who, beside the huge body of the Lygian, looked like a tiny child, emotion seized upon knights, Senators, and the mob alike. Her frail figure, her unconscious condition, the frightful danger from which the giant had just rescued her, and, finally, her beauty and the devotion of the Lygian all combined to touch the popular heart. Some even thought that it was a father demanding pardon for his daughter, and pity flamed up in them the more. The people had had enough of blood, of death, of torture. With voices strangled with sobs they demanded that Lygia and Ursus should be forgiven.

Meanwhile Ursus continued to parade the arena with the young girl balanced in his arms, and to implore both with eyes and gesture that Lygia's life should be preserved to her. Suddenly Vinicius leapt from his seat, crossed the partition-wall of the tier, and rushing up to Lygia, covered with his toga the naked body of his betrothed. Then he tore open his tunic at the breast, and, exposing to view the scars which he had received in Armenia, extended his arms towards the people.

Upon that the popular frenzy surpassed anything that the amphitheatre had ever witnessed. The entire populace fell to stamping its feet and shouting. Voices which had hitherto been suppliant now became menacing, and thousands of spectators turned towards Cæsar, and shook their fists at him, with the light of fury gleaming in their eyes.

Nero prevaricated; for although he felt no real hatred of Vinicius, and cared not greatly whether Lygia lived or died, he would have preferred to see the young girl disembowelled by the bull's horns, or torn in pieces by the fangs of wild beasts. His cruelty, added to his depraved imagination, found a voluptuous pleasure in such spectacles. Yet here was the mob seeking to deprive him of that pleasure! Fury showed itself on his fat-disfigured features, since, apart from anything else, his conceit forbade him to submit to the popular will, even though his native cowardice urged him also not to oppose it.

So he set himself to scan those around him, in the hope that at least among the Augustans he would see a thumb pointing downwards, in token of death. But Petronius extended his hand with the thumb upwards, and, with a slight nod of defiance, looked Cæsar straight in the eyes, while the superstitious Vestinus, who, though prone to emotion, was much afraid of phantoms, but not at all of men, also gave the sign of pardon. Thereafter the same thing was done by many others; on seeing which, Cæsar removed the emerald from his eye with an expression of anger and contempt. Tigellinus, however, who wished at all costs to win a victory over Petronius, leant over his master and whispered:

"Do not yield, my lord. We have behind us the Prætorians."

Nero turned towards the spot where, at the head of his guard, there was standing the ferocious Subrius Flavus—a man who hitherto had been devoted to him, body and soul. And as Nero looked he saw an unwonted sight. The forbidding face of the old tribune was bathed in tears, and with his raised hand he was making the sign of the cross!

Meanwhile rage had taken complete possession of the multitude. Under the incessant stamping of feet a cloud of dust had wrapped the amphitheatre in an obscurity whence came shouts of "Ahenobarbus!" and imprecations upon "the matricide and the incendiary." Nero took alarm at this. In the Circus the people were absolute masters. True, his predecessors, more especially Caligula, had more than once taken it upon themselves to oppose the popular will, and so to risk certain disorder and probable rioting; but Nero was less favourably situated. In the first place, as a comedian and a vocalist, he had need of the favour of the people; in the second place, he wished, in his struggle with the Senate and the patricians, to have the people on his side; and, finally, since the burning of Rome he had been forced to conciliate the mob by every means in his power, and to divert its anger in the direction of the Christians. Consequently he knew that it would be dangerous to show further resistance, since sedition born in the Circus might soon involve the whole city, and produce incalculable consequences.

So, after glancing at Subrius Flavus, at the centurion Scævinus, and at the soldiers in general, and seeing everywhere only frowns, agitated features, and angry looks at himself, he gave the sign of pardon.

From top to bottom of the amphitheatre there arose a storm of applause. The people assured the lives of the condemned, and from that moment onwards the latter were under the people's protection, and no one, not even Cæsar, might dare to persecute them further.

XXVI

Four Bithynian slaves carried Lygia carefully towards Petronius' villa. Vinicius and Ursus, as they walked beside the litter, spoke not a word, for, after the emotions of the day, neither of them had the strength left to converse. Vinicius was still in a half-dazed condition. He kept telling himself that Lygia was safe, that neither prison nor death in the arena any longer menaced her, that their misfortunes had come to an end, and that he was taking her home, never again to be separated from her side. It all seemed to him the dawn of a new life rather than reality. From time to time he would lean over the open litter, in order to gaze, by the light of the moon, at the dear face which seemed asleep, and to murmur once more to himself:

"It is she! Christ has saved her!"

He remembered now that in the spoliarium whither he and Ursus had carried Lygia they had found a physician, who had assured them that she was still alive, and that she would live; and at the thought his breast swelled with such impetuous joy that he began to turn faint, and, unable to walk unsupported, to feel obliged to lean upon Ursus' arm. As for Ursus himself, he kept glancing at the star-bespangled heavens, and sending up prayers.

Thus they made their way swiftly among newly-built houses the whiteness of which gleamed the whiter under the rays of the moon. The city was deserted. Only here and there were a few groups of ivy-garlanded persons singing and dancing before their porticoes, and celebrating, to the sound of the flute, the holiday period which was to end with the games. Just before Petronius' villa was reached Ursus ceased praying, and said in a low voice, as though he feared to awake Lygia:

"My lord, it was the Redeemer who saved her from death. When I caught sight of her on the horns of the aurochs a voice in me cried, 'Defend her!' And beyond a doubt that voice was the voice of the Lamb. Prison had impaired my strength, but for the moment He restored it to me. He too it was who inspired the bloodthirsty mob with the idea of interceding for us. May His will be done!"

"Yes, glorified be the name of the Saviour!" replied Vinicius.

More he could not say, for great sobs were choking his bosom. He felt an irresistible yearning to throw himself upon the ground, and, prone there before the Saviour, to thank Him for the miracle which His mercy had accomplished.

Soon, however, they reached the villa, and were met by the whole body of servants, who had been warned beforehand by a slave. Already at Antium the majority of Petronius' domestic staff had been converted to Christianity by Paul of Tarsus; wherefore Vinicius' sad story was well known to them, and they were overjoyed to see the victims who had been rescued from Nero's cruelty. That joy increased the more when Theocles the physician gave it as his opinion that Lygia had suffered no serious injury—that, though prison life had weakened her strength, the latter would soon return.

She recovered consciousness the same night, and, on waking in a splendid cubiculum that was lighted with Corinthian lamps and perfumed with verbena, could not at first understand where she was, nor what had happened, since her memory carried her only up to the moment when the executioners had bound her to the horns of the shackled aurochs. Indeed, on perceiving Vinicius' face bending over her in the tender lamp-light, she imagined that she was no longer in this world below—the disordered state of her ideas leading her to accept it as a natural circumstance that he and she had halted somewhere on their way to Heaven, in order that she might recover a little from her weakness and her fatigue. No longer conscious of any pain, she smiled at Vinicius, and tried to ask him a question; but her lips succeeded only in uttering an almost inarticulate murmur, in which he could distinguish nothing but his name.

Kneeling down beside her, he laid a hand upon her beloved forehead, and said:

"Christ has saved you, and has restored you to me."

Lygia's lips moved again in an indistinct murmur, her eyelids closed, and she sank back into the profound slumber which Theocles had expected as the probable and most favourable sign. Vinicius remained beside her, absorbed in prayer, with his whole soul flooded with fathomless adoration. Then he too lost consciousness. Several times Theocles entered the cubiculum; several times, also, Eunice raised the curtain before the door, and cautiously inserted therein her golden head. At length the cranes which were kept in the garden began to call aloud as daybreak drew near. Still Vinicius remained prostrate at the feet of Christ—seeing nothing, hearing nothing, but with his whole heart purged in a flame of ecstasy. For already, though on earth, he had ascended to Heaven!

THE LIGHTHOUSE-KEEPER

By HENRYK SIENKIEWICZ

Translated by Monica M. Gardner

I

It so happened that the lighthouse-keeper in Aspinwall, not far from Panama, disappeared without leaving a trace. As this occurred during a storm it was supposed that the unfortunate man must have gone too near the edge of the island rock on which the lighthouse stood, and been washed away by a wave. This was the more probable, because his boat was not found the next day in its rocky niche. The post of lighthouse-keeper therefore fell vacant; but it had to be filled as soon as possible, because the lighthouse is of no small importance, both for the local shipping and for the vessels going from New York to Panama. The Mosquito Gulf abounds in sandbanks and reefs, through which navigation is difficult even in the day, but at night, especially in the fogs that often come up on those waters, heated through with the tropical sun, almost impossible. At such times the light of the lantern is the only guide for the numerous ships. The task of finding a new lighthouse-keeper devolved on the Consul of the United States who lived in Panama, and it was a task of no small difficulty; first, because it was absolutely necessary to find a successor to the post within twelve hours; secondly, because this successor had to be trustworthy beyond the average, and it was therefore impossible to accept just the first who came; and lastly, because there was generally a dearth of candidates for the post. Life in a lighthouse tower is an extraordinarily hard one, and does not at all appeal to the natives of the south, lazy lovers of a free vagrant existence. The lighthouse-keeper is almost a prisoner. With the exception of Sundays he cannot stir from his island rock. A boat from Aspinwall brings him a stock of provisions and fresh water once a day; the men who bring these depart immediately; and in the whole of the little island that measures an acre, there is not one other human being. The lighthouse-keeper lives in the lighthouse, and keeps it in order. In the day he gives signals by hanging out different coloured flags, according to the indications of the barometer, and in the evening he lights the lantern. That would be no great labour, if it were not that to get from the bottom to the lantern on the top of the tower he has to mount more than four hundred winding and exceedingly steep steps; yet the lighthouse-keeper must sometimes make that journey several times a day. To sum up, it is a claustral life, and even more than claustral, for it is a hermit's life. It is, therefore, not surprising that Mr. Isaac Folcombridge was in great perplexity where to find a permanent successor to the late lighthouse-keeper; and his joy may be imagined when that successor most unexpectedly appeared that very same day. He was a man already old, seventy years or more, but hale, erect, with the movements and bearing of a soldier. His hair was quite white; his complexion was as sunburnt as a creole's, but judging from his blue eyes he belonged to no southern race. His face had an oppressed and sad, but honest, expression. Folcombridge took a fancy to him at the first glance. There was nothing left to do but to examine him, which resulted in the following conversation:

"Where do you come from?"

"I am a Pole."

"What have you been doing up till now?"

"I've led a roving life."

"A lighthouse-keeper must be fond of staying in one place."

"I need rest."

"Have you ever been in any public service? Have you got any testimonials of good official service?"

The old man drew out from his breast-pocket a discoloured silk rag, resembling a strip of an old flag, unrolled it, and said:

"Here are my testimonials. I won this cross in '30. This second one is Spanish from the Carlist war, the third the French Legion's; the fourth I got in Hungary. After that I fought in the States against the South, but there they don't give crosses. But here's a paper."

Folcombridge took the paper and began reading.

"H'm! Skawiński? That's your name? H'm! . . . Two flags captured by your own hand in a bayonet charge. You've been a plucky soldier."

"I can be a good lighthouse-keeper too."

"You'll have to go up the tower over there several times a day. Are your legs strong?"

"I've crossed the *plains* on foot."

(They call the immense prairies between New York and California *plains.*)

"All right! Do you know anything about life at sea?"

"I served three years on a whaler."

"You've tried different occupations?"

"It's because I never could find peace anywhere."

"Why?"

The old man shrugged his shoulders.

"Fate."

"You look to me too old for a lighthouse-keeper."

"Sir!" the candidate burst out in agitated tones. "I am very tired and battered about. You see I've gone through a lot. This post is one of those I've most longed to get. I'm old. I need rest. I need to be able to say to myself: You are going to settle down here now, you're in port. Oh, sir! this depends only on you. A post like this mayn't fall vacant again. It was lucky that I was in Panama. . . . I implore you. . . . So help me God, I'm like a ship which, if it doesn't get into port, will founder. . . . If you want to make an old man happy . . . I swear that I'm an honest man, but . . . I've had enough of all that wandering."

The old man's eyes were so beseeching that Folcombridge, who was kind and simple of heart, felt touched.

"Well!" he said. "I accept you. You are the lighthouse-keeper."

The old man's face lit up with unspeakable joy.

"Thank you."

"Can you go to the tower to-day?"

"Yes, of course."

"Well, then, good-bye. Just one word: for the slightest negligence in your duty you'll be dismissed."

"All right."

That same evening, when the sun had sunk to the other side of the isthmus and after a gorgeous day night without twilight had set in, the new lighthouse-keeper was evidently at his post, for the lantern cast as usual its sheaves of brilliant light over the water. The night was absolutely calm, still, a true tropical night, saturated with a bright mist that formed a great rainbow-coloured ring with faint melting edges round the moon. Only the sea was restless, because the tide was coming in. Skawiński, looking from below like a little black dot, stood on the balcony close to the mighty lantern. He tried to collect his thoughts and to take in his new position. But his mind was too oppressed to be able to work properly. He felt somewhat as a hunted beast feels when it at last finds shelter in an inaccessible rock or cave. The time for rest had come for him at last. A feeling of security filled his soul with speechless delight. Yes, from this rock he could afford to laugh at his old wanderings, his old misfortunes, and failures. He was, in fact, like a ship whose masts had been smashed by the tempest, its ropes, its sails rent, which the storm had sent hurtling from the clouds to the bottom of the sea, on which the waves had beaten, the foam spat—and yet which had come into port. Memories of that storm now passed swiftly through his mind in contrast with the tranquil future which was now to begin. He had told Folcombridge a part of his strange vicissitudes, but he had not mentioned thousands of other adventures. His misfortune had been that as often as he pitched his tent and lit the fire on his hearth to settle down for good, the wind tore away the tent pegs, scattered the ashes of his fire, and brought himself to ruin. Gazing now from the balcony of the tower on the shining waves he recalled all that he had passed through. He had fought in the four quarters of the globe—and during his wanderings had tried nearly every calling. Hardworking and honest, he had often made a little money, and in spite of all his precautions and the greatest prudence had always lost it. He had been a gold-digger in Australia, searched for diamonds in Africa, had been a Government hunter in the East Indies. When at one time he had started a farm in California a drought ruined him. He had tried trading with the savage races inhabiting the interior of Brazil; his raft capsized on the Amazon, and he himself, unarmed and nearly naked, had taken refuge in the forests for several weeks, eating wild fruit, each moment exposed to death from the jaws of beasts of prey. He had opened a blacksmith's forge in Helena, in Arkansas, and it was burnt to the ground in a great fire that raged through all the town. Next, he fell into the hands of Indians in the Rocky Mountains, and it was only by a miracle that Canadian hunters rescued him. He served as a sailor on a vessel plying between Bahia and Bordeaux, afterwards as a harpooner on a whaler; both ships foundered. He had a cigar factory in Havana, and was robbed by his partner while he was lying sick of dysentery. Finally, he went to Aspinwall; and here he had surely come to the end of his misfortunes. For what more could overtake him on this island rock? Neither water nor fire nor man. As a matter of fact, Skawiński had experienced little harm from mankind. He had more often met good men than bad.

Yet it seemed as though all four elements persecuted him. Those who knew him said that luck was against him, and so explained it. He himself at last became a little bit of a monomaniac upon the subject. He believed that some powerful and avenging hand was pursuing him everywhere, by land and water. He disliked speaking about it; but sometimes, when asked whose hand it was, he would point mysteriously to the Polar Star, and say that it came from there. As a matter of fact his misadventures were so persistent that it was curious, and could easily have made any one get that idea into his head, especially the man who experienced them. Yet he had the patience of an Indian, and the great and quiet resisting power that springs from rectitude of soul. During his service in Hungary he received several bayonet thrusts because he refused to seize the strap shown him as his means of safety and cry: "I surrender!" Similarly he never gave in under his troubles. He crawled upwards as laboriously as an ant. Thrust down a hundred times, for the hundred and first time he would calmly begin his journey over again. In his way he was something quite extraordinary. That old soldier, scorched in God knows what fires, steeled in adversity, beaten and moulded, had the heart of a child. When there was an epidemic in Cuba he caught it because he gave away all his quinine, of which he had a large stock, without keeping so much as a grain for himself.

There was also this curious thing about him, that after so many disillusions he was always full of confidence, and never lost hope that all would still be well. In the winter he was always filled with fresh life, and foresaw great events. He waited for them impatiently, and for many a year lived on the thought of them. But one after the other the winters passed away, and all that Skawiński won by waiting was that his hair turned white. Finally, he grew old. He began to lose his energy. His patience began ever more to resemble resignation. His old tranquillity changed into a tendency to sensibility, and that hardened soldier was beginning to degenerate into a fretful child, liable to melt into tears at the slightest pretext. Besides which, from time to time, he was gripped by a terrible homesickness, which the most trifling circumstance would rouse: the sight of swallows, of grey birds resembling sparrows, snow on the mountains, or some tune like one he had once heard. At last he was overpowered by one thought only: the thought of rest. It took complete possession of the old man, and absorbed all other desires and hopes. The eternal wanderer could now picture in his dreams nothing more desirable, nothing more precious than some quiet corner where he might rest and tranquilly await the end. Perhaps it was just because some curious freak of fate had cast him forth by land and sea, with scarcely breathing space, that he now imagined the greatest happiness a man could have would simply be not to wander. That modest happiness was now indeed his by rights, but by now he was so used to disappointment that he thought of it as men are wont to dream of something unattainable. He dared not expect it. But now, suddenly, in the course of twelve hours, he had obtained a post that seemed chosen out of all others in the world for him. Hence, it was not surprising that after he had lit his lantern in the evening he was as though stunned; that he asked himself if this were true, and he dared not answer, Yes. Yet at the same time reality spoke to him with invincible proofs; therefore one hour followed after another, and he was still on the balcony. He gazed; he drank his fill; he was convinced. He might have been seeing the sea for the first time in his life. The lens of the lantern flung into the darkness a mighty cone of light, beyond which the old man's eyes were lost in a distance, that was pitch black, mysterious, and terrible. Yet that distance seemed to be running towards the light. Long, jagged waves rolled out from the darkness and, roaring, reached as far as the foot of the little island, and then their foaming manes were visible, glittering, rose coloured, in the light of the lantern. The tide was fast coming in and pouring over the sandbanks. The mysterious language of the ocean was approaching from the deep, ever stronger, ever louder; at times like the thunder of cannon, then as the soughing of mighty forests, again like a far-off confused clamour of human voices. At moments, a hush. Then a few great sighs beat on the old man's ear, then, sobbing—and again, sullen explosions. At last the wind blew the mist asunder, but drove before it the black, ragged clouds which were veiling the moon. It began to blow rougher from the west. The billows leapt with fury on the lighthouse rock, licking the masonry supports with foam. A storm growled in the distance. On the dark heaving waste a few little green lamps flashed, hanging on the masts of ships. These little green dots now rose, now sank, now wavered to the right, now to the left. Skawiński went down into his room. The storm had begun to howl. Out there men on those ships were battling with the night, with the dark, with the waves; but inside the room it was quiet and still. Even the echoes of the storm but faintly penetrated the thick walls, and there was only the rhythmic tick-tack of the clock that seemed to rock the tired old man to sleep.

II

Hours, days, and weeks began to slip away. Sailors say that sometimes when the sea is very rough something calls them by their name out of the night and darkness. If the infinite ocean can thus call, then it may be that when a man grows old another infinitude, darker still, and more mysterious, calls him too; and the more wearied he is with life the sweeter to him is that call. But if he would hear it there must be silence. Besides which, old age is fain to withdraw into solitude as though in anticipation of the grave. The lighthouse was a sort of grave to Skawiński. There is nothing more monotonous than that life in the tower. If young men consent to undertake it, after a given time they resign the post. Therefore a lighthouse-keeper is usually a man no longer young, gloomy by nature, and sufficient to himself. When he chances to leave his lighthouse and goes among men, he walks in their midst like a man woken out of a deep sleep. In the tower all those small trifles which ordinary life trains us to consider important are lacking. Everything with which the lighthouse-keeper comes into contact is huge, without concrete or definite form. The sky is one element, water the other; and between those immensities one solitary human soul. It is a life in which a man's thoughts are one continual dream, and nothing rouses the lighthouse-keeper from this dream, not even his tasks. One day is as like another day as two beads on a rosary, and the changes in the weather are, in fact, the only variety. Yet Skawiński was happier than he had ever been in his life before. He rose at daybreak, breakfasted, cleaned the lens of the lantern, and then sitting in the balcony gazed far out to sea; and his eyes could never have their fill of the pictures that he saw before him. On the immense background of turquoise blue there was usually a flock of swelling sails, shining so brilliantly in the rays of the sun that he had to close his eyes against the excessive glare. Sometimes the ships, taking advantage of the eastern equatorial winds, went by in a long line one behind the other like a string of gulls or albatrosses. The red buoys pointing out the road rocked on the waves with a light, gentle motion. Every day at midday a huge greyish pennon of smoke appeared among the sails. It was the steamer from New York bringing passengers and cargo to Aspinwall, drawing behind it a long frothing trail of foam. From the other side of the balcony Skawiński saw as if on the palm of his hand Aspinwall and its busy harbour, inside the latter a forest of masts, ships, and boats, and a little farther off the white houses and spires of the town. From the height of the tower the little houses looked like gulls' nests, the boats like black beetles, and the human beings moving about on the white stone breakwater like minute specks. In the morning the light easterly breeze carried with it the confused clamour of human life, dominated by the whistles of steamboats. Midday brought the hour of the siesta. The activity in the harbour stopped. The gulls hid themselves in the crevices of the rocks, the waves died down and seemed asleep; and then the moment of silence, unbroken by a single sound, came down on land and sea and lighthouse. The yellow sands, from which the waves had rolled back, glistened like spots of gold on the waste of water; the pillar of the tower was cut out sharply against the blue sky. Streams of sunlight flowed from the sky on the water, on the sands, and on the rocks. At such times a sort of sweet faintness swept over the old man. He felt that this rest which he was enjoying was an exquisite thing, and when he told himself that it would last, he wanted nothing more. Skawiński was intoxicated with his own good fortune, but because a man soon grows used to his better lot in life he gradually acquired faith and confidence; for he reflected that if men build homes for invalids, then why should not God give shelter to His invalids when the end is nearly here? Time passed on and confirmed him in this conviction. The old man lived in the company of the tower, the lantern, the rock, the sandbanks, and solitude. He also made friends with the gulls who laid their eggs in the rocky clefts, and in the evening held their parliaments on the roof of the lighthouse. Skawiński usually threw them the remains of his food; but they soon grew so used to him that when he did this he was surrounded by a perfect storm of white wings; the old man went about among the birds like a shepherd among his sheep. At low tide he went out on the low-lying sandbanks on which he gathered appetising shellfish and beautiful pearl-mussel shells which the retreating waves had washed up on the sand. At night, by the light of the moon and the lantern, he went after fish with which the crevices of the rocks swarmed. He ended by falling in love with his rock and his treeless island, covered with sturdy little plants exuding a sticky resin, the only thing that grew there. The distant views made up to him for the barrenness of the island. In the afternoon, when the atmosphere became very clear, the whole of the isthmus could be seen, covered as far as the Pacific with the most luxuriant vegetation. It seemed at such times to Skawiński as though he were looking at one gigantic garden. Clusters of coco-nut trees and mighty bananas were grouped like superb, tufted bouquets close behind the houses of Aspinwall. Farther away, between Aspinwall and Panama, an immense forest was to be seen, above which a reddish vapour rising from its exhalations always hung after sunrise and towards nightfall; a true tropical forest, soaked in its lower depths with stagnant water, entangled with lianas, murmuring like one wave of gigantic orchids, palms, milk-trees, iron-trees, and gum-trees.

Through his official telescope the old man could see not only the trees, not only the widespreading leaves of the bananas, but even troops of monkeys, of great marabouts, and flocks of parrots flying like a rainbow cloud over the forest. Skawiński knew that sort of forest at close quarters, because after he had been wrecked on the Amazon he had wandered for weeks under the same sort of trees and among the same sort of jungles. He had seen how under their lovely smiling surface danger and death lay hidden. In the nights he had spent within them he had heard close at hand the menacing voices of monkeys and the roar of jaguars; he had seen huge snakes swaying like lianas on trees; he knew those sluggish forest ponds overflowing with crampfish and swarming with crocodiles. He knew what dread a man lives under in those unfathomable jungles where a single leaf is ten times his size, which swarm with bloodthirsty mosquitoes, tree leeches, and gigantic poisonous spiders. He knew all this for himself. He himself had experienced it. He had won through it all himself. Therefore it was all the greater delight to him to look out from his height at those *matos,* to admire their beauty, and yet to be shielded from their treachery. His tower guarded him against all evil. He only indeed left it at intervals, on Sunday mornings. He then put on his long blue official coat with silver buttons, hung his crosses on his breast; and he carried his milk-white head with a certain pride when, as he came out of church, he heard the creoles say to one another: "We've got a proper lighthouse-keeper!" "And not a heretic, though he's a Yankee!" But he returned to the island immediately after Mass, and was glad to return, for he still felt some lurking distrust of the mainland. On Sundays, too, he would read a Spanish newspaper that he bought in the town, or the *New York Herald,* borrowed from Folcombridge, searching through them for their scanty news of Europe. Poor old heart! In that watchtower and in another hemisphere it still beat for his country. Sometimes, also, when the boat that daily brought him his provisions and water landed at the island, he came down from the tower for a chat with the watchman, Johns. But he was noticeably growing more of a recluse. He ceased going to the town, reading newspapers, or coming down for Johns's political discussions. Whole weeks passed without his seeing any one or any one seeing him. The only sign that the old man was alive was the disappearance of the provisions left on the bank, and the light of the lantern that was lit each evening as regularly as the sun in those parts of the world rises out of the water. This was caused not by homesickness, but by the fact that homesickness had passed into resignation. The whole world now began and ended for the old man on his little island. He lived upon the thought that he would leave his island no more until his death, and he frankly forgot that there was anything left beyond it. Moreover he was becoming a mystic. His gentle blue eyes began to be the eyes of a child, eternally gazing, as though fastened on something far away. In his continual isolation and in surroundings that were of no ordinary simplicity and grandeur the old man began to lose the consciousness of his own identity; he was ceasing to exist as a separate personality, and was becoming ever more one with that which surrounded him. He did not reason about it, he only instinctively felt it; but in the end it seemed to him that the sky, the water, his rock, the tower, and the golden sandbanks, and the swelling sails and the gulls, the incoming and outgoing tides, were all one great harmony and one mighty, mysterious soul; and he was submerged in that mystery, and felt the presence of that soul which was living and at rest. He sank into it, he was cradled by it, memory fled; and in that captivity of his own separate existence, in that half-consciousness, half-sleep, he found a peace so great that it almost resembled death.

III

But the awakening came.

One day after the boat had brought water and a stock of provisions, Skawiński, coming down an hour later from the tower, saw that besides the ordinary load there was another packet. On the outer cover of the packet there were United

States postage stamps, and the address, "Skawiński Esq.," written clearly on the rough canvas. His curiosity greatly excited, the old man cut through the canvas and saw books. He took one in his hand, looked, and laid it down again. Then his hands began trembling violently. He shaded his eyes, as though he could not trust them; he thought he was dreaming; the book was Polish. What could this mean? Who could have sent the book to him? At the moment he had forgotten that quite at the beginning of his career in the lighthouse he had read one day in a *Herald,* borrowed from the consul, of the foundation of a Polish Society in New York, and that he had immediately sent the society half of his monthly salary, for which as a matter of fact he had no use in the tower. The society had sent him the books as a token of gratitude. They had come in a natural way, but at the first moment the old man could not grasp this idea. Polish books in Aspinwall, in his tower, in his solitude, were to his mind something extraordinary, like a breath of old days; a sort of miracle. Then it seemed to him as to those sailors in the night, that something had called him by his name in a voice greatly loved, but well nigh forgotten. He sat for a minute with closed eyes, and he was almost certain that when he opened them the dream would vanish. No! The packet on which the afternoon rays of the sun were shining lay distinctly before him, cut open, and on it the open book. When the old man once more stretched out his hand for it he heard in the stillness the beating of his own heart. He looked. It was poetry. The title was written on the cover in large letters, and below was the name of the author. That name was not a stranger to Skawiński. He knew that it belonged to a great poet, whose works he had even read after the year '30 in Paris.[1] Later, when he was fighting in Algeria and Spain, he heard from compatriots of the ever increasing fame of the great prophet-poet, but at that time he was so familiar with a gun that he never took a book in his hand. In the year '49 he went to America, and in the adventurous life he led he scarcely ever came across any Pole, and never a Polish book. So it was with all the greater haste and with the more wildly palpitating heart that he turned the title-page. Then it seemed to him that something sacred was beginning to take place on his lonely rock. It was indeed a moment of great peace and stillness. The clocks of Aspinwall had struck five o'clock in the afternoon. Not a single cloud cast a shadow over the bright sky, only a few gulls floated in its blue depths. The ocean was rocked to sleep. The quiet waves near the shore scarcely so much as rippled, as they melted gently away on the sands. The white houses of Aspinwall and the lovely groups of palms smiled in the distance. There was indeed something sacred, and quiet and solemn. Suddenly in the midst of that peace of Nature the trembling voice of the old man rang out; he was reading aloud to make what he read easier for him to understand:

Lithuania, my country, thou art like health.
How much to prize thee can only be told
By him who hath lost thee. All thy beauty
  to-day
I see, and I sing, for I pine after thee.[2]

Skawiński's voice failed. The letters began to swim before his eyes. Something

[1] Adam Mickiewicz, the greatest of Polish poets (1798–1855), who, after the Polish Rising of 1830, together with hundreds of other Poles, lived in exile in Paris.

[2] The opening invocation of Mickiewicz's most famous poem, *Tadeusz.* This poem is a song of the manners of the Lithuania of the poet's boyhood, filled with exquisite word-paintings of the scenery and skies of that country, and set on the background of a passionate patriotism. It culminates in the march of the Polish Legions through Lithuania in Napoleon's Russian campaign of 1812, from which the Poles hoped for the restoration of their nation.

snapped in his breast, and ran like a wave from his heart higher and higher, stifling his voice, clutching his throat. . . . A moment longer: he mastered himself, and read on:

Holy Virgin, who dost guard Czenstochowa bright,[1]
And shinest over the Ostrian Gate![2] Thou who the castled rock
Of Nowogródek,[3] and its faithful people shelterest!
As by a miracle thou grantedst me, a child, return to health,
When by my weeping mother 'neath thy protection placed,
My dying eyes I opened, and to thy shrine on foot
I went straightway to thank God for my restoréd life;
So thou shalt grant us to return by a miracle to our land.

The rising wave burst the barrier of will. The old man uttered a loud cry, and flung himself on the ground; his milk-white hair mingled with the sand of the seashore. Forty years had passed by since he had seen his country, and God knows how many since he had heard his native language; yet here at this actual moment that language had come to him of its own accord; it had crossed the ocean, and found the lonely recluse in the other hemisphere; that language so beloved, so dear, so beautiful! In the sobbing which shook him there was no grief, but only a suddenly awakened, infinite love, beside which all else was as naught. That passionate weeping was simply his entreaty for forgiveness from that loved, distant country, because he had grown so old, lived so intimately with a solitary rock, and forgotten so much, that even the homesickness of his soul had begun to wear away. And now he had "returned by a miracle"; and his heart was torn within him. The moments passed one after the other. He still lay there. The gulls flew over the lighthouse, crying intermittently, as if uneasy about their old friend. It was near the hour when he used to feed them with the remains of his provisions, so a few of them flew down to him from the top of the lighthouse. Then more of them kept coming, and began gently pecking him, and fluttering over his head. The rustle of the wings roused him. Having wept his fill, he now felt full of peace and radiant joy; his eyes shone as if they were inspired. Unconsciously he gave away the whole of his provisions to the birds, who swooped upon them, screeching; and he himself took up the book again. The sun had by now passed over the gardens and the virgin forest of Panama, and was slowly sinking beyond the isthmus, towards the other ocean, but the Atlantic was still all glowing. The sky was quite light, so he read on:

Till then carry my yearning soul
Unto those wooded hills, those meadows green.

Twilight had blotted out the letters on the white page; a twilight as short as the twinkling of an eye. The old man leant his head on the rock and closed his eyes. And then, "She who guards bright Czenstochowa" took to herself his soul, and bore it "to those fields painted with many-coloured grains." Long red and golden trails were still burning in the sky, and on those shafts of light he fled to the beloved land. The pine woods roared in his ears, his native rivers gurgled. He saw it all as it used to be. It all asked him: "Do you remember?" Did he remember! Besides, he saw;—wide fields, green unploughed strips dividing them, meadows,

[1] The shrine of the Blessed Virgin, honored above all others in Poland, that is hallowed by the most sacred of national traditions.

[2] The shrine of the Blessed Virgin in Wilno, where Mickiewicz studied as a university student.

[3] The town in Lithuania where Mickiewicz lived when a boy.—M.M.G.

woods, and hamlets. By now it was night. At that hour his lantern was used to shine over the darkness of the sea: but he was now in his native village. His old head was bowed on his breast, and he was dreaming. Scenes passed one another before his eyes swiftly and a trifle confused. He did not see the house where he had been born because war had wiped it out; he did not see his father or mother, because they had died when he was a child; but he saw the village as though he had left it yesterday; the row of cottages with faint lights in their windows, the dikes, the mill, the two ponds lying over against each other, and ringing all night with choirs of frogs. Once, in that village of his, he was on sentry duty at night. That past now suddenly rose before him in a series of visions. He is again a lancer on guard. The tavern is looking out from the distance with streaming eyes, and ringing and singing and roaring in the stillness of the night with the stamping of feet, with the voices of the fiddles and double-basses. "U—ha! U—ha!" The lancers are dancing till their ironshod heels send out sparks, while he is bored out there alone on his horse. The hours drag on slowly. At last the lights go out. Now as far as the eye can see is mist, impenetrable mist. It must be the damp rising from the meadows, and folding the whole world in a grey-white cloud. You would think it was the ocean: but it is the meadows that are there. Wait a little, and you will hear the corncrake calling in the darkness and bitterns booming in the reeds. The night is calm and cool, a real Polish night. In the distance the pine forest murmurs without wind—like the waves of the sea. Soon the dawn will whiten the east; yes, the cocks are crowing already behind the hedges. Each takes up the other's voice, one after the other from cottage to cottage; suddenly the cranes, too, cry from high up in the sky. A feeling of life and health sweeps over the lancer. They were saying something over yonder about to-morrow's battle. Ha! He'll be going too like the others with a shout and fluttering of flags. His young blood plays like a trumpet, although the night breeze has chilled it. But now it is dawn, dawn! The night is waning. The forests, the thickets, the row of cottages, the mill, the poplars, steal out of the shadows. The well-sticks creak like the tin flag on the tower. That dear country, beautiful in the rosy light of dawn! Oh, beloved, beloved land!

Hush! The watchful sentry hears footsteps approaching. They must be coming to relieve the guard.

Suddenly a voice rang out over Skawiński's head.

"Hi, old chap! Get up. What's the matter with you?"

The old man opened his eyes, and gazed bewildered at the man standing before him. Remnants of the visions of his dreams struggled in his brain with reality. Finally, the visions grew faint and vanished. Johns, the harbour watchman, was standing in front of him.

"What's all this?" Johns asked. "Are you sick?"

"No."

"You didn't light the lantern. You are going to be dismissed from the service. A boat from San Geromo has been wrecked on a sand-reef. Luckily no one was drowned. If they had been you'd have been tried for it. Get into the boat with me. You'll hear the rest in the Consulate."

The old man turned pale. Indeed, he had not lit the lantern that night.

A few days later Skawiński might have been seen on the deck of a vessel going from Aspinwall to New York. The poor old man had lost his post. New ways of a wanderer's existence had opened again before him. Again the wind had blown the leaf away to cast it forth by land and sea, to make sport of it at its will. During those few days the old man had grown very shrunken and bent: only his eyes shone. But in his breast he carried into the new roads of his life his book, which from time to time his hand grasped as though fearful lest that too should be taken from him.

YANKO THE MUSICIAN

By HENRYK SIENKIEWICZ

Translated by Jeremiah Curtin

It came into the world frail, weak. The gossips, who had gathered around the plank bed of the sick woman, shook their heads over mother and child. The wife of Simon the blacksmith, who was the wisest among them, began to console the sick woman.

"Let me," said she, "light a blessed candle above you. Nothing will come of you, my gossip; you must prepare for the other world, and send for the priest to absolve you from your sins."

"Yes!" said another, "but the boy must be christened this minute: he cannot wait for the priest. It is well even to stop him from becoming a vampire."

So saying, she lighted the blessed candle, and taking the child sprinkled him with water till his eyes began to blink; and then she said:—

"I baptize thee in the name of the Father, Son, and Holy Ghost. I give thee Yan as name; and now, Christian soul, go to the place whence thou camest. Amen!"

But the Christian soul had no wish whatever to go to the place whence it came and leave its lean little body. It began to kick with the legs of that body as far as it was able, and to cry, though so weakly and pitifully that, as the gossips said, "One would think 't is a kitten; 't is not a kitten,—what is it?"

They sent for the priest: he came, he did his duty, he went his way,—the sick woman grew better. In a week she went out to her work. The little boy barely "puled,"—still, he puled on till in the fourth year the cuckoo brought him sickness in spring; still, he recovered, and with some kind of health reached the tenth year of his life.

He was always lean and sunburnt, with bloated stomach and sunken cheeks; he had a forelock of hemp color almost white and falling on clear staring eyes, looking at the world as if gazing into some immense distance. In winter he used to sit behind the stove and cry in silence from cold, and from hunger too, at times when his mother had nothing to put into the stove or the pot. In the summer he went around in a shirt, with a strip of cloth for a belt, and a straw hat, from beneath the torn brim of which he looked with head peering upward like a bird. His mother, a poor lodger, living from day to day, like a sparrow under a stranger's roof, loved him perhaps in her own way; but she flogged him often enough and called him "giddy-head" generally. In the eighth year of his life he went to herd cattle, or, when there was nothing to eat in the cottage, to the pine woods for mushrooms. It was through the compassion of God that a wolf did not eat him.

He was a very dull little fellow, and, like village children, when spoken to put his finger in his mouth. People did not even promise that he would grow up, and still less that his mother could expect any good from him, for he was a poor hand at work. It is unknown whence such a creature could have come; but he was eager for one thing, that is, music. He listened to it everywhere, and when he had grown up a little he thought of nothing else. He would go to the woods for the cattle, or for berries, but would come home without berries and say stammering,—

"Mamma, something was playing in the woods. Oi! oi!"

And the mother would say: "I'll play for thee, never fear!"

And in fact she made music for him, sometimes with the poker. The boy screamed and promised that he would not do it again, and still he was thinking, "Something is playing out there in the woods." What was it,—did he know? Pines, beeches, golden orioles, all were playing,—the whole forest was playing, and that was the end of it!

The echo, too! In the field the artemisia played for him; in the garden near, the sparrows twittered till the cherry-trees were trembling. In the evening he heard all the voices that were in the village, and thought to himself that certainly the whole village was playing. When they sent him to work to spread manure, even then the wind played on the fork-tines.

The overseer caught him once standing with dishevelled forelock and listening to the wind on the wooden tines: he looked at the boy, and unbuckling his leather belt, gave him a good keepsake. But what use in that? The people called him "Yanko the musician." In the springtime he ran away from the house to make whistles near the river. In the night, when the frogs were croaking, the land-rail calling in the meadows, the bittern screaming in the dew, the cocks crowing behind the wicker fences, he could not sleep,—he did nothing but listen; and God alone knows what he heard in that playing. His mother could not take him to church, for as soon as the organ began to roar or the choir sang in sweet voices, the child's eyes were covered with mist, and were as if not looking out of this world.

The watchman who walked through the village at night and counted the stars in the sky to keep from sleeping, or conversed in a low voice with the dogs, saw more than once the white shirt of Yanko stealing along in the darkness toward the public house. But the boy was not going to the public house, only near it. There he would cower at the wall and listen. The people were dancing the *obertas;* at times some young fellow would cry, "U-ha!" The stamping of boots was heard; then the querying voices of girls, "What?" The fiddles sang in low tones: "We will eat, we will drink, we shall be merry;" and the bass viol accompanied in a deep voice, with importance: "As God gave! As God gave!" The windows were gleaming with life, and every beam in the house seemed to tremble, singing and playing also; but Yanko was listening.

How much would he give to have such a fiddle playing thinly: "We will eat, we will drink, we shall be merry"! Such singing bits of wood! But from what place could he get them,—where were they made? If they would just let him hold such a thing in his hand even once! How could that be? He was only free to listen, and then to listen only till the voice of the watchman was heard behind him in the darkness,—

"Wilt thou go home, little devil?"

Then he fled away home in his bare feet, but in the darkness behind him ran the voice of the fiddle: "We will eat, we will drink, we shall be merry," and the deep voice of the bass: "As God gave! As God gave! As God gave!"

Whenever he could hear a fiddle at a harvest-home or some wedding, it was a great holiday for him. After that he went behind the stove and said nothing for whole days, looking like a cat in the dark with gleaming eyes. Then he made himself a fiddle out of a shingle and some horsehair, but it would not play beautifully like that one in the public house,—it sounded low, very low, just like mice of some kind, or gnats. He played on it however from morning till evening; though for doing that he got so many cuffs that at last he looked like a pinched, unripe apple. But such was his nature. The poor child became thinner and thinner, only he had always a big stomach; his forelock grew thicker and thicker, and his eyes opened more and more widely, though filled oftener with tears; but his cheeks and his breast fell in more and more.

He was not at all like other children; he was rather like his fiddle formed of a shingle, which hardly made a noise. Before harvest, besides, he was suffering from hunger, for he lived most frequently on raw carrots, and also the wish to possess a fiddle. But that wish did not turn out well for him.

At the mansion the lackey had a fiddle and he played on it sometimes at twilight to please the waiting-maid. Yanko crept up at times among the burdocks as far as the open door of the pantry to look at it. It hung on the wall opposite the door; the boy would send his whole soul out to it through his eyes, for it seemed to him that that was some unattainable object, which he was unworthy to touch, that that was some kind of dearest love of his. Still he wanted it. He would like to have it in his hand at least one time, to look at it near by. The poor little fellow's heart trembled from happiness at the thought.

A certain night there was no one in the pantry. Their lordships had been in foreign countries for some time, the house was empty, the lackey was at the other side with the waiting-maid. Yanko, lurking in the burdocks, had been looking for a long time through the broad door at the object of all his desires. The moon in the sky was full, and shone in with sloping rays through the pantry window, which it reflected in the form of a great quadrangle on the opposite wall. The quadrangle approached the fiddle gradually and at last illuminated every bit of it. At that time it seemed in the dark depth as if a silver light shone from the fiddle,—especially the plump bends in it were lighted so strongly that Yanko could barely look at them. In that light everything was perfectly visible,—the sides with incisions, the strings, and the bent handle. The pegs in it gleamed like fireflies, and at its side was hung the bow in the form of a silver rod.

Ah, all was beautiful and almost enchanted; and Yanko looked more and more greedily. He was crouched in the burdocks, with his elbows pressed on his lean knees; with open eyes he looked and looked. Now terror held him to the spot, now a certain unconquerable desire pushed him forward. Was that some enchantment, or what? But the fiddle in the bright light seemed sometimes to approach, as it were to float toward the boy. At times it grew darker, to shine up again still more. Enchantment, clearly enchantment! Then the breeze blew; the trees rustled quietly, there was a noise in the burdocks, and Yanko heard, as it were, distinctly,—

"Go, Yanko, there is no one in the pantry; go, Yanko!"

The night was clear, bright. In the garden a nightingale began to sing and whistled with a low voice, then louder. "Go! go in! take it." An honest wood-owl turned in flight around the child's head, and cried: "Yanko, no! no!" The owl flew away, but the nightingale and the burdocks muttered more distinctly: "There is no one inside!" The fiddle shone again.

The poor little bent figure pushed forward slowly and carefully; meanwhile the nightingale was whistling in a very low voice, "Go! go in! take it!"

The white shirt appeared nearer and nearer to the pantry. The dark burdocks covered it no longer. On the threshold of the pantry was to be heard quick breathing from the weak breast of the child. A moment more the white shirt has vanished; there is only one naked foot outside the threshold. In vain, O wood-owl, dost thou fly once again and cry: "No! no!" Yanko is in the pantry.

The great frogs began to croak in the garden pond, as if frightened, but afterward grew silent. The nightingale ceased to sing, the burdocks to rustle. Meanwhile Yanko crept along silently and carefully, but all at once fear seized him. In the burdocks he felt as if at home, as a wild beast feels in the thicket; but now he was like a wild beast in a trap. His movements became hurried, his breath short and whistling; at the same time, darkness seized hold of him. A quiet summer lightning flashed between the east and west, and lighted up once more the interior of the pantry, and Yanko on all fours with his head turned upward. But the lightning was quenched, a small cloud hid the moon, and nothing was to be seen or heard.

After a while a sound came out from the darkness, very low and complaining, as if some one had touched strings unguardedly, and on a sudden some rough, drowsy voice, coming out of the corner of the pantry, asked angrily,—

"Who is there?"

Yanko held his breath in his breast, but the rude voice inquires again,—

"Who is there?"

A match became visible on the wall; there was a light, and then—Oh, my God! curses, blows, the wailing of a child, and crying "Oh, for God's sake!"—the barking of dogs, moving of lights behind the window, a noise through the whole building!

The next day Yanko stood before the tribunal of the village mayor.

Was he to be tried as a criminal? Of course! The mayor and elders looked at him as he stood before them with his finger in his mouth, with staring and terrified eyes, small, poor, starved, beaten, not knowing where he was or what they wanted of him. How judge such a poor little misery, who was ten years of age, and barely able to stand on his legs? Send him to prison,—how help it? Still it was necessary to have some small mercy on children. Let the watchman take him and give him a flogging, so that he won't steal a second time, and that's the whole business.

It was indeed!

They called Stah, who was the night watch.

"Take him and give him something for a keepsake."

Stah nodded his dull beastlike head, thrust Yanko under his arm as he would a cat, and took him out to the barn. The child, whether he failed to understand what the question was, or whether he was frightened—'t is enough that he uttered not a syllable; he merely stared like a bird. Did he know what they were doing with him? Only when Stah took the handful to the stable, stretched it on the ground, and raising the shirt from it struck a full blow, only then did Yanko scream, "Mother!" and as long as Stah flogged him he cried, "Mother! mother!" but always lower and weaker, until after a certain blow the child called mother no longer.

The poor broken fiddle!

Ai, stupid, angry Stah, who beats children that way? Besides, this one is small and weak, hardly living.

The mother came, took the little boy,

but had to carry him home. The next day Yanko did not rise from the bed, and the third day, in the evening, he died quietly on the plank cot under hemp matting.

The swallows were twittering in the cherry-tree which grew at the cottage; the rays of the sun entered through the window pane and colored with the brightness of gold the dishevelled hair of the little boy and the face in which there remained not a drop of blood. That ray was as it were a road upon which the soul of the boy was to go away. It was well that it went out by a broad shining road in the moment of death, for during life it went on a thorny one, truly. Meanwhile the emaciated breast moved with another breath, and the face of the child was as if absorbed in listening to the sounds of the village which came in through the open window. It was evening, so the girls coming back from hay-making were singing, "Oi, on the green field!" and from the stream came the playing of pipes. Yanko listened for the last time to the sounds of the village. On the matting lay the shingle fiddle at his side.

All at once the face of the dying boy lighted up, and from his whitening lips came out the whisper, "Mother!"

"What, my son?" answered the mother, whom tears were choking.

"Mother, will the Lord God give me a real fiddle in heaven?"

"He will, my son, He will give thee one," answered the mother; but she could speak no longer, for suddenly in her hard breast burst the gathering sorrow, and groaning only, "O Jesus! O Jesus!" she fell with her face on a box, and began to wail as if she had lost her reason, or as a man wails who sees that he cannot wrest from death the beloved one.

In fact, she did not wrest him; for when she raised herself again she looked at the child. The eyes of the little musician were open, it is true, but fixed; his face was very dignified, gloomy, and rigid. The ray of the sun had gone also.

Peace to thee, Yanko.

On the second day the master and mistress of the mansion returned to their residence from Italy, with their daughter and the cavalier who was paying court to her. The cavalier said,—

"Quel beau pays que l'Italie!"

"And what a people of artists! *On est heureux de chercher là-bas des talents et de les protéger,"* added the young lady.

The birches were murmuring above Yanko.

THE LIFE AND WORKS OF HENRYK SIENKIEWICZ

By GEORGES ALBERT-ROULHAC

HENRYK SIENKIEWICZ was born in 1846 in Wola Okrzejska, not far from Warsaw. His childhood was spent here in a fine house standing at the end of a drive planted with poplars, its entry steps adorned with ivy. Inside were vast reception rooms, their walls studded with icons. The house was surrounded by a park, with birch trees whose branches were silhouetted against more somber clumps of trees. The domain extended into vast pasture lands, coppice, and heath.

His early education was carefully supervised: he had an abbot for a tutor, as well as a French governess. He was surrounded by a large and devoted domestic staff, who were like a second family to him. Sienkiewicz, in a short story called "Stary Sluga" (The Old Servant), portrays one of them—Nicholas, an old grumbler type with a heart of gold.

Unfortunately, Sienkiewicz left no private diary. But one of his critics, M. C. Cooken, notes that Sienkiewicz's mother was probably the model for a gentle and good woman whose shadowy presence appears in one of his first novels, *Hania*. Cooken also sees his father in the same story personified in an old Polish nobleman faithful to the codes of honor and religion. The great medieval traditions were so strongly upheld in this family that when a son came of age, he was feted in a ceremony very similar to that of the consecration of a knight in the eighteenth century. As for Sienkiewicz himself, young Henryk, the principal hero of *Hania,* may be a self-portrait. The very sensitive adolescent of the story with a highly developed imagination and a rare generosity reminded his friends of the troubadours of the Middle Ages.

The social milieu in which Sienkiewicz grew up attributed as much importance to physical as to mental training and we may assume that from an early age he would have been a first-class shot and an excellent horseman—like the Polish youth he describes in *Hania,* who with one leap of his horse clears the park gate railings.

Henryk Sienkiewicz left his home to continue his studies in Warsaw at the university, and, in accordance with the tradition of good families, he was entrusted to the care of a professor who supervised his final education. This professor, from what we know of him, was a free thinker and regarded religion as an antiquated superstition. This was no doubt confusing to the young man, coming as he did from a tradition-steeped background, but his later life shows clearly that this was merely a test from which he ultimately emerged with a stronger faith.

In Warsaw, Sienkiewicz came to know a group of fellow students, who were soon aware of the superior qualities of their friend. Among them was a strange student whom Sienkiewicz depicts in *Hania* in the character of Selim. He was the son of a colonel and a Circassian girl, and "His eyes had nothing of the Tartar; they were large and black, sad and veiled. When Selim fought with a fellow student, they became elongated and gleamed like a wolf's eyes."

Portraits of Henryk Sienkiewicz, painted about the time he completed his education, show an elegant, well-poised figure; his forehead was well developed, his nose aquiline, and his moustache flowing. His eyes sparkle with intelligence and life, and a masculine energy further animates these harmonious features.

As soon as he was freed from the scholastic yoke, Sienkiewicz began to write articles and short stories for reviews, using the pseudonym of Litwos. His first novel *Na Darno* (In Vain) appeared in the Warsaw paper *Korona Warszawska.* The desire to escape and see the world, common to so many at this age, attracted him first to Paris, where he made a prolonged stay, and then to the United States. His travels in California and the Far West, where he shared the life of the farmers, produced his *Listy Z Ameryki* (Pages from America). The work consisted of three long short stories or novellas: "Dla Chilba" (For Bread); "Piaski (Across the Savannah); and "O.R.S.O." Here, he relates the hopes, disappointments, and sufferings of the Polish immigrants who came to the forests of the New World in search of liberty and who found only poverty. These simple moving tales had the same appeal to the Poles then as the books of Pierre Loti perhaps had for the French; and they were equally successful. Perhaps more Spanish in tone than Polish, "O.R.S.O." gives a poetic view of California.

Soon after he returned to Poland he was married, but death soon robbed him of his wife, leaving him with two children. Work became his consolation, and, in a sense, misfortune contributed to the maturing and strengthening of his gift. He published mostly short stories. *"Bartek Zwyciesca"* (Bartek the Conqueror) caused the greatest stir; it is the tale of a simple-minded and good-hearted Polish peasant who, after fighting bravely in the campaign of 1870 in France is left with no recognition for his bravery. On his return to civilian life he goes steadily downhill until finally his house is put up for sale, and his wife and children are cast out into the street.

"Janko Muzykant" (Yanko the Musician) is another small masterpiece. Yanko, a poor village boy with a passion for music, steals a violin which has been left in the castle hall. He is caught and arrested. Under the lash administered as punishment by an imbecile executioner, he dies.

These two early stories give some idea of Sienkiewicz's main preoccupations: to combat the selfishness of the squire class while helping the humble and suffering; and to propagate the principles of love and charity. Pity and emotion dominated his character. He dreamed of a classless society which would elevate the minds of the masses and provide them with more freedom. He was surrounded by writers who shared his ideals, men like Lubowski, Balacki, and Lam.

Other novels followed: *Latarnik* (*The Light house-Keeper*), *Pamietnik Poznanskiego Korepetytora* (*The Journal of a Posen Teacher*). Sienkiewicz's contemporaries agreed in their praise of the verisimilitude of his settings, the easy flow of the narrative, and his keen observation of real life, dedicated more by the heart than the intellect.

Sienkiewicz was doubtless a naturalist, but his naturalism differed greatly from that of Zola, or even Flaubert. He took no particular pleasure in describing the repellent, but drew his characters from the people he saw around him in everyday life. Rather than trying to idealize them, he attempted to penetrate the innermost depths of their souls, making them act and speak in keeping with their own virtues or faults. His work reveals a melancholy irony and a deep sympathy for the outcasts of fortune.

Eventually, Sienkiewicz the moralist turned historian; or rather, the moralist applied his intensive research to the Polish nation as a whole. The sad history of Poland is full of continuous struggles with neighbors, uprisings against oppressors, and frequent dismemberments. Successive partitions of Poland were perpetrated by Prussia, Russia, and Austria during the eighteenth century, and by France when Napoleon was infatuated by Marie Walewska; the insurrections of 1830 and 1863—each followed by a fearful repression—were also part of the dramatic convulsions of this unhappy nation. But Poland had known its day of power and glory. Sienkiewicz could remember when Poland was, next to Russia, geographically the largest state in Europe; and the time when Sobieski saved Vienna from the Turks, and Hungary from the yoke of the infidel. He was also well aware of the distant clamor of desperate battles waged by his ancestors against Asiatic hordes with Tartars and Cossacks in their ranks. Indeed, all the memories of those glorious days which stirred the Polish people so deeply, inspired Sienkiewicz to write his celebrated trilogy: *Ogniem i Mieczem* (*By Fire and the Sword*), published in 1884, was followed at two year intervals by *Potop* (*The Deluge*) and *Pan Wolodyjowski* (*Pan Michael*). In these lively epic pages, the author's prodigious imagination evokes the life and trials of seventeenth-century Poland. It is, however, reasonable to consider these three works—to which must be added *Krzyzacy* (*The Knights of the Cross*) (1901)—in which the atmosphere of the fourteenth century is so brilliantly reconstructed, as entirely different from the work of Walter Scott or Alexander Dumas. Sienkiewicz uses fiction as a vehicle for truth; the poetic vein and the esthetic sense in no way diminish his realism.

Sienkiewicz could have rested on his laurels. In Polish eyes, if not in those of foreigners, he was already a great writer, the creator of definitive pictures of his martyred country, and a great patriot who consoled them and revived their faith in the future. But for a man who was preoccupied with the meaning of universal life and human destiny there can never be rest.

With such philosophical problems in mind, Sienkiewicz wrote two novels in which he analyzed the movements of human sensibilities and will, the ebb and flow of passion, and the conflicts between the senses and reason. *Bez Dogmatu* (*Without Dogma*) appeared in 1890. The novel is written in the form of a memoir in which the author appears to speak for himself, and is an open attack on the doctrines of men like Auguste Comte and Spencer who were so much in fashion at the end of the nineteenth century. The hero, Ploszowski, is an idler who, at the same time, is endowed with great analytical faculties which enable him to observe himself and his useless life. These speculations land him in doubt, depriving him of all ethical sense. Sienkiewicz concludes by letting us see that a lack of belief is the fundamental vice and the destroyer of all existence.

Less clear-cut are the conclusions in *Rodzina Polanieckich* (*Children of the Soil*), the second novel of this period. Toward the end, a glimmer of faith is kindled in the soul of the hero. Circulating around the main characters are a number of symbolic figures sketched from life, such as Snobbism, Social Hypocrisy, and even certain Utopian currents of thought running through the younger generation.

In 1895, Sienkiewicz, having already achieved a great reputation in his own country, suddenly and dramatically joined the ranks of internationally famous writers. Although he was a modest man and his literary fortune never turned his head, the commercial success of *Quo Vadis?* was very great.

As he wrote to one of his biographers:

> It is possible that there were more translations of *Quo Vadis?* than of any other novel. Apart from translations in the main languages, English, French, German, Spanish, Italian, even Russian, I have them in Swedish, Danish, Dutch, Hungarian, the Slavonic languages, Portuguese, neo-Greek, Armenian, Finnish and many others. There is even one in Japanese, and last year a publisher in Constantinople sent me an Arab translation. As for the number of volumes published, I read twelve years ago in an English review, *Black and White,* that the sales of the English translations of *Quo Vadis?* than of any lion. Since then, many new editions have been printed, especially in France, where there are innumerable other editions, some de luxe, and some popular selling for a franc or fifty centimes.

His reading of *The Annals of Tacitus* and his long stay in Rome had prompted Sienkiewicz to write a novel about the Eternal City. On a visit to a small chapel not far from the old Capuan Gate, a half-effaced inscription on a stone caught his attention: *"Quo Vadis, Domine?"* The inscription refers to the legend of Saint Peter, who, fleeing from the Neronian persecutions, met Christ on the Appian Way; and to his question *"Quo Vadis, Domine?",* Christ answered: "Because you have abandoned your flock, I am going to Rome to be crucified once more."

Thanks to his great knowledge of the origins of the Church and his historical and archeological studies, Sienkiewicz was able to complete the book very quickly, most of it being written at Saint-Maur, and in Brittany.

The publication of *Quo Vadis?* in Poland and the stir it caused in Europe inevitably raised the problem of the historical novel, which has been so often discussed and never resolved. Adversaries claim it to be a false style, which cannot be truly classed as history, because most of its characters are fictitious, because the details of everyday life are invented, and because it is impossible to refer to the authentic documents which form the indispensable basis of every serious historical study.

Nevertheless, why deny the historical novel a priori the right to a special place between history and fiction, possessing a definite style of its own? Pure history, however important, is accessible only to a minority. Sienkiewicz knew this and thought to give the mass of other readers the opportunity to familiarize themselves, even superficially, with a different historical epoch. How many people would have remained ignorant about Roman life had Sienkiewich not taken the trouble to write his illuminating historical novel? He defined his work thus: "This book treats of a subject, and resurrects memories, which are common to all peoples. It takes place in that Rome which, because of its great past and its influence on the destinies of other nations, should ideally belong to all peoples."

The beginning of the twentieth century coincided with a neo-Christian movement. The Panama Canal scandal and the Dreyfus affair had perturbed the public, and there were signs of a revived idealism. Readers were beginning to tire of a surfeit of naturalism and to demand something more than the analytic mood of contemporary morals. Parisian adultery, even when dissected by Paul Bourget, seemed to have had its day. The ground, therefore, was well prepared for the growth of a series of historical subjects: Tolstoy's *War and Peace, Force* by Paul Adam, *The Disaster* by the Margueritte brothers bear witness to this, as did, in the theater, *Cyrano* and *Madame Sans-Gêne*.

Quo Vadis? proclaimed the superiority of faith in a merciful God over a corrupt and godless civilization—in other words, the superiority of mind over matter. The skeptics found nothing in the book to interfere with their lack of conviction, while others sought consolation in the story of the early Christians' struggle against a brutal power. *Quo Vadis?* brought people together in Neronian Rome.

Sienkiewicz never intended to write a thesis, only a historical novel, and his approach to the subject is above all that of an artist. He is skillful enough never to rely on Divine Intervention; and the psychological evolution of his characters, such as the conversion of Vinicius, is made plausible by the interplay of human passions and the demands of circumstance. If Petronius seems to us a modern dilettante, subtle, intelligent, and dedicated to the cult of beauty, it is because Sienkiewicz felt he was such a man.

The affectionate admiration of the Polish people for Sienkiewicz was revealed in 1900 on the occasion of the twenty-fifth anniversary of the beginning of his literary career. His compatriots opened a national subscription for him, and delegations from many Polish towns solemnly presented him with the award. It took the form of the title deeds to the Oblengorek estate, where he could shoot and fish, and, above all, meditate in peace in the shade of century-old trees.

After the award of the Nobel Prize in 1905, Sienkiewicz lived a tranquil existence, varied with journeys (he was nomad by nature) and open-air cures on his estate in the Carpathians. His last book, *Pustynia i Puszcza* (*Through Desert and Jungle*), was addressed to youth. Here, with an imagination which had lost none of its power, he depicted the reactions of a boy of twelve confronted with certain extraordinary situations.

When World War I broke out, Sienkiewicz took refuge at Vevey in Switzerland. He did so not to escape the rigors of war, but to organize help for his Polish brethren. It was from here that he issued his famous appeal to the civilized world on behalf of his country, once again besieged: "Gunfire destroys our towns and villages. From the banks of the Niemen to the peaks of the Carpathians, across the length and breadth of our plains, we see the specter of famine. Has not my country Poland a right to your help?" Death came unexpectedly at Vevey in 1916, before he had the joy of witnessing the resurrection of Poland, for which he had so long fought.

His work as a novelist has been questioned. Indeed, he occasionally doubted his talent himself. Once he wrote to a friend, "The peasant who stores his crops knows perfectly well that he is filling his barn with wheat and rye which will benefit the health of mankind. The author who writes in complete good faith may at moments wonder if he is providing bread or poison."

The Polish people themselves were never in any doubt about the effective help which their great writer had brought them. They never ceased to regard him as a living emblem of their country, a standard bearer of their national claims. This collective gratitude was fully expressed at the state funeral which took place in 1924, when Sienkiewicz was interred in the Warsaw Cathedral next to the Primates of Poland.

Georges Albert-Roulhac is a French literary critic and historian.
Translated by Anthony Rhodes.

THE 1905 PRIZE

By GUNNAR AHLSTRÖM

All the Nobel Prizewinners are open to criticism for one reason or another, and Henryk Sienkiewicz was no exception. Everyone believed that the Prize had been given him because of *Quo Vadis?,* which some critics felt cheapened the award. Even in the opinion of many readers the novel was simply a best-seller within everyone's reach rather than a work worthy of taking its place among great literature. There seemed to be something suspect about popularity: it was too often associated with a taste for the banal and colorless.

The Swedish Academy, however, had not glorified the merits of this novel or attached any special importance to it during the course of its deliberations. The work of the presumptive laureate had been judged in its totality, with full knowledge of the facts.

The Sienkiewicz candidacy had been renewed from one year to the next with the help of Swedish admirers since 1901. By 1905, the definitive choice had come to fruition. Fifteen names had been proposed, including those of Tolstoy, Carducci, Selma Lagerlöf, Swinburne, and Kipling. On this occasion, an important part was played by Alfred Jensen, a specialist in Slavic literature whom the Academy had consulted, and who had both introduced and translated Sienkiewicz in Scandinavia. Opinions remained divided for a long time: certain factions were in favor of dividing the Prize as in 1904 and awarding one half to a Polish woman writer, Elise Orzeszko. In any case, it was Poland and the Slavic world at the front of the stage. Finally, it was Sienkiewicz alone and undivided who triumphed.

It was 1905. World politics influenced feelings, and academic judgment was colored by them. To honor a Pole who was in the public eye and covered with glory was to deliver a discreet rebuff to Russia's autocracy, that reactionary scarecrow of Europe. Seen in this light, *Quo Vadis?* concealed unsuspected propaganda resources. The description of Nero's depraved empire had some bearing on the present, and the awarding of the Stockholm prize stimulated political comment. The Paris daily newspaper *Le Siècle* presented the case thus: "*Quo Vadis?* is considered to be the incontestable masterpiece of Polish literature because, without appearing to, it embodies a material symbol, the symbol which has inspired all the great writers and sublime poets of suffering Poland. From this point of view it is a book which follows in the tradition of the patriotic poetry of Mickiewicz, Slowacki, and Bogdan Zaleski. The links have not been broken. In this story of a people sunk into decadence but upheld by an inner life, people have chosen to see the efforts made by Poland in the struggle against incessant perfidious tyranny and their apparent hope of resurrection."

It was hardly a propitious moment at which to honor the champion of a nation suffering under the oppressive autocracy of the Czar. The Russian part of Poland was in the throes of trouble and strikes, and a state of siege had been declared there. The postal service had ceased to function and normal communication with Warsaw had been interrupted. The Swedish Academy was obliged to send a special emissary, Alfred Jensen, to Cracow via Vienna, with instructions to contact the laureate through Austrian Poland in order to deliver the happy news. Jensen managed to get a telegram sent across the Russian frontier, asking Sienkiewicz to come to Cracow on important business. A few days later, when railway communications had been restored, Sienkiewicz appeared. On November 29, he wrote the following letter:

Please forgive me if my answer is somewhat late in reaching you, but immediately after my meeting with Mr. Jensen, I was recalled to Warsaw for a few days, and I did not want to write to you from there, knowing that our letters (especially those to foreign countries) are often censored by the authorities. The secrecy required could not therefore have been maintained until the arranged date.

I am now back in Cracow and hasten, Sir, to write and thank you warmly for your flattering and kind letter.

The news which you send makes me truly happy, the more so as this glorious distinction with which you are honoring me is not given to myself alone. I accept it for my country and for our literature—that ancient literature which is so rich and colorful, and yet so completely ignored that often its very exponents are thought of and quoted as being Russians, whether mistakenly or intentionally.

It must however be admitted that latterly things have certainly changed: this international Prize awarded by the Swedish Academy is a solemn confirmation of our role and of our part in the intellectual and cultural movement of the world.

I shall do my utmost to come at the appointed time, and I would like to express my thanks and gratitude to your Academy and to your noble nation.

And at the appointed time he came, a pale little man, with white hair and a small pointed white beard, a kind of aged Napoleon III.

Translated by Camilla Sykes.

Carl Spitteler

1919

"In special appreciation of his epic, *Olympian Spring*"

Illustrated by R. MARTIAL

PRESENTATION ADDRESS

By HAROLD HJÄRNE

CHAIRMAN OF THE NOBEL COMMITTEE
OF THE SWEDISH ACADEMY

The Swedish Academy, in accordance with the statutes of the Nobel Foundation, has awarded the Nobel Prize for Literature for 1919, which was not awarded last year, to the Swiss poet Carl Spitteler for his epic, *Olympischer Frühling* (Olympian Spring, 1906).

Of this work it can be truly said that its "significance has become apparent only in recent years," and that all doubts that prevented a full appreciation had to be carefully considered until its merits, not immediately obvious, could be fully recognized not only as ornaments of the poetic form but above all as the artistic and harmonious expressions of a superior genius of rare independence and idealism.

This is not to say that we in any way subscribe to the opinion that this poem represents the fruit of a persistent struggle with the darkness of thought rather than of a lucid liberal inspiration. The original gap between the poet's art and its appreciation by critics and readers does not in this case point to a shortcoming on either side, but rather proves the deep and rich meaning of the work, which needs careful critical judgment to be revealed in its entirety.

Spitteler's *Olympischer Frühling* achieved popularity in Switzerland and Germany only in the revised final version of 1909. But with every year and especially since the end of the war, interest in it has grown and its circle of readers has widened; this year's printing is expected to run into several thousand copies. That is a considerable number for something as out of step with the times as a verse epic of 600 pages about the gods of Olympus, which because of its genre must be read as a whole and which demands the leisure and concentration of the reader. The writer, who has for decades devoted all his energies to such an enterprise, has indeed deliberately and ruthlessly isolated himself from hectic contemporary life and has given little thought to the modern demand for adequate material compensation.

He has done nothing to soften these contrasts. On the contrary, he has intentionally chosen a subject and an approach which were bound to bewilder and even repel many readers of different dispositions and inclinations or of different backgrounds of taste and education, as they tried to understand the poetic world that he opened before their eyes. From the beginning he was bold enough to appeal to their patience and endurance to follow him to the end of his curious paths, illuminated only by the clear and uninterrupted thread of the action and the soliloquies and dialogues of the heroes, which are highly dramatic despite the epic framework. The connoisseur recognizes Homeric traits, but to his surprise he is led on toward an unknown and never anticipated goal.

But for the rest, what a harsh and striking contrast between Homer's Olympus and Spitteler's idiosyncratic mythology! Nothing could be more unjust than the reproach that he likes to attract philologists and other disciples of scholarship by means of recondite allusions and profound symbols borrowed from their disciplines. His Olympians and heroes, his myths and oracles only rarely remind one of the style or tone of the older Greek poet-philosophers. They can neither be derived from the latest findings of classical scholarship nor cited as evidence of the poet's dependence on any kind of allegorical interpretation. Equally misguided are those who have spoken of a third part of *Faust*. Spitteler does not imitate anyone, not even the aging Goethe in his attempt to reconcile Romantic passion and classical balance in the masks of Faust and Helen. Spitteler's mythology is a purely personal form of expression which grew naturally out of his education and which gives shape to the living turmoil of struggling characters that he evokes in order to represent on the level of ideal imagination, human sufferings, hopes, and disillusions, the vicissitudes of different human fortunes in the struggle of the free will against imposed necessity. Why should he care that the current esthetic enlightenment finds it difficult to accept this seemingly fantastic mixture of dream and reality with its willful abuse of mythological names?

Even if I attempted to give a careful and comprehensive summary of the action of *Olympischer Frühling,* I could not give a clear picture of the wealth of its content, of the radiant vividness and moving power of the changing episodes, nor of their firm interrelation in an effective whole. Suffice it to say that the brilliant life of Olympus and the cosmos, manifesting itself in pleasure and trials of strength, ends in impotent despair in the face of human ingratitude, license, crime, and misery. Hercules, the mortal son of Zeus, equipped with all perfections by his father, his relatives, and friends, but at the same time burdened with the curse and hatred of Hera, the queen of the gods, must leave Olympus to accomplish ungrateful tasks of pity and courage on earth.

The Olympians, with their deeds and adventures, their victorious fights and their quarrels among themselves are in reality supermen whom the poet values only inasmuch as they are able to curb their whims and desires.

Above them all there is an inexorable universal law that assumes shape in gloomy powers of fate. Below them and closer to us are the mechanizing, soulless powers of nature which gods and men should put into their service for the benefit of themselves and of others, but which, abused by malice and pride, drive them into folly and ruin. The epic is full of airships and other curious inventions and its gorgeous buildings with cupolas and stately porches leave Homeric simplicity far behind. But the plot of the impudent flatfoot people to deprive Apollo of his universal rule by means of an artificial sun and their overweening attempt to attack him in the air by means of a treacherously constructed vehicle and poison gas testify to the decay that threatens mankind when it pushes too far a self-confidence based on material power.

Spitteler describes such pranks and the strange quests and enterprises of his heroes with a playful humor reminiscent of Ariosto. His style has a great variety of tones and colors ranging from solemn pathos to the careful brush strokes of the similes and the lively descriptions of nature, which reflect his native Alps rather than the regions of Greece. The iambic hexameters with their alternating masculine and feminine rhymes carry the flow of his masterly language, which is always powerful and splendid, never without vitality, and often unmistakably Swiss.

The Academy takes pleasure in expressing its admiration for the independent culture of Spitteler's poetry by awarding him this Prize. Since Mr. Spitteler has been prevented by illness from attending this ceremony, the Prize will be forwarded to him through the Swiss Embassy.

There was no formal Acceptance Speech by Spitteler.

PROMETHEUS AND EPIMETHEUS

By CARL SPITTELER

Translated by James F. Muirhead

PART ONE

INTRODUCTION

It was in the time of his youth. Health reddened his blood, and his strength waxed daily.

Then spake Prometheus, full of abounding life, to Epimetheus, his friend and brother.

"Up, brother! Let us be other than the many who swarm there in the common crowd.

For, if we rule our life by the common example, we shall earn but a common reward, and shall experience nothing of noble happiness or travail of the soul."

And the other was kindled by his word. So they set forth, and, where the valley was at its stillest and nestled most snugly among the hills, they chose their home, each of them building his house on one side of the clear brook.

And there they dwelt apart from all the people, and they went not to sacrifice to the Gods of their Brothers and went not to buy the proper ideas in the market, and when the others sang they did not join in.

And they stretched a barrier across the path and closed the valley carefully with bolt and lock. And they accepted no law and no custom; and their only commandment was the whispering of their own souls, as they wandered in meditation through wood and grove or along the fragrant and blooming slopes of the hills.

And, above all, their manners and their speech were alien, for they used "r" where all others used "l," and they bent backwards, where others crossed themselves, to show the devout and humble reverence of their heart.

And thus arose here and there a misunderstanding, and it came to pass that, if chance or a social impulse brought them into touch with their neighbours, the game stopped at once and the friendly chatter ceased. And they found no place for the sole of their foot and they suited nowhere and were everywhere strange and unwelcome guests.

And of an evening, when they, like the others, came out on the common highway to enjoy the summer air, the Elders of the people sat in the sunshine before the gate and whispered and spoke complacently to each other:

"Whence do these men come? Their bearing is not unseemly, but something is lacking that I greatly miss."

And his neighbour answered in the same spirit and said:

"And there is also something excessive

in it, something that displeases me in every way."

And there was no one who was not offended by their bearing, each from a different standpoint.

DECISION

And in the twelfth year, when autumn was passing into winter, the time came for the Angel of the Lord to choose one from the multitude of men and to appoint him king, in his stead, over all the earth.

And a dim rumour of this news spread abroad among the people; and each one reported it secretly to his neighbour; and the neighbour doubted it and disputed it —but yet, doubtful as he was, passed it on.

And while these doubters did their work, the whole people were stirred to an undefined impatience, greedy for something new.

Then the Angel of the Lord issued one morning from the richly ornamented gate of his palace, and took his way straight to the highest peak of Heaven. And after him came a great troop of worshipful attendants.

And he came at last, after a long walk, to the airy watch-tower, which dominated the whole kingdom of Heaven, where the cold winds struggled rudely with each other, where is heard the angry cry of eagles and of falcons, while far off, in the clouded distance, spread all the valleys and all the mountain peaks. And the Angel advanced to the parapet, and took a hasty survey of all the immeasurable tract around him. And as he found everything in order, and as no new thing was there to astonish his gaze, he turned with set purpose towards the darker side, where eternity with its black shadow touched on the world of existence, bathed in air and shining light.

And he gazed towards the dark mountain, where the days, one after the other, climbed out of the eternal abyss, with short and slow steps, bending knees, and hanging heads, like the porters who bear the bulky and back-breaking luggage of the easy-going townsman from the summer valley to the snow-clad peak. And not one of the great troop sang or spoke or laughed, but from time to time one of them bowed more deeply and covered his face with his hands, sobbing so that his shoulders shook with the laboured drawing of his breath, and his back trembled violently.

And thus sadly they pursued their way along the crooked path; and when the first of them at last reached the forest which separated the mountain's top from the land of earth, he paused for a while and balked, like a lamb that smells the odour of blood. And thereafter he passed through the portal of the wood in sorrowful resignation.

And this was the scene that the Angel long considered with great attention, not purposelessly or casually, and not as one enjoying a fair prospect, but as one whose consciousness is wholly absorbed in the picture before him.

But he gazed with a definite purpose in his mind, and questioned, and measured, and calculated, and compared with his thought all that his eyes saw in the profound distance. And so he remained for a long space; at last his bearing became certain and assured, and thereafter he braced himself, and turned and spoke to his attendants, who stood motionless behind him, in attitudes of respectful expectation:

"Betake yourselves forthwith to the land of earth and the race of men, and go from village to village announcing this behest in my name:

'I have resolved to set a King over you,

so that there may be one on earth who shall rule for me the Kingdom of God, so that it may suffer no injury in the time when my business calls me elsewhere, and so that he may protect it if ever sickness should befall me and for a time paralyse my strength and impair my will.

And so, when seven times the morning has reappeared over the valley, ye shall all leave your task and devote yourself to adorning the country for a worthy reception of the chosen one and to preparing a banquet for a joyous greeting.

And forty days ye shall devote to this purpose, and thereafter each of you must return to his home and do penance and purify his soul with prayer and worship for seven days. And on the eighth day ye shall assemble on the common outside the town, where with my own lips I shall announce to you the one my judgment has chosen.' "

So he spake, and all hastily scattered, eager to execute his command. He himself, however, gladly chose to wait a little longer in the airy watch-tower. Stepping to the side, where a massive table stood on a base of white and gleaming stone, he sat down on the wide bench, leaning his back against the table, and looked down with leisurely gaze, through the rails of the parapet, into the abyss, with the green and blue straths and the cloud-wrapped mountains, with the falcons and the eagles, which flew round the cliff, screaming in their excitement.

And thus, as the Angel of the Lord commanded, so it came to pass; when the eighth day appeared, the people left their cares behind them, formed themselves into groups, and adorned with garlands and gay streamers the town and the valleys and the hills and all the level countryside. Everywhere were animation and a joyous tumult; and old and young, man and woman, vied with each other in the lively, welcome, and gay-hued work.

And this they did for a long space, until the sun had set forty times behind the lofty wood; and thereafter they returned to their homes, to refresh their spirits and compose themselves through devout and sacred contemplation.

And now seven solemn days overshadowed the land; no sound was heard and no breeze ruffled the still atmosphere; the smoke rose silently from the mountain, and over the lower ground spread mysteriously a soft and vaporous mist.

And on the seventh day, the eve of the Sabbath, Prometheus paced thoughtfully up and down in the garden of his house, and gazed silently through the mist, while the dead leaves rustled under his feet.

And already, ravaged by the long autumn, the pride of the garden had waned, and the golden foliage hung but sparsely on bush and tree, and but few dark-red blossoms glimmered through the mist. And yet a rich and pregnant silence brooded over all, hallowed by the soft twittering of the blackbird as it flitted through the forsaken wood, dreaming of summer's departed gaiety and joy. All around there seemed no living thing left, and no movement was to be seen, except where a solitary sunbeam played over the green sward, chasing itself like a child, disappearing and reappearing, slipping through the hedge, trembling on the leaves, and resting on the ground.

And as Prometheus thus wandered quietly and his countenance shone bright and cheerful as if from inward peace, and his gaze dwelt on the rays of sunlight, while his thoughts roamed far and wide, the Angel of God drew near to him unawares, and lifted up his voice and spake earnestly to him with weighty words: "Prometheus, bold stranger from the lands of men!

I have marked thee now for many

days, and I have well observed the strength of thy spirit, and the bountiful richness of thy nature has not escaped me.

But in spite of all, thou shalt be cast out in the day of glory on account of thy Soul, for she knows no god and obeys no law and nothing is sacred to her pride, either in heaven or on earth.

And therefore hear my counsel and separate thyself from her, and I shall give thee a conscience in her stead, that will teach thee the *'Heits'* and *'Keits'* [1] of things, and will lead thee in the strait path."

And Prometheus answered and said, with high resolve:

"O Great and Mighty Lord, who allottest glory or shame to the Children of Men as seemeth to thee good, verily, I give thee thanks, for the spirit of thy speech is mild and I feel the friendliness behind thy words.

But it does not lie with me to judge of the face of my Soul, for, lo, *She is my Lady and Mistress, and She is my God in joy and sorrow, and all that I am, I owe to her alone.*

And so I will share my honour with her, and, if needs must, I am ready to forego it altogether."

And at these words the brow of the Other clouded, and he began and warned and spake—and his eye revealed more than the words of his mouth: "Prometheus, all-too-bold is thy temper, and all-too-quickly thy lips prepare for resistance!

But there is an important issue between thee and me, and the fate of thy whole life lieth under thy tongue!

And therefore weigh my counsel once again: it will come about, if thou canst not accept it and free thyself from thy froward Soul, so shalt thou lose the great reward of many years, and the joy of thy heart, and all the fruits of thy richly endowed nature."

And again Prometheus stood fast and spake with undismayed courage:

"Oh High and Lofty One, Thou who holdest the happiness of earth in thy treasure-house, and without whose grace there can be no good thing in the heart of a man!

Mayhap thou knowest this tale of the land of men: there was once a man, who was anxiously warned by his friends, saying unto him: 'She is a wicked woman, and will lure thee to death and sin.'

And the man smiled quietly and said: 'Well, if it must be so, I go to death and to sin.'

And so it is with me, and neither in joy nor in sorrow can I be without her beloved whispering."

And on this answer the Angel turned, and bowed his head, and departed. And he passed slowly through the narrow valley and went step by step, with hesitation and lingering.

And at the innermost reach of the valley he paused and stood and tarried, as one who expects to be called back, and as one who hopes that his friend may yet alter his resolve.

But Epimetheus, in his house on the farther bank of the brook, was well aware of all that had passed and had fully understood all their words.

And as he saw the Angel standing and waiting on the edge of the valley, he was inspired by the spirit of worldly wisdom,

[1] I.e., distinctions without a difference, the splitting of straws. *Heit* and *Keit* are abstract terminations (corresponding to our *ness*), which are identical in meaning and used quite arbitrarily (from conditions of euphony, etc.). We might represent them by *tion* and *ness, ation* and *ition,* or *ism* and *ity;* but none of the possible English pairs is so neat and "snappy" as the German.

and he stole out of his house and bowed himself and hasted by a secret path, until he stood before the face of the Angel.

And he fell on his knees and prayed and spoke with humble heart:

"My Lord and my God, until now I have strayed in the paths of error, influenced by my elder brother's word and example.

But now my desire is for truth and my soul lies in thy hand, and, if it please thee, pray give me a Conscience that I may learn the *'Heits'* and *'Keits'* and everything that is just."

And as he thus spake, he handed to the Angel a casket richly adorned with gold and precious stones.

And the Angel listened gladly to his prayer and accepted his offering and granted his wish and gave him a Conscience in gracious compliance with his request.

And thereafter he arose and withdrew himself into the folds of the valley.

And it came to pass that as Epimetheus stood upon his feet, he felt that his stature was increased and his courage firmer, and all his being at one with itself, and all his feelings instinct with assured confidence.

And so he returned through the valley with a firm step, following the straight path as he who fears no one, and with free and open bearing, as one possessed by faith in his own right-doing.

But as he was come in front of his brother's house, Prometheus raised his voice and spake to him in bitter greeting: "Whence dost thou come? And wherefore does thy countenance shine as with righteousness and wherefore does thy eye gleam as with treachery?

And, truly, I had rather have seen thee on the scaffold, scoffed at by the rude and vulgar rabble, than know that thou hadst broken our covenant and traded thy free soul for *'Heit'* and *'Keit.'* "

And, so saying, he turned away, and all his affection was changed to bitterness.

ELECTION

And it was once more still in the valley and time crept slowly over the mist-clad fields and the sleepy day sank into the dusk of eve.

But when midnight pealed from the tower, the King of Day approached with silent tread and set himself on the invisible throne of God, while at his feet stood his attendants in reverent silence.

And he sat there motionless and looked out patiently over the night-shrouded land, even until morning came and the hills and valleys laid aside their veils.

But at the first peep of dawn, he beckoned and seized his golden pencil; and the attendants eagerly approached and bowed themselves down and held ready for him his massive bronze-mounted tablets.

And when morning light was fully come, when the race of men awoke and beheld the sacred head, they rose quickly and donned their best raiment and hastened in crowded groups from the hills to the town and from the town to the common in front of the Angel's throne, in order to hear the choice and verdict of their lord.

And at the hour of the day agreed on the messengers appointed came to the Angel and made their report and spake: "Behold, all is ready, and thy people await thee in silent assembly."

And at this word the Angel sprang up, seized his sword, girded himself, and took up his journey to the lands below.

And through the radiant streets of Heaven he marched with shining and festal bearing, and on to the towering wall at the border of Heaven and to the well-built rocky road spanning in noble arch the yawning abyss.

And then began his happy descent, while the varied land of earth spread far and wide at his feet.

And below, at the gate of earth, he was received by the chosen representatives of the congregations of men, who joined themselves to him and led him to his throne and to the great and silent assembly of the people.

And the Angel began and spake to the people in a clear voice:

"My people! My consolation, and the chief reason of all my striving, and the only object of my cares!

I have kept a silent watch on you, and have distinguished those who tower above the mass, and I have noted and tried them one and all, and I have compared each of them with the other.

And two were more prominent than all the rest, and long have I hesitated and have felt unable to decide between their equal strength of mind and the loftiness of their character. But at the eleventh hour I found counsel, and so I have made my choice and have rejected him who made himself his own god in the arrogance of his incurable and sinful delusion.

So that all may learn and so that it may be a proverb to the end of time:

That he who dares to despise my commandment and is a law to himself and does not bow his soul before the everlasting judgments:

That this man shall be cast out and all the rich harvest of his faculties shall be for him as weeds and tares."

And thereupon the Angel turned towards the representatives at the foot of his throne and declared and spake to them this judgment with a clear voice:

"Behold! Make yourselves ready! And go to Epimetheus, where he dwells in the quiet valley, and greet him, and bring him before my throne. But take good heed that no harm comes to his person, for he is your King, and all our hope depends upon him, and I have no second choice whatsoever that could take his place."

And at the sound of this name, there arose boundless joy among the people; and at a sign from the Angel there pealed out in unison the bells of the high temple, sending forth from their harmonious lips the joyful tidings over town and land. And there was answer from the mountain and there was answer from the valley, and the clear and silvery notes of Heaven blended with the deep-toned song of earth.

And about the same hour Epimetheus lingered in front of his house and paced briskly to and fro, while oft-times his ear was intent to listen and his eyes gazed furtively into the distance.

And when all at once the air quivered to the thousand-voiced turmoil of the bells, he set a ladder against the house and began to pluck grapes from the golden vine.

And Prometheus, from his window on the other side of the stream, raised his voice and spake to him:

"What art thou plucking, my brother of the hypocritical deed? Thy look is surely bent on another harvest, and a sweeter fruit, as it seems to me, hangs in front of thy lips.

But I have one wish for thee—and listen carefully to my counsel—there is one thing I wish for thee: that the juice of the grape may never turn sour on thy hands."

But Epimetheus did not heed his counsel; but plucked and garnered with diligence, and turned now and then his head, and let his glance stray over the mountain to the road leading from the far-off land.

And the valley was just taking on colour, and the air was bluer, and through the light mist the noonday sun shone warm and clear, and on the golden foliage poised the sun's friend, the dark, hair-fringed butterfly.—Then steps approached the path, and voices waxed loud and called Epimetheus by name.

And at the great number of the voices and at the strange sound of his own name, Epimetheus turned his countenance in great wonderment.

And when he saw the Elders of the people in festal garb, bowing themselves before him in reverential greeting, he stammered and called out and spake with mighty wonder:

"What do ye wish of me? Surely it is in error that ye call thus on my name."

They, however, repeated their greeting, and bowed low, and delivered the message of the Angel.

And at that the Other cried and spoke with excited gesture:

"What do ye think of me? For, lo, this office is all-too-great for me, and this burden is all-too-heavy, and verily it is beyond the bounds of my strength.

Therefore depart from me, and go ye to seek a better man, suitable for such an office."

But they remained steadfast and answered, and said:

"Thou art the choice of our God, and he has none other man to take thy place."

And after a time of long struggle, since they persisted in their quest and did not yield, and would not hearken to him, his sense of duty prevailed and he climbed down from his ladder in modest wise and went in and made himself ready; and the Elders led him thence.

And while they thus fared through the narrow gorge, a cloud spread over the valley and drifted slowly across the blue lake to the dark forest.

And the cloud began and spoke and said to itself:

"What assembly is that in the valley deep below; is it, perhaps, the newly elected King whose praises the bells peal over the countryside?"

And thus speaking, it set its course, and altered its direction, and followed the procession, always keeping above the leaders in the distant blue.

And when it was quite sure of what it saw, it raised its voice and spoke to its shadow, which lay indolently on the hilltop below.

"Descend, and wake up the valley! Make it live! Make it start in amaze, by speaking to it the words I desire:

'Awake! Awake, thou happy valley! For, behold, light and fame stream from thy recesses, and glory arises from thy depths!

And henceforth thou shalt no longer be known as the modest valley, because thou hast this day been ennobled, and when in the future the wanderer nears thy house, he will stand still, and purify his heart, and collect his thoughts, so that he may devoutly inhale the breath of thy woods and prayerfully greet the consecrated spot.' "

And the shadow did as commanded, and swung itself up, and threw itself down the hill. And it animated and startled everything, telling and announcing the joyful message.

And as Epimetheus passed by, there stood well-known objects all along the way, and they greeted him and spoke the mournful words of farewell:

"Now thou marchest to thy bridal, and thou wilt enjoy the noblest that earth has to offer.

And then thou wilt doubtless forget thy poor friends in this remote valley."

But the Other answered and spoke with moist eyes:

"Verily I say unto you, that even though my foot walked on gold and silver, and though the voluptuous fragrance of the south enwrapped me:

Yet will ye remain quite unforgettable, and oft-times a wistful dream will bring back to me your dear faces."

And at the outlet of the valley, twelve mounted messengers awaited the procession.

And eleven of them, mindful of the prize, tarried on the spot, and each one held his steed back, so that he might, perhaps, be the first to announce the much-wished-for news.

But the twelfth, of bolder mood, dared to ride far into the valley, and when he came to a wayside hill, he pressed his horse to the top of it, and there, rising in his shortened stirrups and bending forward, he spied the land with sharp eyes.

And as, after a while, the rich and well-known costume of the Elders showed clearly on the road, he turned his horse and gave it a sign, and the horse forthwith galloped furiously to the road and along the road, with head flung high, towards the outlet of the valley.

And his eleven companions saw him coming and, glad of their start, set out, bent on the prize.

But he overtook them speedily, and, as the valley became more open, he stormed past them, and swung joyously in his saddle, and stood up in his stirrups, cheering and waving his hat, so that his horse was excited to its utmost speed.

And the people saw him while he was yet afar off, and they understood the meaning of his message; and just as a stream bursts its dam and breaks with thunderous noise over the lowlands, knowing no law and allowing no obstacle to stay or stem its resistless course:

So the serried rows of men broke up and flowed tumultuously towards the highroad, to await their friend and King.

And they waited long in vain; but when he at last appeared, with hesitating gait and perturbed countenance, a stupendous shout of joy arose from a thousand throats, and with enthusiastic greeting they threw themselves upon him, and surrounded him, and encouraged him, and were beside themselves, and knew no restraint. And the unbridled pressure of their affection almost overwhelmed him.

And just as when a beetle, crawling unsuspectingly through the grass, is suddenly fallen upon by a wild troop of ants, which will not leave him alone but drag and push him hither and thither, and rush him along with them, so that his body is absolutely lost in the mass:

So they dragged him along, and the crowd often became jammed before his feet and impeded his progress, and the dense knot was disentangled only with labour and difficulty.

And so, as in their unmeasured zeal they neared the throne—the joyous song of the bells suddenly ceased, and every shouter became devoutly dumb, and the crowd moved respectfully to one side, and ranged and ranked itself, and stood in a circle according to ancient wont and custom.

And an anxious silence gradually spread throughout the whole assembly.

The Angel, however, greeted graciously the sovereign of his choice and grasped his hand and set him on the throne by his side and laid solemnly on his shoulders his own gold-embroidered mantle, and made over to him the sword of justice, and the sceptre, and the crown, and all the other emblems of power.

And he showed him to the people and lifted up his voice and spoke to the assembly:

"Behold your chosen King and Lord! And so honour him, and watch over him, and protect him, and do all that he bids you!

For, lo, he is the best of you all, and if ever he errs, so be it, it will be an error of the noblest kind."

And thereupon he turned his head and spake these words to Epimetheus:

"Behold thy people! Their happiness

now lies in thy hands, and thou art the surety for their every hope!

And, therefore, have mercy upon them, and devote every day of thy life to their service, and for their safety offer all the strength of thy mind, so that hereafter they may teach their children to bless thy name."

And after these words he took him away and led him to the banquet prepared on the high hill before the town, and he bade him take up his abode in the lordly castle, and he showed him everything and handed over to him the massive keys.

And when he had finished all this, and seemed ready to take his departure, he all at once assumed a different mien, earnest and severe, and gave Epimetheus a silent sign to follow him.

And with a mysterious manner he strode across the court of the castle and led the way to the keep, the strongest part of the building, well fortified with stone and iron, and rising over the mighty cliffs on the highest peak of the hill. And they climbed the steep and dark stairway to the top of the lofty tower.

And here the Angel suddenly stopped and turned and raised his voice and spoke solemnly to his friend:

"Here, in this chamber, sleep my children, the consolation of my heart and the future hope of our kingdom."

And, thus saying, he opened with his secret key the concealed lock and entered with devout steps, like one whose foot treads on the sacred pavement of a temple. And where his children rested in the rosy twilight, he bent and kissed them lightly in their sleep.

And thereafter he turned round quietly and carefully closed the huge door and answered and spake, weeping, to his friend:

"This key I herewith entrust to thee, that thou mayest preserve it safely till thy latest breath."

And thereupon he descended the stair and saluted Epimetheus and departed.

But Epimetheus escorted him until he had crossed the threshold of the castle.

In the meantime the people assembled before the hill and loudly proclaimed their passionate longing for their King. And he, in amicable mood, gratified their desire, and appeared again and again in front of his house, until at last the voice of the people became too weary for further jubilation.

But though their lips were weary, their hearts were still athirst; so they pitched a camp below the castle and celebrated a feast, in order that they might continue to enjoy the neighbourhood of their dearly loved King.

And the festival was sincere and spontaneous, inspired by happiness and seasoned with mirth; and every face was made beautiful by its free and cheerful joy.

And in this feast there was neither envy nor ambition among the people, and no severe criticism marred their pleasure. Like brothers they mingled in sweet fellowship; each word was welcome, every song pleased, and every sound enhanced the general good humour.

And while the people amused themselves in this way like children, with song and sound and cheering and noise:

The nobles advanced in a long procession towards the castle, in order that they might offer their courtly homage and bask in the light of the throne.

And in front of the richly ornamented door of the castle, the procession came to a standstill and grew and swelled; and the sight of the beautifully dressed leaders was one of superb and radiant beauty.

And it came to pass at this moment that all the worth and wealth of this earth lay plain and open to the eye; for all that the artist's longing thirst for the pride of man and the beauty of woman could dream of was there in reality, in unhoped for amount and in unthought of strength and wealth.

And in pairs and groups they now entered and did homage, offering gifts and scattering flowers at the feet of the King.

And Epimetheus thanked them simply and returned modestly every salutation, and he bound many a man to him by his words, and many beautiful eyes rested long on the noble and virile lines of his figure.

And the goodly company streamed in and out until the evening, but when the dusk enveloped the land, the King found surcease from the endless commotion. And thereafter he withdrew to his chamber, and shut himself in, that he might in solitude bring order into his thoughts and control the overflowing feelings of his heart.

And he fell upon his knees, and humbled himself, and felt himself of no account; and he let the scenes of the day pass once more across his mind, and combined them, and compared and proved them, and inquired into their hidden meaning.

And for a long space he communed thus with himself, and he could find no limit to the great gifts that had come to him. Then his Conscience became active within him, and consoled him, and spoke with urgent admonition.

"Why dost thou distress thyself? And why dost thou torment thy soul with futile trouble?

Do simply what is right from day to day, and all that God has commanded."

And at these words it came to pass that his soul became thoroughly wearied and quiet, and the burden of his body became heavier, and his limbs no longer obeyed him. And thereupon he laid himself to rest in a state of the uttermost exhaustion.

In front of the castle, however, and at the foot of the hill, the people still tarried, undisturbed by the darkness, and they filled the air with their jubilant outcries.

And, when the night had become totally black and only the stars glittered in the firmament, suddenly a thousand coloured fires flamed up all over the land, and at their gleam the festival renewed its zest, and every heart beat more warmly and the general humour became still more merry.

And so they stayed together in happy communion until the pale dawn, with song and music and dance and play and confidential talk.

And on the selfsame day, while feast and sport prevailed in the land of men, and all cares were absorbed in the general joy:

Prometheus climbed grumbling up the hill, with eyes cast down, his face glowing with shame, and all his feelings sore from the deadly insult.

And he climbed for a long hour and his home-valley lay far-off below him, and the land of earth appeared small and the path became steeper, and above him the peaks of the mountain rose ever more menacingly.

But he pressed onward and upward, escaping from the hateful merry-making.

And so, aimlessly pursuing his way, he came to the crest of the mountain, and there—either because of the calmer air, where no sound was heard in space, or because of the sanctity of the place, as the fir-trees were arranged like the columns of a great cathedral—

He made an end of his journey, and rested, and walked up and down on the soft turf with measured steps, and the continual retracing of his own tracks did not vex him.

And he had done this for hours, and the daylight failed, and the air became dim, and twilight veiled field and wood, and a secret arose from all the valleys.

There was movement in the canopy of heaven, and a thousand grey shadows glided softly over the cloudy space and fell noiselessly, like wool, on the dark earth.

And at first singly or by twos and threes they fell like dew, slowly and sedately, but after a little they became more numerous, just as when endless troops of starlings fly over the fields; and as sheep congregate when they are driven to the upper alps, so the swarm crossed and intermingled, till all the land was buried under a soft white covering.

And till late evening the snow whirled and stormed, but when night came it stopped suddenly and only a few lazy flakes fell. The black and white woods were outlined sharply, and in the dark heaven glittered the stars.—

And about this time the march of Prometheus became more violent and his whole being was withdrawn and fearful.

And oft-times he lingered and then started again quickly, and oft-times he stood suddenly still and hearkened and gazed searchingly and fixedly towards the gate of the wood in his gruesome expectation.

Just as in the North Country a sleigh glides over the frozen heath, and the horse stops abruptly and shies, and tosses his head, and pricks his ears, while he shudderingly smells the neighbourhood of the wolves,

So the face of Prometheus was stricken with terror, and his whole body trembled in alarm.

And while he thus listened and held his body back as if in readiness for flight, and while his eye quailed before the black fir-trees,

There arose wonderful colours out of the snow, and under every tree the grass moved, bending sideways and tossing to and fro as if buffeted by a storm-wind, and as if scorched by the glow of an invisible fire.—

And the play of colour became more and more vivid, and the blades of grass moved ever more violently. Then, all at once, a gleam as of the sun shone from the forest, and, behold, a woman appeared, transcending nature in her divine radiance and in the pride and nobility of her beauty.

And at this apparition the blood of Prometheus rushed through his veins in mortal terror, and his whole being searched up and down for rescue, and implored his soul for succour, and moved frantically hither and thither, until at last it seemed to sink helpless and motionless into the deepest depth of his heart.

And he would gladly have taken flight, but the commanding power of her gaze fixed him to the spot, like a bird fascinated by a serpent, which flutters in vain and finds all its powers paralysed by the strong will of its adversary.

And the woman approached with royal steps, and her celestial form came nearer and yet nearer, and the emanation of her beauty reached him, and the marvel of her countenance took him captive, and all his feelings were bewitched and bedazzled by the wondrous grace of her limbs.

Then, suddenly, he took courage and summoned all the strength of his will, and crossed himself and prayed and turned to flee.

But he found himself within a circle of fire, which defied every prayer and all his holy spells.

And thereupon he resigned himself and stood still, and awaited her approach with forced courage and with feigned calmness. But this was a terrible strain and the effort exhausted all his strength, so that he was at the end of his tether and could no more. He could not rally himself either in defence or in greeting, but stood senselessly like a stone or a statue, and his whole soul and all his will were absorbed in the effort not to blench.

And the Goddess approached him and laid both hands in greeting on his shoulders, inclined her head, and looked at him, glance for glance and eye to eye. And at her gaze his life died and rose again, his blood first seethed and then froze, and all his feelings became enslaved to her in boundless and self-forgetting love.

And after a pause of speechless gaze, the Goddess opened her lips and began and spoke—and her look shone strangely as in twilight, and her mien became baffling and illusive.

"Prometheus, my friend, I warned thee at our meeting in the meadows, by the brook, when the flowers began to show their colours at dawn.

And I warned thee and told thee that I was a wayward Goddess, who would lead thee aside, in untrodden ways.

Thou, however, didst not hearken unto me, and so it is come to pass, as I foretold, that thou hast let them, on my account, rob thee of the glory of thy name and the happiness of thy life."

And it came to pass that at the sound of her voice, and even more at the fragrance of her breath, which softly played on his face, he began to stagger, like a drunken man, and suddenly he threw himself on the ground, wrung his hands, and sighed and implored her with fervent longing:

"Oh thou, my Goddess and the light of my life! Thou, my bliss, Thou the joy of my heart!

Blessed be the day when I first gazed into the night of thy eyes! Hallowed be the spot, where the music of thy voice was revealed to me! All the days of my life will I go and kiss, and kiss again, the sacred ground!

And even though I am bereft of all else, so shall I be immeasurably rich, if only thou remainest and callest me 'my friend' with thy sweet lips and lookest down on me with thy proud and gracious countenance."

And while he thus bore himself, in the frenzy of his ardour, a strange trembling played about her lips and her eyelids quivered, opening and closing quickly. And behind her soft and delicate eyelashes something menacing lurked and prowled, like the fire that steals through a house maliciously and stealthily, or like the tiger that winds through the jungle, showing amid the dark leaves glimpses of its striped and yellow body.

But after a time, her mien became once more stark and motionless, and once more she tried and proved him, beginning to speak in a changed voice:

"But now it is too late, and no repentance can now avail thee, and no retreat is allowed thee; and thou must be my slave, and must serve me without wage, and must do whatsoever I command thee."

And Prometheus answered and spoke, with ardent and yet humble look:

"So be it, and this is the petition of thy slave: bind me with cords, forge me with iron, and fetter me with chains to thy gracious being!

Let the light of thy countenance be ever upon me, and let thy strong will be my sweet reward, declared to me by thy joy-giving lips."

And again her eyelids quivered and her eyes shone. And all at once, like the spring of a lion or a peal of thunder, her whole manner changed into boundless disdain; hate distorted her beautiful features and wrath overspread her countenance.

And convulsively, with strange eyes and pale lips, she took up her parable, and her lips quivered with passionate excitement:

"Prometheus, stand up and hear what I bid thee!"

And he gazed shudderingly at the terrible figure before him, and tremblingly he arose, hardly able to obey her behest.

And with slow and solemn bearing she stepped forward, and silently reached out and grasped his right hand, and drew it towards her, and then let it go again. And Prometheus followed, obedient to her will.

And thereupon she took a ring from her finger, and looked at it and consecrated it with prayer and spell, and pressed it to her heart, and blessed it with her lips.

And, once more grasping his right hand, she slowly and solemnly slipped the ring on his finger.

And when she had so done, she stepped back, and began and spoke with anger-choked voice:

"I have heard all that passed in the lonely valley, in the sunshine of a windless day, when thou knewest my face and saidst of me 'my lord' and 'my god,' and didst not shun destruction, and insult, and shame for my sake.

And I heard it all and I have sworn to myself: 'so be it, thou shalt not repent it.'

And now, as it is their pleasure to deny thee this day, the day of glory, the day of election, so have I chosen thee, to be my bridegroom and to be betrothed to me, until I redeem the ring again, and have prepared for thee a bridal day, when I shall repay with interest all that thou hast to-day renounced for my sake.

And this I offer thee in expiation, and now receive my blessing, to bind our compact."

And quite beyond himself through bliss and happiness, and, drunken with delight, he fell on his knees and gazed thirstingly at her face and hung passionately on her glance, and his whole being thrilled with confidence and youth.

She, however, laid her hands in benediction on his head, and began, and blessed him and spake with a clear and loud voice:

"Accursed be all that thou doest! Accursed by day and by night be thy emotions! Accursed be thy hope!

And human happiness and joy shall never come to thee, but that which is known in the land of men as heart-break shall be thine in full measure: renunciation, wounded feeling, unsatisfied desire, and suffocating struggle in the silent watches of the night.

And day after day, year after year, will see thee in this state of perpetual damnation, and thou wilt have neither rest nor sabbath, and thou shalt look with envy on every beast of the field that exhausts itself with work, and sleeps, and loves, and dies in the natural order of things.

And that is my price, and for this thou shalt be my wooer.

But beyond all this approaches the high day, the day of glory, the day of rapture, when I shall reveal my body to thy gaze and open my bosom to thy longing, and will give myself to thee, heart to heart, limb to limb, eye to eye.

And for a single hour I shall dwell with thee, and yet for this hour all future generations shall envy thee."

So she spoke. But Prometheus remained on the ground in profound travail of soul, and he gratefully clasped her knees, and covered her hands with his kisses.

And for a time she suffered him to continue, and then she began and admonished and spake to him mildly:

"And now I depart from thee, for, lo, a great work awaits me, a work of huge labour, and the utmost haste is needful that I may bring it to an end."

And, so saying, she loosed herself from his grasp and prepared to leave him.

But at her action his love flamed up in

him, burst its bonds, opened violently the door of his voice, and desired and spake with passionate longing:

"And wilt thou then abandon thy friend so? Behold, thou takest my very life with thee, and only death and nothingness remain for me, if thou departest!

And even if haste is thy aim, even so it is the use and wont of lords and masters to bestow a last greeting and a final command. So do thou follow this custom with thy servant, by indulging him for a moment and granting him another word or two from thy lips.

For, behold, a moment of thy countenance is an eternity! And the least of thy words will be for me an imperishable gift, at which my heart can refresh itself in the time of utter barrenness!"

And at the impetuosity of his craving the heart of the Goddess softened, and she began and turned back and answered and spoke graciously to him these pregnant words:

"This, then, is my last greeting and the final expression of my will.

I know that two animals dwell with thee in thy house, and also some little ones.

And these animals do not know my face, and these little ones will lead thee astray.

And, therefore, when, going from hence, thou reachest thy valley-home, thou shalt slay these little ones for my sake, and afterwards the older animals will die of themselves.

And this shalt thou do, and in doing shalt glorify my name."

And thereupon she again turned away and made as if to go.

But the Other held her fast once more, and besought and spoke with desperate entreaty.

"Of a verity thou hast gifted me overrichly, and it ill beseems me to entreat thee once again.

But it is the way of the world that in the exceptional hour the fount of grace flows without ceasing, and good fortune offers itself without reserve to the man of its choice.

So, therefore, turn to me for one last time and tell me when I shall again see the splendour of thy limbs and thy sweet mouth and thy beloved eyes?"

And once again she stayed her steps, and, pointing to the neighbouring hill, took up her parable and spoke in riddles:

"It is easy to see from hill to hill, and what does it matter about the valley? Even so will the time of my reappearance be nigh thee."

So she spake and saluted and vanished among the dark pine-trees.

And thereupon it was as if a light had gone out; the air seemed cold, the wood and field seemed dark, and the whole earth was empty.

And for a space it was as if a magic glow and play of colour still hung on bush and tree, and bright-hued threads stretched through the gloomy air, and dream-like eyes gazed out of the black caverns of the forest.

And it withdrew but slowly, as when, after the sun has long sunk below the horizon, the rosy glow still beautifies the mountain, and disappears, and returns, and refuses to leave the peaks of snow and ice.

But when at last every breath had wholly vanished, and the world was left to the dregs of commonplace existence,

Then Prometheus arose and strode from thence, inspired with courage, as one to whom great good luck has come and as one who has received a gift transcending his expectation.

And once more the joyful tumult of the people reached his ear, and the whole countryside, far and near, was lit up by the festival.

But now this seemed to him stale and alien, and at his recent annoyance he smiled with a feeling of complete superiority.

And when, after long wandering through bush and brake, he had finally reached his home-valley, and when only one bend of the path concealed his house, and when the dark tree-tops of his garden had come into sight over the edge of the way,

A little dog came running to meet him through the night and the darkness, and welcomed and caressed him, smelling and sniffing after the manner of dogs. And it raised its voice and spoke in amaze:

"Whence dost thou come? And what has touched thee?

And truly I trace a godlike odour about thee, and thou seemest also to have remembered me in thy talk?"

And Prometheus answered and spoke, with downcast mien:

"In truth we have thought of thee; but I advise thee not to speak of thanks in this matter."

And thereupon he seized the whelps, as they lay sleeping in their warm bed, and strangled them, faithful to his divine command.

And while he was slaying them, the mother licked his hand and looked up into his face with mournful submission. But when he came to the last of her children, the little dog beseeched him and spoke out her modest wish:

"Peradventure thou wilt leave me this last one, and I shall hide it away in the forest, so that thou shalt never be aware of his presence, and his life will be to thee all the same as his death."

And Prometheus could not reject this prayer and spared the whelp and departed in peace.

And when he reached the front of his house, there stood a lion in the doorway and looked at him searchingly and spoke and asked with severity:

"Come now, what bringest thou me as a gift? For I saw a Goddess walking through the wood, and I saw her following thy track, and I saw her conversing with thee on the snow-clad summit of the mountain."

And Prometheus answered and spoke in deep embarrassment:

"Truly, I bring thee a gift, but I fear it is one that will give thee little joy."

And thus saying, he entered the house to fulfil the behest of the Goddess.

And when he had done the deed and only one of the lion-cubs remained, Prometheus lifted up his voice and spoke with conciliatory mien: "Perchance, if it please thee, I may spare the last of thy children."

The lion, however, threw herself fiercely on the cub, and tore its body limb from limb. And then he turned and approached his master with bloody jaws, and said unto him with fierce and blazing eyes:

"Take, now and thus, the thanks that I give thee in greeting and response for thy deed.

And it shall so be that from this day on I shall hate thee and I shall hate thy body, and never wilt thou be able to placate me. And yet, so long as that ring is on thy finger, I shall have no power against thee and I shall have no leave to hurt thee, and thou shalt dwell safely by my side in spite of all my grim hatred.

And if you have treated me so to no end, and if once the ring is loosened from thy finger, and if death comes to precede thy marriage, and if thou lookest to end without glory and without name,

Then, behold, I shall double thy death and shall tear thee to pieces, drinking joy from the poignancy and multitude of thy agonies.

So mark this well, for it is my last word, and thou needst not ever hope that I will depart from it."

And thus he expressed his thanks. But

Prometheus blessed the lips and face of the distant Goddess, and, thereafter, he gave up and laid himself to rest after the many and strange happenings of the day.

And the two animals followed his steps, and laid themselves to rest. The little dog curled up, sobbing, at the door of his chamber, and closed her eyes, and buried her head; but she could find no ease, so she got up again, and put her bed in order, and tried it again from the other side. But in vain; from neither side could she attain the boon of sleep.

And so she lay, moaning, outside the door. But the lion entered his master's own room, and prepared his sleeping-place by his master's bed, and there, crouching on his belly, burying his head between his mighty paws, he gazed without ceasing straight at the face of Prometheus, who felt, even in the deepest slumber, the dark and malignant glow of the hate-filled eyes.

Close

And about the hour of midnight the Royal Day descended from his throne and put away his pencil and handed his written tablets to his attendants. Then he girt his raiment about his loins and made himself ready to journey to the distant and fathomless deeps beyond the other mountain.

And, quietly, by airy paths he proceeded through the night-shrouded land, and behind him came the Apostles, four in a row, keeping step, and six feet always treading in the same tracks. And when he was come to the festal mountain, where the loud and multifarious exultation of the people filled the air, he stood still and pondered for a while. Then he suddenly branched off to one side, alone and refusing all escort, and took his place opposite the palace of Epimetheus and looked searchingly into its dark windows.

And so he tarried for the greater part of an hour, and thereafter turned again aside, and made his way solemnly to the house of Prometheus, and gazed at it in the same way. And the while he often looked over also at the brilliantly illuminated palace.

And so he remained, until his eyes smiled at the clear idea that came from his long thinking. And thereupon he returned to his escort and proceeded with them softly, through the woods and over the fields, and across the mountain and down the valley, to his distant, eternal, and boundless goal.

SURVEY

And so the High Day came to an end, and thereafter the earth resumed its normal mood, and the sun shone, from a paler heaven, with sober, yellow light.

And everywhere, over the whole land, people donned their week-day clothes, and toiled and moiled, and worried and worked after the fashion of men: each for himself, and his wife, and his children.

Epimetheus

But it was otherwise with the King in his goodly palace, for he took upon himself the care for his whole people as if for a child, and his labour was solely for the welfare of others.

And so he began and lifted up his voice and spoke to his Conscience, with anxiety and trembling:

"Behold! Thou must prove thyself henceforth as a true friend, by correcting me without fear, and ruling all my actions, and taking no heed of the weakness of my heart;

For, lo, the welfare of my people is placed in my hands, and anything that I do will cast its shadow over all time and all lands."

And, thereupon, he arose and went

down into the kindgdom, where he settled disputes, and stopped evil-doing, and gave wise counsel, and created order everywhere, and relieved many necessitous cases by the consolation of his lips and the rich gifts of his hands.

And this he did for a year and a day, never wearying, never finding any appeal inconvenient, and never refusing a hearing to anyone who sought his presence.

And after a year and a day the fruits of his hand became manifest. And when, of an evening, his gaze swept over the whole countryside, there was no village so small that it did not yield response to his labours. And when, of a morning, he walked in the fields, his footsteps were followed by many with praise and thankfulness and with the unfeigned gestures of real affection.

And so great was the power of his virtue, and so strongly influenced was every spirit in his favour, that when, on his path, two men were fighting with fierce and furious hate, they would draw back with ashamed faces and agree to make it up and offered up their long feud as a sacrifice to him.

And when the criminal suffered the penalty of his misdeeds in the stocks or the pillory, he would rail at law and justice, but he honoured the name of Epimetheus by reverential silence.

And from the high watch-tower of Heaven the Angel looked down on his chosen minister and appraised his behaviour with a keen eye.

And when he perceived the gratitude of the people and saw the Kingdom of God flourishing under the hand of his chosen one, his spirit trembled within him, and he sighed and lifted his voice and prayed and uttered his blessing with deep emotion.

"All hail, Maja, my blessing! Wing thy way to the valley of earth, there to tarry in the house of the King and to serve him day and night, so that his heart may swell and his eyes grow bright at the fulness of his happiness."

And so he spake; and Maja hasted away at once on light wing and wafted herself, like a fragrant shadow, down to the variegated fields of earth.

And when she reached her goal, the form of her body was materialised and she became in all points like an earthly maiden, in whom still slumbers her secret strength, while her slender youthful body sways artlessly and lightly.

And when she found herself on the flowery mead, in full sunlight and clad only in woman's natural charms,

A soft blush mantled her cheek, and she sought a hiding-place for a time, taking refuge in the cool shade of the neighbouring wood.

But after a short time, mindful of her task, she wound her hair (disordered by her rapid flight) into a knot with deft fingers, and dried the celestial dew on her brow, and shook the sun-dust from her white shoulders.

And then she arose and looked around her once more, and walked, with light steps and all unseen, to the palace of the King; and there she at once began her wondrous work.

And when Epimetheus stayed at home, she was always near him, and in all his goings and comings he was aware of her influence.

And when he walked abroad in his kingdom, she opened the window and clapped her hands thrice. And at this signal, the gay and slender daughters of the sun hastened up, crossed the window-sill, and began to play and frolic throughout the spacious mansion, until evening came and the repeated summons of their mother warned them from the far-off hill. And when night filled the world, Maja went round the house, looked to the locks on the doors, shot the bolts, and extinguished the lights. And when all was in due order, she glided on rosy toes to the King's bedside and held her divine hands in benediction over his eyes.

And it came to pass that under the shadow of her hands, his soul felt weary and his sleep became deep. And when, from time to time, her delicate fingers stroked his brow, her youth streamed into his blood, so that in his sleep he received strength after all his toils.

And about the midnight hour, she betook herself to rest, seeking her modest couch, either on velvet rugs in the rich hall, or on the hard floor under the roof, or (in summer) in the quiet nooks of the garden.

And her only pillow was her own soft, white, and rounded arm.

A few hours of sleep were enough for her, and while it was still night she rose up and went to the spring, to bathe her shining eyes. And then she entered the garden, where she wakened the buds and made the flowers open their mouths at the caress of her lips.

And, next, she went back and busied herself in the house, putting everything in its proper place and blowing away the dust with her fragrant breath.

And when she came to the magic casket, in which lay hid a treasure of wonderful tones, her delight was almost too much to bear. She laid her fingers on the black and white keys, counted three and five and eight—and evoked a morning song of invisible and harmonious voices.

And long she listened to the sweet melody, until at last, mindful of her duties, she blamed herself, and went off, and began her work again. And she brought about order, with hand and voice, and with the magical strength innate in her soul.

And this she did day by day, and in a short time the house became sanctified. And when the Spirit of the World moved through the land of an evening, seeking the distant creator,

He passed through the middle of the palace, and the King's ear heard the dread rustling of his wings;

And when, in the morning, the hidden stream of life poured forth, and divided into branches, and trickled through hill and dale, to feed the very roots of existence,

It finally settled under the house of Epimetheus and wound thrice round the hill in graceful loops.

And over the whole earth there brooded an interval of deep rest; but in the house of the King the Present sat enthroned in all its fulness.

Prometheus

And while Epimetheus thus took pleasure in the rich abundance of his office and the dignity of his lot:

There crawled, at midnight, out of the dark grave, a worm, that raised itself up, and sniffed, and nosed around, and coiled itself in a ring, and bent its head from side to side.

And, all at once, it set out and made its way with definite purpose over the field, and from the field to the path; and it followed the path, unfalteringly, always heading in the same direction.

But its progress was slow and its goal was far-off, and ever and anon it had to stop to regain its breath;

But it always started again with renewed vigour, and stretched itself and wriggled and pushed and dragged its smooth body along. And so, before the peep of day, it reached the house of Prometheus, and crept through the door, and made itself a nest, and dwelt therein in comfort and content.

And when Prometheus went forth each morning to his daily task, the worm came to his hand, and he nourished it with food and drink. And it drank out of the same glass and fed out of each of his dishes.

And it was a true and loyal guest, and shared in every toil and every adventure of Prometheus.

But before the breath of the worm, peace fled from the house, while impatience and discord entered in. And so Prometheus was at war with himself, and became his own enemy, and used the rich and varied gifts of his genius to torment himself.

But, in spite of all, his spirit knew neither repentance nor shadow of turning. And it happened, when he saw his brother in the distance, walking up and down in the busy land of men, surrounded by the acclamation of his people and shone upon by the blessing of Heaven:

Then he fell on his face and prayed and with dogged obstinacy spoke this defiant word:

"A god of mercy art thou, oh my Soul, rich in grace!

And, therefore, if ever the cursed day shall come when I shall sin like the children of men before thy face: then do thou put my name to shame and slay my body. Any penance will seem to me just, and all other punishment from thee shall be welcome to me.

But one thing I beg that thou wilt not do—on account of my true love, with which I have served thee now for many a year—this one thing leave undone: *do not suffer me to grow like this man."*

JOURNEYING

And one evening, as Prometheus was praying according to his daily wont, the Angel of God stood in the garden of his palace, while Doxa, his tall and beautiful comrade, sat on the wall in front of him. And the bearing of the Angel was peaceful and he was meditating as he beheld how the sun was on fire with its own rays, and how the valleys and the mountains were empurpled by the reflection of the great conflagration.

But Doxa, whether from the all-too-sombre nature of her own being, or from the effect of a recent dispute, did not share in his action but turned her proud back on all the glory, looking morosely over her shoulder and picking with her fingers at the joints of the wall. And her eye lit up only when she succeeded in her mischievous task and detached a fragment of stone from the wall, so that it rolled down upon the ivy, which held the shady corners of the garden close-locked in its firm embrace.

And while she thus gazed distractedly at the scene below, like a thunder-cloud that, pregnant with destruction, hangs over the ochre-coloured field, delaying its stroke, menacing the whole land, and yet uncertain where to discharge its fury,

There ascended, in the distant valley, the prayer from the heart of Prometheus, a speedy messenger posting to the home of the haughty Goddess.

And on other days he followed quickly a straight and direct path to his goal, reaching it without mishap and fulfilling his mission truly.

To-day, however, whether betrayed by an evil spirit, or from too great presumption, he made a wide circuit, then flew inland towards the royal palace, but passed by the house, though keeping as close to it as possible.

And he came straight to the narrow path skirting the ivy on the garden wall.

And when he beheld the mighty pair, he squared his shoulders and raised his head, and passed by with fixed gaze, making no salutation. And so it was that, when their glances crossed, he smiled with his eyes, and his lips curled slightly.

And this he did without any conscious

will, but by some secret and involuntary impulse.

And the Angel suffered it with lofty dignity, like a lion teased by some foolish little animal—its eye twinkling, looking aside, annoyed, and yet patient, if the jest is not carried too far.

His consort, however, took it quite otherwise. The depths of her heart were filled with a darkly glowing hate, and hate, too, welled in full stream from her midnight eyes, from her tight-shut lips, and from her majestic body.

And she felt hatred not alone for her enemy's face, but for his whole body, and for every movement of his limbs.

And it was thus only that she acknowledged his presence. And when he had passed on, she turned her head and gazed at his back until he was out of sight.

And when he finally vanished amid the bushes, and when the object of her hate could no longer be seen, she turned round again and spake to her lord slightingly and with blame.

"How long wilt thou endure this barefaced scorn, and for what does thy long-suffering wait?

For, lo, the heart of Prometheus is sickening of all-too-great comfort. So put an end to his good time, and take away his leisure, and let him taste the real savour of the earthly life. So, perchance, his spirit will once again become lowly, and his soul be purged of all unwholesome sleekness."

And stung by his wife's taunt, the Angel's anger was aroused and he called to one of the servants standing at the door of the palace and spake this command to him in firm tones:

"Haste thee to earth and to the valley of Prometheus, and lead him straightway into a strange land, and set him there to some mean and servile task. But see thou hurt not a hair of his head, for this is a truly worthy man, and it may well be, that in good time, when he has repented, I shall be able to make use of him again."

So he spake, and the servant hurried off at once, zealous to begin his mission.

And darkness had already covered the land, when the unwelcome messenger reached the house of Prometheus, and began to speak in respectful tones:

"Wake up with wailing! Make thyself ready with tears!

For this day thou must leave thy home hill and valley, and must betake thyself to menial service in a strange land!"

But Prometheus answered and spake with calm assent:

"Here is no wailing! Here are no tears! For, lo, I have expected thee, and therefore be thou welcome."

And, thereupon, he prepared himself for the journey and girt up his loins, and, when all was ready, he set out and walked on quietly alongside his guide.

And before he had reached the gate of the garden, there was a patter of footsteps behind him, and, lo, his little dog came, running round and round him, with coaxing whines.

But Prometheus began and spoke sternly to the little creature:

"Where dost thou come from, and what dost thou think to gain by thy coaxing?"

And the little dog wriggled, and cowered, and stretched herself flat on the ground.

Prometheus, however, when he saw the disobedience of the dog, raised his hand and spoke sharply:

"Go home at once, for, lo, we journey to a far-off land, where I can make no use of thee."

And the little animal crouched low, and whined, and whimpered, because she felt the rebuke;

But even as she cried, her eye sought that of her master, blinking and winking.

And after a spell of impatience, her

master's anger abated, and his face was troubled, and his arm fell to his side involuntarily.

Then the little dog was encouraged to make a further effort, and crawled up to him on her belly, begging and praying with fawning gestures.

"If the land is far-off, my feet are sound and strong; and if thou dost not need me, I can keep away to one side."

But Prometheus abided by his refusal and spoke again in displeasure.

"Thou desirest a foolish thing, for truly our journey does not lead to happiness, and if thou knewest what awaits us in that land, thou wouldst, perhaps, prefer to stay at home."

But the dog was persistent, and kept on acting as before, and followed her master at a distance, and when he threatened and scolded, she remained behind, and turned back sadly, and pretended to go home.

But after a little, there she was again, fawning and begging and following steadily at a discreet distance.

And Prometheus began and spake to himself, in wonder and amaze:

"And so I have escaped my enemy, the grim hater?"

And even as he spoke, two glowing eyes appeared in the dark, close to the way, and, behold, the lion lay in wait, couched and ready for a spring.

And Prometheus answered and spoke to the lion, with quiet composure:

"In vain, my friend, dost thou lurk there, because the might of my God still protects me, and the time of the sacrifice is not yet!

If, however, thou wilt listen to good counsel, so much the better. Use the happy chance of to-day, leave thy grudge behind thee, and accompany me to the new country."

But the lion would not listen to his request, but crept off, growling, and walked along at some distance, to one side of and below the path.

And now his menacing look was seen among the bushes; and now he sprang noiselessly over stream and gully. And often he climbed up to the top of the bank, and the loose stones started under his mighty feet and rolled noisily down into the valley.

And so this curious procession fared through the narrow valley, each apart from the other, veiled in darkness, and wrapped in solitude. And none spoke a word, nor was any sound heard, except their own footfalls, echoing regularly in the black stillness.

And Prometheus was a little in advance, to the left of the way. And, as he walked, he gazed away from the gorge towards the night-clad fields, listening to the grass-halms, whispering secrets to each other.

And to the right of the path paced his guide, looking aimlessly downhill, and carefully avoiding the glance of his companion.

And when, in this silent order, they had nearly reached the middle of the valley, there stood by the way a lime-tree, sleeping and dreaming.

And the tree, raising itself on high, began to whisper in its dreams:

"Who are ye, hailing from the valley of Prometheus and from the beloved home of that quiet thinker?"

And Prometheus disguised his voice, looked up, and said: "A friend of his youth, and, to wit, at a time when his heart is sore. My soul is sick, and when it wails and cries, I can hardly bear it."

And again the tree spoke and asked in its dreams:

"What is Prometheus doing in his quiet home, and what is the aim of his work?"

And again Prometheus spoke in a feigned voice, looked up, and said: "He sleeps and dreams, and it is of days of promise that he dreams, when the wedding-morn will flame over the fields and drive the mists away."

And at this word, the tree remembered the joys of morning, when the birds sing clearly above the ploughed fields—and at this thought it thought on and on, and bowed its head, and lapsed into silence.

And, as they went on their way, a little brook glided sleepily through the valley and its ripples slipped along lazily and quietly.

And out of its weary heart it began and murmured and gurgled and put these questions:

"Who are ye from the gorge of the valley, and how is it that your steps approach from the home of the quiet and patient one?"

And Prometheus disguised his voice, looked down, and said: "I am a sick man, who heard of the skill of Prometheus and of the miraculous healing power of his gracious mistress, and therefore I thought that it might, perchance, come about that they would heal me."

And again the brook began and asked, in its soft murmur:

"What thinks his Soul, his beauteous friend with the proud brow?"

And again Prometheus changed his voice, looked down, and said: "She walks by the clear fountain in her beautiful garden and spins her wedding-robe, and as she spins she murmurs a song, and as she murmurs she thinks of her servant, who dwells alone in a distant land!"

And it came to pass at these words the brook thought of its sisters, who murmur in the dark grove, and he thought on and on, and dreamed, and forgot himself, and became silent.

And as they fared farther, the bearing of Prometheus became of a sudden more anxious, and his steps became more soft; and all the while he looked with stolen glances towards the far side of the valley, where the mountains raised their dark and shapeless masses.

And after a space a winding path branched off on one side, leading to an old hut by a deserted quarry, hidden in the darkness, unnoticed by the guide, and visible only to the eye that knew it was there.

Thereupon Prometheus slackened his pace and kept step with his companion, so that the guide's body shielded his and his shadow always covered him in the axis of the path's direction.

And so, with noiseless step and held-in breath, he strove to pass unseen, fearing most that the loud beating of his heart might betray him.

And even after the side-path lay behind them, and new objects bounded them both on the right and on the left, he still for a long time walked cautiously, avoiding every noise, until a very considerable space lay between him and the hut.

And, thereupon, his bearing became freer and he drew his breath more lightly, like one who had overcome his greatest difficulty and like one who had escaped from an ambush without scathe.

And quietly and regularly their steps resounded throughout the night—and, ere they knew, they had reached the outlet of the valley.

And the guide began and spoke, with the gracious permission of Prometheus:

"Perhaps, if it please thee, thou mightest here turn round for the last time, to greet thy home-valley and bid farewell to thy beloved haunts."

And Prometheus answered and spoke in quiet response:

"Thou speakest in error, my friend! For my home does not lie in that spot, but my dwelling is in the distant future and beyond the dark mountains."

And, thus speaking, he walked stoutly round the last corner of the valley.

And a little thereafter they came to the

populous part of the country, and to the tired and sleeping community of men. And it came to pass, by a freakish chance, that their steps led them close by the royal palace, on its proud hill.

And the black body of the palace shone with lights, and its shadow was cast far over the sleeping fields, and from the windows sounded silvery laughter, and lively talk, and many other cheerful noises.

And Prometheus steeled himself and pressed onward with his head turned away.

The lion also avoided the palace by a wide loop through the fields. But when the little dog, the last of the band, reached the foot of the hill, she kept looking up, and smelling, and sniffing, and questing, and listening.

Prometheus, however, turned round, and warned and scolded her.

"Thou art doing a very foolish thing; take care that thou dost not find how bitterly alien happiness tastes in thine own heart!"

And abashed at her master's reproof, she gave over and reddened and dropped back. Then she stiffened her body, raised her head, and ran on in front with a severe air of conscious virtue.

After a brief space, however, her steps faltered, and when a broad shadow fell across her way, she slunk off secretly and hastened, unnoticed, by a winding path through the garden to the palace. And there she placed both her forepaws on the window-sill and spied out what she could see, with outstretched neck and open ears.

And the rich hall was lit up as bright as day, and goodly men and cheerful women walked up and down in it, greeting each other in friendly talk. And all eyes beamed with a pure and spiritual delight.

And the Queen outshone all the others, but not on account of her jewels or of the magnificence of her dress or of the haughtiness of her bearing.

For she mixed with the crowd as one of themselves, and her dress was plain and without ornament. And she moved easily from one couple to another, animated and organised the friendly assembly, and said a gracious word to every individual after the use and wont of a good hostess.

But while she so passed from one part of the room to another, every eye dwelt with amaze on her noble features. And their gaze at the proud beauty of her figure was like a prayer and followed her steps as in an act of worship.

And, moreover, a spirit of such benignity enveloped her that it made soft and gentle the lines of her head, lit up her eyes and mouth, and tempered the austere impression of her beauty.—

And, suddenly, there was a silence in the great room, and a pale man separated himself from the gay crowd. His garb was black and his bearing distinguished, and his manners were easy and unconscious;

And he looked around frankly and calmly and bowed low in greeting; then he began to recite a poem in a strange, veiled voice.

And the poem was clear and vivid, like the sun shining at noonday; but the brow of the man was dark, and his eyes glowed like live coals in their sockets.

And he spake of the manifold doings of men, and of the secrets of the forest, and of the sorrows and joys of love; and his narrative was complex and artfully constructed.

And the eyes of most of his hearers hung thoughtfully on the lips of the speaker; others, however, stared blankly at the floor before them, while yet others gazed through the windows, and saw his charming pictures shine all the more brightly against the dark background of the night.

And so it was with the King and Queen —who stood far apart, separated by crowds of their guests; and the hearts of both seemed wholly absorbed by the words of the poet.

But when the man spoke from time to time of love and longing, their heads turned, unseen by the guests, and their gaze crossed, and they realised their mutual understanding, and each of them felt the words of the poet with double force.

And when the song was over, the noble guests dispersed and sought their homes, speeded by the farewell and benediction of their royal host.

And the little dog was about to do likewise and was getting ready to depart, when of a sudden a velvet shadow glided through the black night, and, lo, the Queen appeared at the window.—

And the dog crouched down in the grass and lay in wait and hearkened, holding his breath.

And the Queen leant on the sill, pressing her brow against the cool window, and began to look out dreamily over all the dark and invisible countryside.

And whether it was that an earnest word of the poet had found an echo in the depths of her soul, or whether it was that a too-happy scene of her youth was recalled in her heart, her bearing became sad, and her glances became ever more sombre.

And for a while she stood so, forgetting the present and all unconscious of herself —then suddenly her face became bright and beautiful, just as the grey morning sky is brightened by the rosy dawn: and, lo, the King stood beside her, and his shadow fell on her head.

And he gently circled her waist with his left arm, and with his right hand sought hers, which lay on the sill, half-closed, and he grasped it, opened the fist, and pressed the delicate fingers softly backwards.

And at this action, her stately form melted like snow in spring, and her whole being was relaxed in soft charm, as when a May shower sprinkles the flowery meadows.

And for a short space she stayed so, with pleasure prolonging his victory, which meant her own defeat.

But, at last, she raised herself, leaned her body backward, and with the supple muscles of her neck bent her head as far back as possible.

And the King met her action and bent down, so that they stood eye to eye, and with united breath and thirsting lips they gazed at each other, and read each other's soul.

And glorious, it appeared, was the book and clear its text, for in the reading her eye swam in bliss, and they could not have enough of it and read on and on with growing ecstasy;

And their languishing mouths approached nearer and nearer, and when at last the warm and sweet chalices of their lips met, the Queen closed her eyelids, stretched herself, and sighed, and drank. And, then, they left the window, closely clasped in passionate desire.

Prometheus, however, as he no longer heard the pattering footsteps behind him, often looked round, and waited, sent out his voice, called aloud and coaxed, turned in every direction, and tried on every side to find a trace of his companion.

After a time, as his own voice always returned to him empty, he began to speak and to console himself with these words:

"No doubt, she has thought better of it and trotted off home."

And, so saying, he walked on, feeling quite easy.

And he had made considerable progress, when something was seen moving in his tracks, and pattering steps were heard, and, lo, his little dog hastened up to him, with a wild look and a grievous face, while her tears poured on the ground in endless stream.

And the amazed Prometheus began to speak:

"Why dost thou weep? And what grief causes thy rueful countenance?"

And the little dog answered, sobbing: "It is others' happiness in my own heart that makes me feel thus."

And her tears continued to flow and flow.

Prometheus, however, took his dog's grief very much to heart, and (though, perhaps, the long walk may have had something to do with it) his bearing became weary and sad, and he went on with tired steps and a hanging head, a deceptive picture of patience and resignation.

And his steps became ever slacker and his heart grew ever more heavy-laden. But after a time he found relief in sleep from his unbearable grief, and his spirit found rest, and he was aware of nought except the complete exhaustion of his physical frame.

And this was pleasant rather than otherwise, and he would willingly have slept on for ever, and hoped to end his painful journey in this drowsy and apathetic state.

But something stirred within him and raised its head. His thoughts rose silently out of their hollow graves, and sniffed, and hearkened, and looked all round them. And when they noticed the weariness of their master and the slackened arm of his strong will, their bearing became bolder, and they began to whiz and buzz about him, blustering and shrilling in a hateful and hundred-voiced song. Just as when a wanderer strolls at midday through a sultry wood and is surrounded by a cloud of the minute pests of summer, singing and humming in his ears, not giving him a moment's rest, annoying him, teasing him to frenzy, and constantly increasing in number,

So the thoughts of Prometheus buzzed about his brain, and waked him up, and gave him no respite from their irritating song.

And so he lifted up his voice softly, and besought, and spake in sober expostulation:

"My dear friends: Your master, who often allows you time for recreation, at the proper moment, after the successful completion of the work, begs you that you will grant him rest to-day after the time of arduous struggle, as his heart is sick and sad, and sore in need of a little consideration.

And, therefore, dear friends, be silent for a short space, and thereafter, at any other time, you may act just as you list."

And it came to pass, that most of the huge swarm took shame to themselves at his petition, and yielded, and turned away, in compliance with his sober expostulation.

But all the maliciously disposed, when they heard from the master's own lips this confession of his weakness, persisted all the more and came on all the more boldly, and their former rough play was no longer enough for them and they went on to delight themselves in mocking their sick master.

And one of them burst out into this song of jubilant mockery:

"Oh Prometheus, wisest of mortals! Thou who art privileged above all others! And thinkest thyself too superior to be content even with the greatest blessings!

Well, what hast thou now attained? And how doth thy lofty wisdom stand the test?"

And another chimed in with a stronger voice:

"And thou, in the haughtiness of thy delusion, hast despised the good fortune of thy brother, and hast tormented thyself, and hast granted thy own heart neither joy nor peace, but hast richly endowed it with all the innumerable sacrifices of self-denial besides all the other sorrow that is the christening gift of the earth.

And now sleep beckons to the poorest, and his wife sits by the sick man's bed, and children's laughter encompasses the least of men.—

As for thee, however, thy sleep was longing, and loneliness thy wife, and discord thy children!"

And on this his heart turned within him and wept bitterly.

And thus accused by his own heart, and unable with his reason to deprive these reproaches of their truth, Prometheus bore every word in silence and had no protection against them save a heavy and deep-drawn sigh.

And their courage was increased by his silence, and one of them, thinking to excel all the others, came close to his master's ear, and whispered and spake with malicious tempting:

"And even lamentation is forbidden thee, for, lo, there was a day, and in that day there was a moment, when, if thou hadst so willed, thou wouldst have had no need to wander lonely to-day, through the dreary land, greeted by none, with no tear shed for thee, and no sympathetic look to heal the melancholy of thy heart.

And thou thyself wouldst be sitting in place of thy brother in the well-lighted palace, with all the goodliest men around thee, and the joy or sorrow of thy heart would have been a matter of universal interest, and in the day of misfortune, thou wouldst have felt the consoling power of love, and, feeling that, thou wouldst have blessed the very name of misfortune!"

But at this word, Prometheus mastered himself, gave his orders, and spoke in wrath and firm determination:

"Impertinent fool! How darest thou touch the Holy of Holies of my life! For, behold, I have done right; and so would I act again to-day, or to-morrow, or at any other time."

And at his anger, they all scattered and fled in abject terror, and sought quickly a hiding-place where they might take refuge. One crept behind the hedge, another among the bushes, each one taking the nearest path to safety.

And in a single instant the whole huge swarm had disappeared and seemed entirely overcome, so that no new attack was to be feared.

But it was like what happens in a grove of palms, when the wayfarer is attacked by a cowardly troop of naked savages, who run off screaming at the sound of his rifle. Yet, after an interval, they venture on another attack, and abuse him, and try to tire him out, and threaten him with hand and mouth and uncouth gestures.

So, after a short time, the thoughts thrust forth their heads again, and then came out into the open, and at last acted just as before and lost all fear, surrounding and provoking him, at first from a distance and then close at hand.

When, however, Prometheus became aware of the superior power of the enemy, he kneeled down, bowed his head, and touched the earth thrice with his forehead. Then he began this fervent prayer;

"Oh my Goddess, who canst slay with the lifting of thy eyebrows, and condemn to everlasting perdition him on whom thy glance falls unfavourably,

Before thy austere face I swear solemnly to thee, that I have no share in the sinful talk of my thoughts, and I know that I am pure and innocent of any offence. Neither in dream nor in unguarded moments have I ever stained my sacred decision by base repentance.

Do thou, therefore, have mercy upon me and lay not to my charge the sins they commit before thy throne. For, behold, they are mutineers who mock me in the time of need, and traitors who falsely use my name."

And while he so went on his way, sorely depressed and with a heavy and bitter heart, like a wounded bull which drags its sick body painfully over the steppes, stopping now and then to menace with his mighty horns the pack of hungry wolves on his trail,

He came upon a group of happy travellers, singing and dancing by the wayside, round a cheerful fire.

But at the sight of Prometheus they shrank and suddenly became mute.

And Prometheus began and spoke with friendly encouragement:

"My dear brothers, go on and sing me a song in your own way."

They, however, bowed themselves to the ground in servile fashion, and declined and answered and said:

"Honoured Sir, thou seemest inclined to mock us, for, lo, we are humble folk, and there is no sense in our songs."

As, however, he persisted in his request, after a time a maiden approached, with black hair and nut-brown skin, clad in gay but soiled finery;

And she placed herself in the middle of the circle and arranged her dress and greeted Prometheus. And then she stood at full height, and stretched herself, and turned and rocked her lithe body, and finally began to sing and leap. And the glances of her eyes sparkled like flame.

"He is a fool who thinks of life in any other way than we, a vagrant crew, homeless and free from toil, wandering over hill and dale.

And so it goes that in the day of joy, in the time of youth, we quaff the sweetness and pleasure of life, and when the evil days of age appear, we sing: so be it, all is right with the world, for, lo, we have had our fill of earthly happiness, and therefore it is just that we should also know earthly grief and death."—

And as she sang, her face beamed and the zest of life streamed through her graceful movements.

And Prometheus answered and said, seriously and thoughtfully:

"Verily a beautiful song, and truly wiser than the school-room songs sung by professional choirs. It would take but little to make me sing it with you.

But there is one and only song, wiser still, to which I cling, so that you cannot convert me to your view; and on account of this song you will be worsted in the struggle with my opinion and with my troubled and tormented life."

And the girl lifted up her voice and asked and said:

"Perchance, if thou art so gracious, thou wilt tell us this song to our great healing and profit."

Prometheus, however, laughed sadly: "Verily, it would please thee little for me to teach it thee, for it is a difficult song and the way to sing it is troublesome beyond all measure.

And it is also a sad song, and, besides, the song has no end at present.

However, if, after a year and a day, a happy chance should make us meet again, then I surely promise to teach you the song, with its ending."

And so he spake and sighed, and then he took the path over hill and dale, leading him to a strange people in an unknown land.

SURVEY

And their journey lasted till daybreak. But with the first gleam of morning light they reached the unloved land, and there they stationed themselves in the market-place in patient expectation.

And when the people assembled at their wonted hour, they came up and inspected the man and asked of what arts he was master.

And Prometheus answered and spoke, with genial smile:

"I am innocent of arts! But I shall serve you truly and honestly to the best of my modest ability."

But this reply did not satisfy the hirers, so he was left alone for a long time and was the last man in the whole market to find an employer.

But when the tower-clock struck at noonday, there approached a man, foolish from his birth and now also weak-minded from age, and he addressed Prometheus with all the simplicity and kindliness of his nature:

"Verily, his face seems to me honest, and I shall perhaps be able to engage him at a low wage."

And he spake and closed the bargain. And so Prometheus entered into this man's service and followed him to his house—he and his two animals.

And at first the service was a hard one. And it so happened that, when in the morning he led his master's herd to graze outside the town gate, the beasts began to eat the apples on the adjacent trees and paid no attention to his efforts to restrain them;

And in the evening the cattle moaned and writhed and were in great distress, whereupon the master complained and said to Prometheus: "This comes from eating too much grass, so let us quickly buy some figs from the dealers in the market."

And when Prometheus was set to building by his master, the latter began at once to find fault: "Verily, thou seemest to have no idea of beauty, for thou art building the house with square corners, and all the lines are straight."

And so saying he ordered him to build all the walls and partitions on a slant.

And when the job was ended, the structure collapsed, with rumbling and cracking.

Thereupon the man wept and screamed: "This is the second time that thou hast brought misfortune upon me! For, behold, the house had too many corners. So begin again, and see that thou scrupulously avoidest every right angle."

And this was the nature of his service. But after a time his friends came to the employer, and spoke to him, and asked him in profound amazement:

"How is it that thy house is so clean and so light? And how is it that thy possessions have increased and that all goes well with thee?"

And so it came about that Prometheus found his service much more bearable. And after a time he became quite indispensable to his master, who followed wherever he stood or went and sunned himself in his cheerful mien and in his rich and many-sided character.

But while his service was thus going on in an easier manner, a knock came to his door one evening, and, lo, there was the worm from his home-valley. And the worm came in and greeted him with these friendly words:

"It was a long way and a hard journey, but I got here at last. So let us rejoice in the renewal of our companionship."

And with that it shook the dust from its body and settled down for a quiet rest.

And Prometheus answered and said to the worm:

"Thou art very welcome and comest just at the right time! For, behold, I am menaced by an unworthy happiness, and my heart is enmeshed by the dishonouring embrace of a baseborn comfort. So do thy duty and blow it away with thy powerful breath!"

And the worm did as it was asked, and even more. For, in its dealing with his unworthy happiness, it involved over and above his finest feelings to boot.

THE LION

And after a year and a day, whether it was the breath of the worm or possibly the unwonted air of a strange land, the lion fell sick and could not eat a morsel and stared fixed and amazedly at the same point, while his whole body shivered violently.

And so it went for a long time—and finally the thing drove him out to seek relief afar off.

And he wandered about in a wide land and for a whole day, and when he got back in the evening, his body was weary to the death and his energy was broken. But in spite of all, he found no relief from the burning fever of his plague.

And thus he scoured the country every morning. And Prometheus, either becoming used to the continued sickness or reassured by the undiminished strength of his friend, gradually became consoled and spoke to himself comfortable words:

"No doubt all this is caused by the unknown country, and in good time it will doubtless come out all right."

And so he neither spoke nor thought of it any more. But one morning, as he was pasturing his master's kine according to his daily use and wont, the royal animal appeared, with crippled back and dragging his hind-legs pitifully in the dust.

And at this sight Prometheus was smitten with such pain as he never had felt in all his life before, and he cried out bitterly and uttered these words with unmeasured grief: "Thou noble animal! There is nothing like thee on earth. When they saw thee in the pride of thy youth, all the people marvelled at thy mien, and stood still, looking after thee and whispering to each other in the utmost amaze:

'Truly a noble youngster! From what stock has he sprung? What a rich fulness of unheard of gifts he will one day manifest!'

And every good man was thy friend, and no hope of thy growth seemed too great:—and now I have to see thee in this state! All thy promise murdered by my guilt—an irreplaceable loss for the world and an incurable wound for myself!"

And thus lamenting, he followed the lion with his eyes, and every movement of his limbs pierced him to the heart.

And the lion took no heed of his words, but strode mutely past him, to undertake his daily roaming through the land.

And his gait was slow in very deed, and every step was a grievous toil, and it seemed as if his strength must give out at any moment.

But either from obstinacy and the clear and determined resolve of his will, or because he was urged on by the increasing agony of his sickness, he never gave out, but dragged on his ailing body and pressed forward over stock and stone, through wood and field. And his only guide was the hope that perhaps in some far-off spot he might find relief from his merciless adversary.

And his flight had lasted for more than an hour, while the country became wilder and wilder, and a little later he found himself in a narrow gorge, hemmed in by huge rocky walls.

And for a time he was at a loss, gazing all round, measuring the height of the walls, and then looking sadly at his palsied limbs.

But everywhere the cliffs rose vertically, broken by no gateway and by no path. And while he waited thus, little streams tumbled from all points of the gloomy rocks, assailed his ear with incessant rustling, and splashed his head with troublesome spray.

And thereupon he waxed impatient and his eye became full of anger. He could bear it no longer, but lashed his tail and tossed his mane, bent his head back, opened the red cavern of his mouth, and lifted up his voice against all this vague and senseless uproar.

And the tone of his voice was angry, like the barking of wolves in a snow-bound forest, and like the howling of the wind over a storm-tossed sea. And his roar filled the air, drowning every other sound with its fearsome cadence.

And this served him as a *Test;* and thereafter he lowered his head and with the full strength of his lungs repeated the terrible roar ten times in succession.

And this was the real *Opening* of the performance. So he went on to fill the empty house of the aether with the rolling thunder of his voice, like the avalanches that fall from the mountaintops into the valleys, so that the cliffs on either side resounded and trembled. And all the spirits of the air, that nestled in the rocky walls like birds, awoke in a fright and fled, losing their way in their dumbfounded panic. And they swept up and down with screams of terror, recoiling at every point, colliding with each other, and crushing each other, so that the ears of the great soloist were deafened by the thousandfold repetition of their cries of dread.

And for a long while he kept on with this performance, redoubling his rage by the echo of his own voice. And while he roared, he stared in front of him with hate-burdened eyes and whetted his glances on the hard stones. Then, suddenly, his pain and anger obsessed him with mad fury, and he began to climb with frantic effort.

Wherever there was a narrow ledge of earth and vegetation, he dug his claws into it and dragged up his crippled body by his straining sinews. But where the face of the rock was smooth and refused him any foothold, he growled and bit at the stone with powerful teeth, and let the whole weight of his body hang on his mighty jaws.

And so step by step, with incredible pains, he climbed the livelong day from morn till eve.

But several times he was at the end of his strength, and in his sober senses he would never have persisted. But the demon within him let him neither pause nor rest, until at last the cleft opened and the warm, sun-soaked aether flooded it with light.

And at this he collected his forces for one supreme effort and managed to reach the top in one more agonizing spasm. And, lo, he found himself in a fairer land; more beautiful things clustered round him, and the circumambient air was more balmy. The miracle of a happy chance had transported him to the blessed fields of Heaven.

And quite beside himself at this discovery, he collected his energies with hasty zeal and took up his journey with new zest. But it was too much for him. He broke down wholly and fell on his side, gasping and groaning in complete helplessness.

And it was just the time that the sun assumes its lovely farewell face and greets its much-loved earth with its last soulful glance, while the meadows and forests waft their responses, giving thanks for the rich delights of the day, sighing desire, breathing contentment. Just as a woman who has given herself body and soul to her beloved man, when he makes to leave her, continues to lie on her couch, bathed in recollection, intoxicated with happiness, faint from the storm of love. And, when his right hand is actually on the latch, she turns towards him again with her voluptuous body, stretches out her inviting arms, and with love-drowsy eyes sighs out an adieu. And the kissing of her soft mouth repeats it, and the swelling of each muscle repeats it, and each languishing limb repeats it, so that the separation is conquered and reconciled by the exuberance of the pleasure.

And it was at this hour that the people of Heaven wandered up and down in long rows, on the high bank of the land, singing their songs of joy, looking down calmly into the depths below, and drinking in the fragrant zephyrs, while their long shadows swam, as it were, in a sea of molten gold.

And when they were aware of the deep-mouthed groaning that filled the air, they hastened to the spot, discovered the lion, clustered round him, and looked down on him, half with pity, half with gruesome wonder.

And some of them began to speak to the lion: "Whence dost thou come? And what is the god of thy country?"

And the lion answered and spoke in a dissimulating voice:

"I come from the land of earth as an ambassador to God. Perchance ye can put me on the right way?"

And the people looked at each other and then turned round, and began to speak, with consideration and sympathetic gestures:

"Thou seemest to have been misled by evil counsel. For, behold, God does not live in these parts, and no road leads to him from here, and no one of our people has ever seen him.

Tell us, however, the import of thy message, for, perchance, an opportunity may offer for us to forward it."

And the lion again answered and spoke again in the same voice:

"Well, then, pray give God a greeting from the land of earth, and tell him that the whole world is bathed in happiness, and that every creature gives thanks to his creator, and that every moment is a moment of bliss.

And this you may do, if it seems good to you in the plenitude of your good will."

And all was still for a short time. Then they began again with their interested questionings:

"So be it! But why dost thou groan so? Thou seemest to be ill? Where is the chief seat of thy pain?"

And once more the lion replied and spoke with patient obedience:

"I sigh because of the intensity of my inner sensitiveness, and the chief seat of my pain is the point where memory of my former strength meets my present consciousness."

In the meantime more and more loiterers had collected on the spot, so that the inner ring became ever closer, while the outer circle expanded.

Just as snow covers the stone more and more thickly, or as flies cluster round fruit, or as bees swarm round their queen, or as a dying hare amid the clover, still breathing and still able to raise his head, sees the air full of moving bodies, where the crows and the ravens are flying towards him in unbroken files and fluttering round him with greedy cawing, and the air becomes grey with the approach of new swarms.

Whereupon the place became odious to the lion, and, moreover, his body was sorely in need of rest, so he overcame his fatigue and started on his homeward way, avoiding the pity of strangers at any cost, as is the use and wont of the proud.

And the people perceived his intention with regret, for they would gladly have asked more questions and let their emotions run riot.

But the goodness of their heart made them give way to him, and they willingly made room for him to pass.

And so, without let or hindrance, he had nearly reached the entrance again—

when, lo, by a happy chance, the Angel of the Lord came through the fields, enjoying the cool of the evening with Doxa, his tall and beautiful friend.

And he saw the group of people and directed his steps towards them, but at first without much interest, as one who happens to notice something unimportant and as one who despises the foolish wonder of the vulgar crowd.

And at sight of him the procession halted and reverently made a passage for him.

And he approached arm in arm with his friend, bending calmly forward and as yet he had noticed nothing. He had already turned his body a little to one side, and had set his lips for a smile, meaning to retrace his steps after a glance or two at the crowd.

And this was his intention as he turned round. But no sooner did his eye light on the lion than his face became extraordinarily serious, and he advanced rapidly and looked anxiously down at the suffering beast.

And while he thus looked, his eyes filled with tears and he became sunk in reflection.

And the Goddess was displeased at her lord's action and shuffled her feet impatiently, bent her head to the side, swayed her back and her hips, and pressed his arm gently with her fingers, inciting him to move on.

But the Angel never looked up, and when the pressure of her fingers became more marked, he released his arm from her too great importunity.

Whereupon she swung herself violently round and went on alone, muttering.

And for a space the Angel stood there, dumb and deeply moved. Then he collected himself, greeted the lion, and began to speak with agitated voice:

"Art thou not named Prometheus,[1] and doth not thy master live in exile in a strange land?"

And the lion raised himself up and answered yes.

And thereupon the Angel continued and consoled him in a soft and sympathetic voice:

"Well, then, do not despair but go with good courage home! For, lo, in this very hour I shall essay to heal thee."

And the lion thanked him feebly and dragged himself along and began once more his painful journey. The Angel, however, hastened by a straight and secret path to the valley of earth and to the home of Prometheus in the strange country.

And about the same hour Prometheus was searching along the boundary, distressed on account of his sick friend and anxious owing to his all-too-long absence.

And the Angel came upon him unawares, and began in haste to speak to him these gracious words:

"Prometheus, my son, elect by the wish of my heart to no mean task! Hearken, I shall end this strife and rescue thee from the unloved land and I shall set apart for thee an honourable office, wherein thou shalt find rest and peace."

And at these words of kindly approval, the heart of Prometheus trembled and sighed, as when release is brought to a prisoner. Or as when a sick man, who has lain for years on a bed of pain and still suffers unbearable torture, known to himself alone, and has been long a stranger to good health, and has given up all hope, suddenly and incredibly receives the announcement of complete cure.

And his face had already cleared and he had already opened his lips to express his thankfulness, when an inner voice was

[1] The lion really represents part of Prometheus.

heard speaking to him with severe menace:

"What dost thou yearn after? What cause has thy heart to be moved?

My decision is right and just; hearken quietly to what I command."

And thereupon this voice spoke proudly through the lips of Prometheus:

"I desire no office at thy hands! Never shall I desist from this conflict until thou hast admitted the righteousness of my cause and until thou standest before me with words of thanks in thy mouth and with hot tears of penitence in thine eyes!

For, behold, thou hast made a proverb about us, but I, even I, will furnish a rhyme for it!"

And at this arrogant answer the Angel turned away and departed in shame and confusion of face, like one who has lost his self-respect and like one who rues the foolish waste of his compassion.

And after a long time the lion returned home, weary unto death and tortured by pain, but with new fire gleaming in his eye.

And he approached his lord with questing mien and sought to read his looks —but thereupon the fire of his eye died out and he dragged himself away slowly and utterly collapsed.

And after lying there for several hours, he raised himself and spoke to the little dog, which loyally abode by her friend's couch:

"Why is the darkness so great? The night seems to me to have no end, and no glimmer of dawn appears!"

And the little dog answered and spoke in amaze:

"Thou art dreaming, my friend, and thine eyes must be overcome by weariness! For, behold, the golden orb is high in the heavens, every task of the day has long since been begun, and morning is even now giving place to noonday."

And the lion again raised his voice and spoke:

"Very well then; let us leave this gloomy chamber, for here darkness is all around us; and these walls prevent every desire of my eyes."

And at those words the little dog looked, and lo, her friend's eyes were wide open, and the light of day shone full on the noble face of the lion.

Thereupon the little dog crept into the bushes and there sobbed out her heart in pitiful wailing.

And it came to pass that when the lion heard this sound, he was amazed for a short time, till the grievous blow that had befallen him broke upon his consciousness.

And for a while he remained mute, revolving in his mind his bitter grief, but calmly, after the manner of noble souls, and then he began to speak in a soft and subdued voice:

"Why dost thou weep, my friend? And why dost thou take my affliction so sorely to heart?

"For I have done thee many a wrong, and I was but a hard friend to thee, and there was eternal feud between us and between our children.

Still, though my outer bearing may have seemed rough, I was always loyally disposed towards thee. Verily I should gladly have done thee a favour at any time, and I have oft-times communed with myself as to how I could best serve thee."

And it came to pass that on these words the little dog came up to him and bathed him with her tears.

And so they remained together the livelong day, seeking each to console the other with their mutual love;

But when midnight shrouded the land, the lion began all at once to listen, raised his head, and then began to smell the ground.

And the little dog was amazed and began to speak to him:

"What dost thou hear? What has fallen on thy ear? For the air seems to me wholly empty and I cannot hear a single sound."

But the lion went on as before, and his bearing became ever more impatient, and he growled as in anger.

And all at once he stood up and spoke to his friend with firm determination:

"My friend, thou seest that I am ripe for death, and in a very little while I shall trouble thee no more.

Mayhap, therefore, thou wilt do me a last service and help me for the last time."

And the little dog assented, mutely and with sobs.

Thereupon the lion continued and spoke with insistent desire:

"Thou seest, I lie here blind and helpless, and every path is barred to me. So do thou lend me thine eyes and lead me hence to my home-valley, that I may greet my dearly beloved children for the last time."

And the little dog answered in profound astonishment: "What dost thou mean? How shall I interpret thy wish? For are not thy children dead, strangled by the stern decree of our master?"

And the lion replied: "Verily, I thought as thou thinkest; but now I distinctly hear the well-known sound of their voices. Moreover, at the time I begat them in the mountains the spirit of God moved in the tempest, and therefore, I fear, they could not die.

So, delay no longer and do me the service of guiding my steps, for, lo, this is my last walk, and hereafter, thou wilt be free of any trouble from me all the days of thy life."

And at this word they set out and proceeded slowly towards the far-off valley, one following the other.

And toil and trouble they had more than enough; but when the evening of the second day was melting into night, they had reached their goal, and their reverent feet were treading the soil of their homeland.

And the lion spoke to his friend: "Let us now find a place of ambush, where we may, unseen, see whatever may befall."

And the little dog agreed, and they laid themselves down behind a bush, on a hill overlooking the valley, and there waited patiently and quietly.

Hour after hour they spent thus, but they heard nothing, and utter silence brooded over the valley. The moon rose slowly, and the silence was unbroken save for the unchanging murmur of the brook far down amid the shady willows.

—And while they so waited in vain, midnight struck on the heavenly tower, and was echoed by the bosom of the earth, and resounded from mountain to mountain through the deep veins of ore.—

And both listened to the solemn tones. Then, suddenly, the teeth of the little dog began to chatter, and she whined and whimpered in a low tone.

At this the lion's heart sank and he asked: "Tell me why thou art whining, and what terrible object meets thy gaze?"

And his companion replied in a whisper: "I see thy children rising from the dead, and I see them alive again, and they are moving about quite plainly."

And the lion said: "Are they all there, and is no one of the large litter absent?"

And the little dog looked again and counted, then replied in a whisper:

"One only is wanting, and it lies like a clod on the ground, and I cannot make out whether it is alive or dead."

And the lion went on with his questions:

"Are they all sound and well? Has the death-sickness been cured? Are they growing bigger? Are they flourishing? Do they move their limbs freely and strongly?"

And the dog looked at them once more, and once more whispered her reply:

"The bloody spot still cleaves to their necks, and they crawl about with difficulty, like seals when they drag their smooth bodies over dry land."

At this information the lion could no longer master the wild anger of his heart, and he crashed headlong out of the bush, braced his forelegs against the hard ground, raised high his heavy head, and greeted the still night with a terrific roar.

And his cubs scattered, whimpering, in all directions, each seeking safety where it might.—

But the lion had already changed his position, and, tearing up the turf with his mighty paws and claws, had thrown himself over the bank. And so he rolled rapidly down, stemming his fall with his legs and ploughing up the ground with his nails, until in a few moments he reached the bottom of the slope and lay panting on the level floor of the valley:

And coated with mud and earth, his mane matted with twigs and gravel, he rose up, and, trusting to his ear alone, pursued his ghastly hunt, the blind and crippled father chasing his wounded children.

And so began a grisly massacre in the valley, and the mountains re-echoed with screams and appeals for mercy.

But the loss of his sight proved no obstacle to the all-too-great keenness of his ear, and he overtook his victims everywhere—in the wood, in the grass, in the dark caves of the rock. No hiding-place and no flight could save them. Whether they crawled behind the house, or threw themselves, mad with fear, headlong into the stream, he seized them, tore them limb from limb and with a soft but ghastly sound crushed their tender bones between his strong teeth.

And the fearful execution lasted long, until at last the whole brood was slaughtered. And he turned back, and, wherever a sigh or gasp was audible, completed his bloody work.

And when the silence all round was absolutely complete, except for the peaceful rippling of the brook, he dragged himself back and spoke to the little dog, who listened to him shuddering in every limb.

"So that is accomplished. Now let us go home and die."

And the little dog obeyed his wish, and led him thence.

And as the evening of the second day was darkening into night, they reached their home again. And then the lion lay down to die, fighting the accursed battle for three long days.

And the little dog sprang hither and thither, whimpering, despairing, powerless, unable to furnish either help or counsel. And every now and then she licked the lion's face, in a vain attempt to alleviate his sad sufferings.

And at the head of the sick lion sat his Lord, motionless as if made of stone, with his body turned away from the death-bed. He neither wept nor wailed, and his rigid features betrayed neither feeling nor pity. All the same he kept turning his gaze on the lion, and when, now and again, the lion writhed in the extremity of his agony, his eyebrows twitched and he bit his lips.

And he spoke no word during the whole time. When, however, the end came on the third day, he stood up and with firm tread and solemn earnestness he approached the lion. Crossing his arms, he kneeled on the ground, saluted the dying beast, and spoke with bowed and humble head these words:

"My friend, thou art now about to die, and wilt never more return, and never again shall I see thy face.

So consider once more the old friend of thy youth, and open thy lips, and do not depart from me in grudge and enmity."

And at these words the lion called on the last remnant of his strength, and stretched himself and raised himself with a mighty and painful effort. And with all his hate concentrated in one last glance, he glared at him with his blind eyes—and then fell dead on his side.

Close

And as he so lay, never to move again, Prometheus sprang to his feet, stretched out his arms, and circled round him slowly. And he began to speak in a loud and emphatic voice:

"All ye things that look down at me at this juncture, and ye, earth and heaven, that compass me about, listen now to my oath and count me a liar if ever I depart from it."

And he continued, turning towards the dead lion: "Hear me now; by thy dead body I swear that, if I have acted bootlessly, and if the ring on my finger breaks, I shall accept the heritage of thy hate and shall revenge thee on myself, offering myself to death, whether from the precipice, or in the sea, or by plunging the steel in my breast by my own hand."

And thereupon he set himself to bury the lion in a corner of the garden.

THE LITTLE DOG

The little dog, however, lay down on her friend's grave, bedewed it day and night with her tears, and refused to leave it.

But after a time her master gave her a clear and urgent order:

"Cease to act so and come away from the grave; otherwise it may come to pass that the poison of his sickness may attack thee also, and so I may lose both my friends."

And the dog, well trained to willing obedience, did as she was told and left the grave slowly and reluctantly.

And the whole long day she stayed near her master, obedient to his strict command; but when the veil of night was spread, she crept off hastily to her friend's grave and wept and sobbed there, until morning came and the approach of dawn revealed what had been hidden by the dark.

And thereupon she slunk once more into her master's room.

And so she acted day after day. And it came to pass that one morning, when Prometheus greeted the dawn, he raised his voice and began to speak sternly to his little friend: "Why dost thou look so weary and why are thine eyes so red, and wherefore does thy body shiver with cold?"

And she replied, with some confusion of face: "I look weary from having slept too long, and I feel cold because I dreamed of winter."

And so she followed the same practice with great regularity for many days, varying her routine in no degree.

And one morning, just like other mornings, the sun mounted cheerfully in the sky, the dew sparkled in the grass, and the birds trilled in the hedges.

The little dog came back sadder than usual, her body shivered and shuddered worse than ever, and her eyes were more than ordinarily red.

And she crept about the room as if seeking something with hazy eyes, and she turned round in circles. Her teeth chattered, and she would snap suddenly in the air with a hoarse, throaty howling. And thereafter she crawled under the bed and rolled herself into a ball, sobbing and barking, and her legs jerked convulsively.

And she lay there for seven days, refusing food and drink, and paying no heed to her master's call, no matter whether he coaxed her or ordered her sternly and loudly. She remained as if dead and quite oblivious of all that happened.

But on the eighth day, when Prometheus came home at eventide, she crawled out, greeted him, and began to speak in a feeble voice:

"My lord and master, hear my prayer —the prayer of thy poor child, who has always and unchangeably loved thee in joy and sorrow. My every thought was for thee, and my every feeling concerned thee only—And, oh, these were days full both of beauty and of pain!—

Such days I never see now. Joy and sorrow are for me ended. All my children are dead, my friend is dead, and very soon thou wilt have to bury me also!

And, perhaps, it is better so. For, lo, I have had it all in abundance, and, truly, I would not wish to bear it longer.

All the same, I know not why, my heart is so unspeakably sad and full of woe, that I said to myself, it may be that thou wilt take pity on me, and raise my spirits by some edifying tale."

And so saying, she laid her head on her master's knee, and looked up at him with her loyal eyes.

And Prometheus laid his hand affectionately on his little friend's head, and began to relate to her the following story:

The Valley of Death

In a distant rocky wilderness there was a man who lived poorly, in the sweat of his brow, with his seven sons.

And when the sons went forth in the morning to plough in the fallow field, the father spake these warning words to them, with anxious mien.

"Above all, take care that ye avoid the Valley of Death, which lies to the right, below the grove of palms, for I have often heard from the lips of my parents that it will come to pass that madness will seize whoever enters this valley, and that he will have no more happiness all the days of his life."

Thus he spake day after day, and they listened to his words, and led a hard but honest life, in the sweat of their brow, yet with a contented spirit.

But one day, as they sat down to dinner at the usual time, the father looked at his sons, and counted them, and behold the youngest was missing. And the brothers answered and said to their father, with consoling gestures: "Without reason is thy heart anxious, for behold we left him safe and sound; he stayed behind with his plough and is just loitering a little. No doubt he will soon return."

While they spoke thus, the door opened and behold their brother came in; but his hair had turned white, his countenance was distraught, and the look of his eyes was wholly changed.

In great horror they all sprang to their feet, surrounded him, pressed close to him, and besieged him with anxious questions.

For a long time he stood speechless and gasping, while his eyes were fixed on the far distance.

But at last he controlled himself, opened his mouth, and spoke breathlessly, ashy-pale and shuddering.

"It befell that, as is my use and wont, I was the last to turn towards home. The air of noon was hot, the rocks were scorching, and a brooding stillness lay over the whole land.

When I came with weary steps to the palm trees above the Valley of Death, where a grateful shade cooled my brow, my foot paused without my wish, and without intent my eyes sank, and I looked down at the lead-coloured rocks.

While I looked without thought, resting after the hot walk, a sort of humming sound reached me from the depths of the accursed valley.

For a time I could not believe my ears; but to settle my doubt, I bent down, closed my eyes, and kept my head to the ground.

Now I heard, full and clear, thousands of voices, mysterious and confused.

I sprang to my feet in great excitement and ventured to descend a little, and the strange sound became louder and louder. So I went farther and still farther, even to where the grass stops at the landmark of the boundary.

There I stood for a long time and listened, while my breath choked in my breast and my blood roared and hammered in my temples.

At last I could bear it no longer and spied about furtively, and as no one was to be seen as far as the eye could reach in any direction, I took heart, stooped, grasped a stone, and gently turned it over; and, lo and behold, beneath it swarmed and squirmed and wriggled thousands of soft warm living things.

Beside myself with deadly terror, I lifted a second stone, and it was just the same, on and on, wherever I stopped there was life—life!"

While he thus spake, his senses left him again and he stood dazed, with his eyes rolling distraught.

His brothers began to reassure him, saying: "Take courage, brother, and be not dismayed, probably a bad dream of noonday terrified thee; in any case thou mayst easily learn for thyself the deceit and illusion of this ghostly vision.

For behold, if life existed in the valley, there must also be death, on and on to all eternity. How can thy poor heart believe in such a devilish and crazy dispensation as that?"

At these words the other answered as one beside himself: "That is just what I have seen; death, death everywhere throughout that wide valley."

The others laughed incredulously and signed knowingly to each other. And when the moon shone on the fallow field, they silently arose and hastened to the palms above the Valley of Death.

And after listening for a while, they too ventured to descend. When, next morning, the Father came to waken his sons at the usual time, each of them sat on the floor beside his bed, quite out of his senses and gibbering foolishly.

Thanking him, the little dog answered and spake to Prometheus, his Lord and Master: "Verily this tale has consoled and strengthened me mightily; but please go on, if perchance thou knowest a second story with the same significance."

And Prometheus again lifted his voice and began the following tale, in a monotonous and slow manner.

Sophia

It was one Sunday afternoon in summer, when wood and field were in festal array, the silvery air sparkled and shimmered, and the bells joyously swung out their clear peals far and wide over the town and countryside.

People crowded out of the streets of Heaven, surging through the gate, and making, either in groups or alone, for the mountains, the woods, and the fragrant coppices.

And while they thus disported themselves in the sunshine, every sin was redeemed, all suffering was assuaged, and all trouble disappeared in the clear and blessed light of the day.

Sophia, the eldest and most beautiful daughter of God, sat in her airy castle in the most delightful corner of Heaven. Sighing, she laid her hands on her lap and sadly looked through an open window at the eagle, soaring high in the air, and at the green and boldly formed mountain, casting its shadow across the valley.

Hour after hour she sat there with troubled eyes and patient heart, as one whose wont it was and as one to whom renunciation was a daily habit.

Suddenly she sprang up, crossed the room, and, laying her gentle hand lightly on the banister, glided down the wide steps, and hastened to the gloomy and black-draped room, where her brother, the son of the most high God, lay sick.

Opening the door and standing on the threshold, she began to speak to him, with sadness and tears:

"Would that I had never been called a daughter of God, and had never dwelt in the most beautiful house of Heaven; rather would I be one of the least of those who live down there on earth, unknown and nameless amid the common herd.

For, lo, each of them has a husband or a brother who cares for her, honouring her and taking her to festivals, while joy brightens her face.

But I sit lonely and deserted day after day; for me there is no festival, no one shows any interest in me, no one takes me to the place where I might enjoy sunshine and the breath of the forest."

Slowly her brother raised his head and looked at his sister, who stood before him in all the glory of her beauty, her charming face flushed with animaion, and her whole figure bathed in light. And thereupon he began to answer her in feeble and reproachful tones:

"Beloved sister! comfort of my life, more precious to my heart than my own unhappy self—willingly would I give thee, if I could, my life a thousand times over.

Away with these spurious tears! Do not, light-heartedly and wantonly, let thy face exhibit a disingenuous sorrow! Every day do I wish and pray that thou mayest never experience true suffering or have to shed real tears.

And, as thou knowest, most willingly would I grant thy request. In my soul, however, dwells a bitter woe, by reason of which I can bear neither sunshine nor the fresh air. And the many-sided common life is poison to my heart.

Therefore must I here shroud my grief in darkness and solitude; but do thou go home in peace, content with the unspeakable blessing of thy health and strength."

But she did not hearken to his words, but came closer to him, and tearfully urged her request:

"Verily, thou hast been far too long alone; in this solitude thy disease grows daily worse, and thou wilt never become any better;

So dare to make the effort and tear thyself away from here; peradventure, if thou trustest thyself to the sunshine, it may bring thee healing on its wings."

And as she spake she threw her white arms round his neck, coaxing and caressing him with tender gestures.

And moved, either by her words or by a secret hope in his own heart, he finally yielded. And thereupon his sister hastened away, smoothed her dark and luxuriant tresses, and arrayed her stately figure in a purple robe. Then they arose, left the house, and joined the busy throng passing along the highway.

And it befell that at the sight of them the crowd made way and looked long after them, with uncovered heads and respectful pity.

And the Sick God walked along shyly, incommoded by the glaring light of day and harassed by the crowd, and so he listlessly followed the determined guidance of his sister.

And as, perforce but unwillingly, she pushed along the highroad, she showed the true instincts of a sick-nurse, avoiding so far as she could every greeting, hastening her steps, continually occupied with her charge, and watchful of his every look. And when, after a time, a bypath appeared leading across the fields to a neighbouring wood, she guided her brother's steps thither, and side by side they followed the narrow track.

And now, freed from the turmoil of the crowd and plunged in solitude, they saw at their feet a vast and undulating plain. Over their heads rose the huge dome of the aether, borne airily by slender columns, an immensity of light and space, giving no sense of downward pressure or heaviness, but rather suggesting a helpful arm relieving one of all weight. So the steps of the pair became slower; the Sick God held up his head more freely and began to feel refreshed by the great stillness.

The modest path, with its smooth surface and its elastic resistance, suited him better than the more imposing highroad; and he was pleased that it carefully avoided the arid level tracts and preferred to make a loop, winding so as to reach the spots where his face might be cooled and his body shaded by slender cherry-trees or by the tall stalks of corn. All this was most grateful to him, and he took no offence when now and again the little path allowed itself to play with its noble guests, hiding itself for a time, sinking into hollows, and then suddenly showing again as a russet streak in the distance, saluting them mischievously and inviting them to follow its track.

After a time the Sick God gained sufficient mastery over himself to appreciate the Sabbath-calm around him—covertly, it is true, hardly willing to own it even to himself, and annoyed if his sister's clear eyes seemed to be aware of it. She, however, whether by chance or design, always kept her head averted, so that he could enjoy his secret pleasure unobserved.

And it pleased him to gaze at the luxuriant crops, where the ears were already turning to gold, while the slender halms stood upright, in serried ranks, like an immense and well-marshalled army, man by man and company by company. Over the corn, at more or less regular intervals, towered lofty trees, like the mounted commanders of the army. The warm breeze, moving over the wide expanse, laden with the scent of flowers and of sweet-smelling herbs, was not too much for him. And he bore it patiently, when now and again an east wind passed lightly over the land, ruffled the golden sea, whispered to the trees, and played in the grass, bearing a thousand greetings from distant and happy haunts, telling a glorious tale of harmonious and universal bliss.

But he drew even more benefit from the dark wood, with its sombre colours and deep shadows, which surrounded the blooming fields like a bushy funeral wreath, evoking melancholy thoughts—become, as it were, after a joyous and carefree youth, a serious and mature man, unbowed by misfortune, tempered by scorn and contempt, and undismayed in facing a majority.

At last, after a time, his eye grew used to the scene and became able to endure stronger light. And it was a pleasant novelty to him to find that his vision, so long circumscribed by the confines of a narrow room, could now launch out into the distance, reaching first the white and mist-clad mountains, and then springing up boldly into the clear blue depths of the empyrean.

And at first the realm of air seemed to him pure and noble, indeed, but empty, lifeless, and inchoate. Nowhere was there any trait of animation, nowhere a resting-place for the eye, nowhere a haven for the soul—and he felt that this great space was worthless when compared with the golden kingdom at his feet.

But anon, with a finer understanding, he became aware of motion in the endless space, and saw that hidden floodgates were opening, and that in all the blue caverns of the aether there was a continual bubbling, and foaming, and flowing.

And he noted with amazement how the airy waves, in full stream, mounted towards the silvery palace of the aether, how they entered through the shining gates, and how they filled all the stately halls and bright colonnades with their vaporous body, flowing softly so that no sound should disturb the sacred silence. He saw, too, how they flowed out again through the windows as if from a thousand gates, and how lastly, with praise and prayer, they passed on, like a boundless ocean, to eternity, guided by angels and accompanied by the Holy Spirit, mounted on a tall white-winged steed.

And he learned how to measure the magical depths of this aërial ocean, as, standing on a vast cloud, he plumbed the abyss below him and, in imagination, lifted it up and raised it, to a height three or four times as great over his head. But never did his plummet reach deep enough or high enough, and the blue dome towered in spirals, ever higher, finally disappearing into the void, beckoning to him with a ghost-like hand. And as he thus made his futile measurements, the clouds beneath him were swept away by an overwhelming billow, like a great tidal wave, and not only the clouds, but with the clouds his view, and with his view the whole solid earth, and all its mountains and forests.

And, over him, at the very top of this aërial flood, an eagle floated quietly above the whole expanse, hardly visible to the eye, like a pivot round which the whole globe revolved, or like the tiny kernel of an enormous enclosing husk.

And it seemed to remain fixed in the same spot, no motion discernible and every sign of life as it were frozen.

Then suddenly it began to fly downwards, becoming larger and larger, with the sunlight playing on its dark body. And it turned and twisted in its flight, and finally, with a sideways glide, it began to make a circuit of the round earth below.

And slowly it winged its kingly way, like a star wandering lonely in limitless space, and far below its shadow followed it with gigantic steps over field and forest, over houses and gardens, across river and lake, up and down along the green hills.

And it flew sluggishly, until it came to a point directly below which, on a sacred hill, glittered the city of Heaven, surrounded by dark gardens and enthroned like a gracious queen, hailed and beloved by all the land, and loyally attended by many divers-coloured castles.

Here the eagle twice flapped its wings vigorously, while they gleamed and sparkled in the sunlight, and then it soared upward, higher and higher. And next it diverged in a sweeping circle and sailed like the wind towards the mass of white and fleecy clouds, amid which it vanished.

And for a moment the firmament seemed desolate and empty. But behold, the eagle re-appeared on the other side of the clouds, continued its heavenward flight with renewed energy, and flashed across the red disk of the sun. Then, suddenly, a piercing cry rang out from the remote firmament.

And three times the noble bird impatiently repeated its command, and then it rose and fell in irregular and angry swoops, until it had completed the whole mighty circuit.

Finally it flew off into the unknown and alluring distance, just topping, in its course, the woods below.

And before they reached the middle of the field, whether on account of the solitude or on account of the balmy flower-scented air, the suffering of the Sick God became less and his eyes became clearer.

And his sister noticed this with great satisfaction, and would gladly have given voice to her heart's delight for all the world to hear, and she could hardly contain herself. But strong as this impulse was, her love was still stronger; so she continued quietly on her way, not betraying by the flicker of an eyelid that she had noticed anything, lest she might disturb the secret and delicate process of his dawning recovery.

So they went on their way, and it befell that with every step the Sick God became stronger and the inner rapture of his sister became more difficult of control.

After a while, when the wood was so near that its warm fragrance seemed to fill the air, the path dipped to a small brook, rippling between its soft banks through the lush grass, half-hidden in the narrow hollow, and overshadowed by the tall stalks of corn.

And the flow of the brook was gentle and modest; its behaviour was admirable; there was nothing false or suspicious about it; and its shallow course was clear and limpid.

And in the cool bed of the stream a happy group of naked children were disporting themselves, jumping, splashing each other, shouting and laughing, and churning up the white foam with their feet. Their plump and rosy bodies were lapped in the summer-air, while the water covered them from the foot to the knee.

And one of the biggest ventured now and then to go where the brook murmured in a more hollow tone and flowed more darkly and sluggishly, surely hiding there some secret or mystery.

And gently and tentatively, he put in one foot, disregarding the loud cries of his comrades and controlling his own timidity. And he advanced steadily, with desperate courage, till the wavelets splashed against his thighs and hips.

Then all at once, he hastily drew back, amid the astonished admiration of his remonstrating companions.

The Sick God laughed as he watched the children's pranks, lingered long on the narrow path, and dragged himself away unwillingly.

And when he regained the head of the field, he forthwith opened his long-closed lips and began to talk and ask questions in a perfectly natural manner.

And at this his sister could no longer control her impetuous delight, but threw herself wildly on his breast, passionately kissed his pale lips, his shoulders, and his hands, flung herself at his feet, clasped his knees, and sprang up again. And this she did over and over again, knowing neither bounds nor moderation.

And all the while a torrent of pearl-like tears poured down her happy and radiant face.

And, deeply moved, her brother witnessed the pure and unfeigned stream of her affection, drew her tremblingly to his breast, reverently touched her fair brow with his lips, and blessed her love from the very depths of his heart.

And thereafter the whole world was transfigured for them, and with fresh and vigorous courage they went on their way, arm in arm; and they took delight in everything, and every incident ministered to their delight.

A little later they reached the entrance to the wood.

And here there hung a heavy curtain that hid from their eyes every past sorrow; and there were too a screen and a closed door which shut out all that had gone before, unseen, forgotten, unfelt. All that remained was a stimulating consciousness of a deep and sacred peace.

And this was the sign and seal of his recovery, the definite ending of his long-drawn-out suffering. And what began at high noon was completed by the midnight of the wood. The one, with the flames of its golden crown, charred and burned and consumed the treacherous poison; the other poured balm into the wounds, put an end to the pain, smoothed out the scars, and wiped away every morbid feeling. And as water fills an empty glass, so, with every breath, health streamed into the lungs of the God. And the brother and sister were aware of the magical and life-giving power of the place, and, in order to profit by it to the utmost, they avoided the beaten track, and turned aside, taking good care not to quit the friendly shade.

And so, with cheerful talk, they strolled aimlessly hither and thither for more than an hour, straying far from the path. Their only guide was the wish of their hearts, wherever the green roof arched most invitingly over their heads.

Then, unexpectedly, the wood fell sharply, and to their amazement they found themselves at the boundary of the land.

And the brother began to speak in an apparently disinterested manner:

"Verily it seems to me that we have now come far enough; so, if it please thee, let us retrace our steps."

But while he spoke, she was listening to something; and after a minute or two she lifted her voice and asked in astonishment:

"What sound is this like the pealing of an organ? Is it the wind that we hear howling and roaring in the distance?" But the God heard her impatiently and ignored her question, thinking only by what device he could induce her to go back with him.

But she, either because he was unable wholly to control his expression or simply from woman's native shrewdness, saw what was in the back of his mind, hesitated, and looked searchingly at her brother's eyes, in order to fathom the true meaning of his heart.

And she suddenly grasped his hand and held it fast, and made as if to descend bravely the steep slope before them.

This, however, was not to her brother's taste, so he followed her lead unwillingly, and argued, and resisted, trying again and again to turn back.

But he could not withstand her firmer will, so she drew him along with her, partly by coaxing and partly by sheer force. Thus at last he yielded weakly and accepted her guidance.

So they amicably went side by side down the moss-grown slope.

And the formidable roaring increased in volume; the wood ceased and the light grew stronger, and lo, close to their feet, stretched the vast and mighty ocean.

And at the unexpected fascination of this vision, they both stood motionless, overwhelmed by the turbulent roaring and spellbound by the glory of the blue dome overhead. And they grew dizzy and reeled, and would hardly have kept their feet had they not borne each other up.

And it was some time before they regained enough control even to look about them. And then they observed, close at their feet, a black-coloured bridge crossing the cliffs towards the sea, and leading to a small rocky island crowned by an attractively built pavilion, gay with white and blue paint, and smiling cheerfully over the wild breakers.

And with one will they made for the summer-house, in order that they might enjoy the majestic view from the nearest point.

But it was not enough for their bold spirits to stay in the shelter of the pavilion; so they pressed on to the extreme point of the islet, where the wet rocks glistened black in the sunshine. And here they attuned themselves to the majesty of the scene and deliberately feasted their eyes on its beauties.

Their eyes were filled with fascinated and unceasing astonishment, and they could hardly believe in the reality of what they saw.

For this sea was unlike all other seas; it was never roughened by storm or buffeted by tempest, and its waves were not as other waves.

And the face of the sky was clear and friendly, and far and near no cloud was to be seen. Yet in the very heart of the sea the green water boiled and bubbled, tumbled and whirled and churned itself into milk-white foam.

And every now and again the whole turbulent expanse rose higher and higher, heaved itself up like a mountain, and sang the song of the sea—and then, suddenly, it subsided again with a thunderous roar, and a yawning whirlpool opened in the black abyss.

And so the sea rose and fell in regular rhythm, like the blood in a man's veins, or like the breathing of his lungs, or like the thoughts that at eventide whisper to his soul.

And it befell that when the water rose, marvellous and unheard-of creatures gazed calmly out of the seething uproar; and when the water sank again, a strange breeze issued from the bottomless fissures, and wheeled in weird and unearthly circles.

And drunk with joy, the two Children of God revelled in this scene of beauty and grandeur, sating their eyes with it, while their hearts could not recover from the constantly repeated marvels.

And Sophia stood before her brother on the verge of the cliffs, her face freshened by the sea-breeze, her eyes shining, and her black tresses tossed by the wind.

And she felt no fear when the surf broke thundering at her feet, or when the booming waves danced round her, or when suddenly, each wave grasping the hand of another, they hurried to the shore in long rows, clambering on each other's back and dashing at her feet, with fearsome aspect, gaping jaws, and terrific uproar.

She knew no fear; all this foaming chaos was a delight to her. And when, from time to time, the sea rose, climbed up the rocks, and tossed its white foam to the canopy of heaven, kissing her feet and cooling her brow and cheeks with its fine spray,

The youthful light of her eyes shone with glee, as she stood at the very edge of the rocks, so that she might all the more enjoy the fascinating terror.

For a long time she indulged in this royal pastime, until her vision blended into one the thousandfold confusion and until her spirit became master of the roaring and wrathful flood.

But after a time the action of the ocean seemed to her insipid and lazy, and she turned her gaze on the swallows that wheeled about her in countless numbers. She took pleasure in seeing how they

darted down on the water, how their flights intersected and circled, and how they soared vertically aloft, and then swooped down again in bold curves, mocking at and playing with the sluggishness of the sea.

And after a time this also failed to satisfy her unbridled desires; she began to scorn the restless scene before her. So she directed her gaze to the calm and peaceful shores beyond the sea, which smilingly faced all the foaming turmoil of the waters.

And it lay there pranked in green and gold like the memory of a wedding feast, or like the way in which a youth paints the world in colours to suit his own feelings; every breath was charm, and a soft radiance shone on its brow, and its middle was clasped by a girdle richly adorned with deep luminous colours.

And these hues were very different from those that suffused the world with a watery tint, darkened by the heavy air, stained by earthly use, weary from much travel, with lacklustre eyes and sickly face.

But from the sun emanated rays of serene purity, charged as it were with sap, shining with fiery brilliance, bravely adding light to light, and gaily scorning any timid compromise.

As when in the pure air of the South a parrot swings in a flowering tree, or as when a butterfly spreads its wings over the cup of a lily, so the fair land beyond the sea radiated joy and happiness, while the gold and green of its girdle challenged the pure blue of heaven.

And while the low body of the land was thus bathed in light and bliss, in the background rose a range of quiet and solemn mountains, like the thoughts and aspirations of a noble soul, brooding over the problems of the world. And on the mountains grew forests, with their constantly changing aspects, and boulders, breaking away from the lofty peaks, rolled down like sand into the depths of the stormy sea.

And when the Maiden Goddess was aware of this new and enchanted domain, her soul was possessed by a feeling of pure youth, and she began to drink it all in with renewed zest. And she found it hard to conceive why she had so long ignored it, bewitched by the wild and senseless uproar of the ocean.

And this was the corner-stone of her happiness. Hitherto she had never been able to satisfy her restless spirit for more than a short time. Here, however, she found a peace of which she did not weary, dwelling on it and refreshing her spirit. And now she sat on the shore meditating and noting how all the woods and cliffs merged into the sea; or, anon, she rambled over the velvety meads, through the woods, and past shady hedgerows; or, yet again, standing on the highest glacier of the rosy Alps, she proudly overlooked the endless landscape, and wafted greetings to herself from the blessed and airy watch-tower.

Her actual body remained standing on the foam-flecked rock, but in spirit she wandered up and down in the still, friendly, and homelike Eden.

Her brother Logos stood the while just behind his sister, on the narrow promontory, watching her position and ready to support her slender form with his strong encircling arms.

And all the time, while she lost herself in the ecstasy of her bliss, he kept looking at her face, taking delight in her noble brow, her well-formed nose, her finely curved mouth, and her soulful eyes.

And he did not tire of this occupation, and all the thousand-fold enchantment around him seemed shallow and worthless compared with the treasure he possessed in his beloved sister.

And thus they stood hand in hand and in full accord, in a sort of dream, not marking the passage of the hours, until the sun set behind the dark wood.

Then, at last, they roused themselves and set out on their homeward path, but, unwillingly, often pausing and turning to look back.

And thus, loitering along, they reached the middle of the bridge, where they saw an angler, leaning on the parapet and dropping his line into the foaming stream.

And they meant to pass him with a brief greeting, hardly noting his presence. So they drew to one side and made to walk quietly by him. The angler, for his part, went on fishing, did not look up, and appeared to take no interest whatever in the noble passers-by.

And they had almost passed him, when the fisherman turned his head, revealed his vulgar face, and opened his large and ugly mouth. But he gave no greeting and did not stand up, but continued to rest his gross body and clumsy shoulders on the parapet of the bridge. And, at last, he began and spoke, inspired by the envy with which baseborn louts are wont to regard their superiors:

"No doubt it is all very well, my masters, for you to gaze from the safe shores of Heaven at the stormy and troubled ocean. Perchance, however, they who experience in their own bodies an earthly life and fleshly existence might take quite another view!"

And as at this moment a wave broke over the parapet, he bent clumsily down, scooped up some water in the hollow of his hand, and held it out to them to illustrate his words.

And Sophia looked up with puzzled eye, and then turned and spoke, shuddering, to her brother:

"Is it really from joy that he twitches and gesticulates like this?"

But her brother stood by her side, pale and speechless.

And her brother's bearing made her uneasy, and she found the whole incident very disquieting. So, after a pause, she thought she might put her question better and spoke again, in doubting accents:

"What end does this serve? And what hidden meaning is there in it?"

But her brother and companion did not break his silence.

And thereupon they resumed their journey and made for home by the nearest way.

Evening flamed gloriously through the wood, empurpling every bush and tree and casting blue shadows on the rough white boles of the beech trees.

But they walked on, silently and solemnly, paying no heed to the twilight miracles.

And the dark-haired maiden walked behind her brother and plucked the flowers that bordered the path—but plucked them only to tear them to pieces and throw them down on the ground again.

And this she did unceasingly all the time they were walking. When, however, the wood became thinner, and when, over the uplands, the city of Heaven and their own beloved and familiar home came into sight, she suddenly stood still, drew herself erect, and sighed from the very depths of her heart.

Amazed, her brother turned and spoke to her in a trembling voice: "Why dost thou sigh? And why is thy heart glad, and why dost thou greet thy home with such happy looks?

Verily I say unto thee, it were better to be a worm in the land of men, crushed in a rut by a passing wheel, than the noble and beauteous daughter of God in the sacred fields of Heaven."

And, as he spoke, he saw her turn pale and falter.

And he bitterly repented of his words, but they had been said and could not be unsaid—so he fled with a cry across the field. And his sister went on, alone and unsteadily, to her lofty and shining home.

And all the time that Prometheus was telling this woeful tale, the little dog lay perfectly still and listened breathlessly and with eager attention. And when the story came to an end, she gently breathed her last.

And thereupon Prometheus went forth to bury her in the corner of the garden, beside the lion.

SURVEY AND CLOSE

And, behold, from this time on Prometheus avoided his master's garden, ceased to cultivate the flowers and always made a circuit when he drove his cattle to pasture in the morning.

And his master was surprised and said to him:

"Why is it that thou art so changed? All thy flowers are fading, and thou seemest to avoid the garden on purpose."

And Prometheus answered, not quite frankly:

"That has all come about by pure chance. There happens to be a lilac tree in the garden, and that is a tree I have never been able to abide."

And the next morning, as he was going to the pasture, he noticed that the lilac tree lay on the ground, cut down by his master's order.

And Prometheus made an impatient gesture and exclaimed:

"Verily I am sorry about this tree, and it is an everlasting pity that it has suffered in place of the box tree, which is the one I really dislike."

And it was a different tree every day; but in spite of all Prometheus went on as before and absolutely refused to enter the garden.

Thus by one pretext or another he managed to keep free of the grave during the livelong day; but when the stillness of night filled all space, when every house was dark, when nothing was audible except the sleepy cry of the watchman or the throbbing of his own veins in his empty room, there would come a sound of rustling from the grave, voices became audible, and strange and confused signs of life issued from it without ceasing.

And at first the gruesome sound was but faint—and Prometheus had to strain his attention to hear it, his face pale with terror and his brow wet with sweat. Just as a sick man, who detects the first signs of an approaching paroxysm, still faint and easy to bear, but whose blood already runs cold in his veins, because he recognizes the gentle forerunner of a grizzly horror.

And the noise from the grave became louder and louder, and, all at once, on the stroke of midnight, the ground opened, and from the black depth of the tomb the lion and the dog emerged and set out for their home-valley to execute judgment once more on their dead children.

And it befell when their footfall was heard through the window the walls trembled and the whole house groaned. And Prometheus sprang up, breathless and choking, while his heart throbbed almost to bursting; and so it went with him until the two animals returned from tne far-off valley.

And when dawn lightened the sky, and the first vague sounds of morning were heard, when the cock crew shrill and here and there a lark greeted the still distant sun,

Then they returned, and Prometheus could lay himself down again to enjoy his much-needed sleep. But even in his sleep he found again the pale and grief-stricken faces of his dead friends.

And this was the order of his life night after night, according to the saying with which his Soul had consecrated him in the hour of judgment on the snowclad height above the dark valley: "Thou shalt envy the life even of the beasts of the field as compared with thy own pitiless and manifold sufferings."

Such now was his lot; time brought no alleviation, and things became more grievous for him every year.

Close

And at this period the eyes of Prometheus had become so affected by the constant sight of an alien land that every object seemed to him grey and colourless, even when it was bathed in the most beauteous hues of the ocean of light.

And in this strange land lived a physician, who gave him this advice for the healing of his eyes.

That in the evening, when his work was done, he should go down to the brook that marked the frontier and turn his face towards his far-off home, if peradventure his native air might bring recovery to his sight.

And Prometheus took this counsel, and every evening, at the close of his day's work he allowed himself time to repair to the brook, where he looked across to his distant home and bathed his eyes in his native air.

And though his hope seemed vain and no sign of cure appeared, he persisted in his attempt, trusting that unremitting patience might at last achieve success.

And one evening, when as usual he tarried by the brook, looking fixedly towards the west, he began to speak to himself with an air of doubt:

"What is that moving along the road towards me? The figures seem to have a familiar aspect."

And, after an interval, he continued: "Is that not Epimetheus, my illustrious brother from the lofty palace?"

And the newcomers had noticed him, and stopped on the opposite bank of the stream, and they pitched their camp there and erected a tent, and made themselves comfortable on large and soft rugs.

When all was in order, King Epimetheus stepped forward, supported by a friend on either side, greeted Prometheus, and spoke to him with well-meant words:

"I am heartily sorry for thee, Prometheus, my dear brother! But, nonetheless, take courage, for, lo, I have a salve here, which is a sure remedy for every ill and works equally well in heat and in cold. Moreover, it can be used as a solace as well as for punishment."

And, thus saying, he grasped a staff and tied the box of ointment to it, and reached it carefully with all due solemnity towards his brother.

As soon, however, as he saw and smelt the ointment, Prometheus turned away his head, with loathing and disgust.

At that the King changed his tone, and shouted and began to read his brother a lesson with great zest:

"In good sooth, thou seemest to need a yet greater punishment, for thy present experience does not appear to have made sufficient impression on thee!"

And as he spake, he drew a small mirror from the folds of his robe, and showed everything that had happened, waxing very eloquent and enumerating all the mistakes that Prometheus had made.

And he would have gone on like this interminably, had not his friends interfered: "Remember your rank. For it is now evening and growing very damp, and your wife, in much distress, is awaiting you anxiously in the upper chamber of the castle."

And he was much annoyed by the remonstrance and resisted it vehemently, but at last his sense of duty prevailed and he marched away, though with exclamations of vexation and complaint.

And when the noise of the procession had died away beyond the hill, there came a rippling in the brook and a rustling in the bushes, and a Voice uttered these words, clearly and rapidly:

"Verily, it will be a red-letter day to me, when I see him lying in earth's blackest dungeon, burying his face in the mud on account of the intolerable shame of his name!"

But Prometheus became violently angry and replied: "What a sin this is that thou art committing! For behold, he is my brother, and came hither to comfort me. Do thou therefore take back thy merciless judgment!"

But no answer was vouchsafed him. So the Voice lived on, and hurried off, and followed in the wake of Epimetheus, and wherever he went and wherever he stayed this saying floated over him. But from this day on, the face of Prometheus became set and hard.

OLYMPIAN SPRING

By CARL SPITTELER

Translated by James F. Muirhead

[Excerpt]

HYLAS AND KALEIDUSA OVER HILL AND VALE

The night had fled, pursued by Chanticleer;
The busy day officiously drew near,
While yet the air, though waked by whispering beams,
Stretched in the half-light, drowsy still with dreams.
Behold! there creeps the dew-wet vines among,
Parting with careful hand the tendrils long,
Hylas, fleet Hermes' brother. Through the rows,
Stirred by the morning-breezes, down he goes,
Rallied by blackbirds, by grasshoppers rated;
But now on level ground he lands elated,
When—curse!—a blinding ray, as diamond bright,
The East, the South, are red with vivid light,
All heaven seems to break in fiery brands,
And on the car of flame Apollo stands!
"O brother Hylas, whither now away
Stealing while yet the valley-lands are grey?
Whom to avoid or meet?" Caught in the act,
Hylas blinks upward: "Brother dear, in fact
We think alike, that walking, sleeping, wooing,
By two alone are really worth the doing.
The difference is this—a cloud for thee,
But earthly woods are good enough for me."

So spake he, hurrying on. And soon he could
Plunge in the shelter of a friendly wood;

There he stood still, and feigned a cuckoo-cry—
A turtle-dove cooed softly in reply,
And fresh as morning, for the road arrayed,
Stepped the nymph Kaleidusa from the shade.
A kiss, a laughing word—then through the chace
They run with linkèd arms and equal pace;
Bravely they march, and in their hearts anew
The coloured day, the magic air, the blue,
The enchanted blossoms—freshly born are all,
And eyes look love, though maiden-lashes fall.
For everything that is, or far or near,
To their untroubled gaze gives answer clear—
The whispering grass, the clouds that sail on high,
Can keep no secrets from a lover's eye.
"Hark to the humming bees in shade o'erhead,
Telling the limes about us, love!"—He said:
"O Kaleidusa, I can see and hear
A world of beauty, yet for me more dear
The sound of your fond footsteps on the grass,
The sighs that o'er your bosom gently pass—
For all the organ-tones that ever were
I would not change that little song, I swear!"
And thus they wandered on with sturdy day,
Till rapturous noon upon the thickets lay;
Then tempted by the breath of waters cool
They bathed in dancing brook or shadowed pool,
And, limbs relaxed in dappled hazel-bowers,
Lay side by side, supine, for hours and hours.
But freshening breezes promised fresh delight,
So, stretching arms and legs, they sprang upright,
Leaped, clapped their hands for joy—and soon the two
Ran singing all the glades and clearings through.
No matter where. The way they scorned to learn.

Now evening says to afternoon: "My turn!"
So saying, spreads her pair of dusky wings
And broad on sunlit banks their shadow flings;

Lets fall her purple cloak, whence darkness creeps,
Lured from the shimmering borders where it sleeps.
Then on a bench near by behold her sit,
Open earth's picture-book, and paint in it.
"May I?" asked Kaleidusa. "Would you mind?"
And standing on her tiptoes watched behind.
Mysterious in soft clear tints there grew
Between the o'erarching branches, maidens two,
Morpho and Pantaphila, Pan's girl-brood,
Gleefully changing forms in childish mood—
To birds and beasts their slender selves distorting,
Now as a heron on the breezes sporting,
Now as a roe-deer leaping in the air—
A wish, and once again they both stood fair
And slim, Pan's gentle girls, no more, no less . . .
The village yonder rings with happiness;
Children are playing soldiers: "One, two, three!"
But "Three" is hardly said ere ends their glee,
And at the house-door, thoughtful men, sit they,
And next the passing-bell tolls each away.
"What does it matter?" murmurs the mill-stream;
"Morpho and man and change—it's all a dream.
They call it Nature, I am told. Let be!
It is Ananke's gay-grim fantasy!"

Thus for a while on evening's brink delaying,
The lovers, hand in hand, went fondly straying,
Till softly, dimly, in the vale below,
Red-capped, the twilight-shepherds come and go,
Gathering their herds of dreams to fold and sleep;
And from the brook, aroused from slumber deep,
Sly Pan phantasmal darts on bat-like wings,
Round grove and glade to weave his wizard rings;
While Day with subtle fingers, now set free,
Charms pregnant scents from every bush and tree.
Homeward the lovers turn beneath the moon,
Radiant with memories, ardent friendship's boon,

And when that lurker at cross-roads, Farewell,
Parts them relentlessly, they scarce rebel—
No wish is unfulfilled, no thought can sorrow,
And kisses murmur happily: "Tomorrow!"

But envy on such bliss too well can fare,
And all things now conspired against the pair.
Good sport to break such union, anyway—
And Hylas, going home the selfsame day,
Was ambushed by hedge-nymphs: "Hylas, look here!
Does she use hooks-and-eyes, or does she smear
Lime on your feet, that Kaleidusa-thing?
For to her skirts like any burr you cling,
Or like a carthorse meekly after trot!
Thank God, there still are nymphs, and quite a lot
Fairer than Kaleidusa! Take your pick!
You're charming—it's a shame! Come with us quick—
One moment? You'll be glad. We'll be so kind!"
Hylas rejoined: "I'd better speak my mind.
On Kaleidusa's toe—the little one—
She wears a bead, and this will catch the sun;
And when it does, the path seems all ablaze
With colours which to my enchanted gaze
Are lovelier far than sunlight. I should grieve
To part with hues like those, you may believe.
Moreover, 'twixt her tongue and teeth, you see,
She has a music-box, and sings to me,
And then the whole world sings and my heart sings—
These are her lime, or glue, or such-like things.
If e'er the colours fade, the music cease,
I'll part with her, and take you, if you please."

On homeward path, where ditch and bank are wide,
Bold satyrs tempted her that eventide.
"Peculiar taste at best, I'm bound to say,
O'er stones and stubble trudging every day,
With Hylas, like two mill-wheels on the grind!

What can you see in him? You must be blind.
Are there not satyrs plenty and to spare,
But you must basely with Olympian pair?
I know where money is, if that's your pleasure,
And if you only knew, such hidden treasure!"
Said Kaleidusa: "I will speak my mind.
Ten thousand valleys in the world we find;
A berry grows in each, and there alone,
And every one has flavours all its own.
That's why I wander—I have set my heart
On tasting every one in every part.
And none can tell like Hylas where they grow—
Come, let me pass! The reason now you know."
"All right. You'll soon be sick of this, my friend!"
"On the last day, when all the world shall end."

Thus from seducers' cunning broken free,
They march together towards eternity.

But at the noon-hour on a sultry day,
When in the hazel-grove the lovers lay:
"Look there!" cried Kaleidusa. "On that tree
The writing—what it says I'll have to see!"
Jumped up and read. Thus the inscription clear:
"Caution! Who recklessly lies dreaming here
Shall know in sleep what future he shall find.
Keep off! The future never yet was kind."
"I'm satisfied," said she, "those words to heed.
Fair is the present. That is all I need."
And saying this, returned and with a smile
Sat down, embraced her love, and slept awhile.
And so till seven days had passed and gone;
But the dark word upon the eighth would run
Through Kaleidusa's head. While Hylas slept
Under that tree to dream alone she crept,
A little dazed she was. Scarce closed her eyes,
Ere in her dream she moaned with anguished cries,

And Hylas waked. "Can I believe my ears!"
He rubbed his eyes. "Oh love! Were those your tears?
Your eyes are wet—they hardly seem to see!"
"No, they are dry; they have not wept," said she.
Then, as again they wandered on their way:
"How languid are your feet," he cried, "to-day!
How sorrowful and heavy droops your head!"
"I am not weary; it is you," she said.
But late that evening, in the chill moonlight,
When to Olympus he had taken flight
As ever, and about her caves austere
Yawned, and the world seemed solitary, drear,
She sank upon the ground, and rent the vale
With deep-drawn sobs, like to the nightingale;
Music was in them, music of the heart,
Love and despair and longing—all took part.
Then from the grove there came the sister-pair,
Each took her hand, and pitying stroked her hair:
"Say, sister, what thy sorrow? Can it be
Some word from Hylas thus afflicting thee,
Wounding thy heart? He never meant it so!
Why wilt thou weep the tears of lightless woe?"
"Alas!" she moaned. "Sweet sisters—nay, not he,
Not Hylas, but myself hath wounded me.
I slept beneath the awful tree of fate,
Where they that dream shall know the things that wait.
I saw my love forsake me, pass me by,
No look vouchsafing me, and no reply."
"What's done is done. Thou canst not backward turn."
"Then will I die—yes, die, such doom to learn."
"Wild words—for well thou knowest, sister fair,
Immortal is the wood-nymph's soul of air;
We reckon not with death as mortals use,
At best we change to morning-scents or dews."
She cried: "And such the change I gladly choose!
I will not stay, till he shall thus forget,
I'll have him miss me sorely, pine and fret."

And she stood firm. No tears, no pleading tender
Could wring from her one moment of surrender.

And so the sisters, chanting a sad song,
Were lost the winding forest-paths among,
While she—she wondered, through the night of storm,
What shape her soul could choose, what airy form,
To glide within his heart and there to stay,
Stirring remembrance in him every day.
"This—this?" Her burdened spirit sorely wrought,
But could not find the answer that she sought,
So sick her will, so feverish her brain—
And tears were all the fruit of all her pain.
At last across the sky swept morning's blue,
And lit sad earth with many a laughing hue,
And "Ah?" she sighed, "the piteous hour is near
When through the trees to find me comes my dear!
Not knowing, from Olympus now, maybe,
All glad and sure he wings—ah, woe is me!
My petty pride, my purpose, what are they
If once I hear his voice—up, up, away!"
Swift from the clearing to the wood ran she.
"Courage!" she said. "For so it has to be."
Yet though she thus might urge her fainting heart,
How sweet was life—and she with life must part.

Then in the sea incarnadine o'erhead
Rose the great firebird Phœnix from his bed,
And lighting on a fir-tree preened his wings
Of shimmering flame, and glanced at earthly things;
Then closed his eyes, opened his beak, and sang
His matin-song—like some bronze bell it rang,
Ornate with images, and thus they soared,
The pregnant words that golden voice outpoured:
"What soul, you ask, is this that from the dew
With radiant eyes looks earnestly at you?
Hear! These are tidings from the Son of Light,

Written on vale and field throughout the night
When he, a captive far in desert lands,
Through prison-bars will stretch his longing hands—
Thus daily to dark earth in secret giving
Assurance that he still is loving, living.
Aurosa, whom he loves yet ne'er may meet,
Scans the brave letter, sad and yet so sweet;
At peep of day the forest-gloom she leaves,
From silvered lawns the dewy message weaves
With careful fingers, till she understands
The love-words traced by those beloved hands.
Secret the cipher, to none other known;
The hallowed script is clear to her alone,
Gem of her diadem, Horizon named—
Soon as the first of morning-beams has flamed
She reads the rune: 'In this we meet at last!'
And reason answers love, her heart beats fast.
Then will she hide herself and letter too;
The world is naught to her, so he is true."

Thus from his eyrie sang the great firebird;
The clearing and the flame-red forest heard—
But hark! the voice of Hylas from the hill
On "Kaleidusa!" calling, calling still . . .
Loudly it rang. Or breathless she or frightened,
Or by some sudden hopeful thought enlightened—
Ceasing to run, against a sapling leant
And through her hollowed hands a summons sent:
"O Father Pan! The wood-nymph calls on thee,
Now from her sore distress to set her free!"
Pan stood before her: "Whence this anguished cry?"
Faltering she said: "I long to change, to die."
"Once dead, no wish, no might, can thee restore."
"O Father Pan, I know, and long the more."
"To what, then, wilt thou change thy spirit fair?"
"To some bright ray that comes from everywhere
And seems to Hylas as myself, and so
Will make his yearning and his love to grow."

"Then, Kadeidusa, come—embrace me here."
"Father, kind Father Pan, I shrink, I fear!"
"Was never death but wrestled first with life,
Nor changing form but knows that awful strife."

Sore was the struggle, fierce was Pan's embrace,
Ere the fond soul was torn from out its place,
And Kaleidusa's spirit, breaking free,
Could soar unhindered to infinity.
Not here she was, not there, but everywhere,
Informing all the azure distance fair;
And then she'd have him see her starry crown:
"Hylas, I'm here!" and flashed her glances down.
And Hylas, crying out in sore amaze,
Wept his lost love on whom he might not gaze.
Now from the thicket, sent by Father Pan,
Morpho and Pantaphila to him ran:
"O Hylas, trust our magic! Do not move,
And we will show thee how to see thy love."
So speaking, Morpho with her fingers light
Draws both his hands behind and holds them tight.
"Shut your two eyes," next Pantaphila bids
And softly breathes her kisses on his lids.
"Look up!" And lo! in one heart-warming ray
He knows his Kaleidusa—and away
With longing arms he rushes . . . Hapless wight!
Never shall Hylas touch the radiant sprite;
Though oft he thinks to grasp her, she will still
Elude him, running swift o'er vale and hill.

And so at every hour of every day
His darling torment leads him far astray;
O'er vale and hill he hunts her through the land—
Ever the tricksome gleam escapes his hand,
Though ever flashing: "Come! I wait you here!"
And roguish Kaleidusa laughs: "More dear—
O joy!—more close by far shall be the tie
Than when through woods we wandered, he and I."

BALLADS

By CARL SPITTELER

Translated by Ethel C. Mayne *and* James F. Muirhead

KRONOS AND THE OLD MAN

At dead of night, through cloud-rack's beetling masses,
And fettered as a criminal might be,
The exiled Kronos, bowed with sorrow, passes
Out from his high Olympian sovranty,
Leaving that blue-and-golden habitation
For grim Cocytean shores of desolation.

The captive's car, by two mute guards preceded,
Is followed by two more as mute as they;
His anxious questionings are all unheeded—
Deaf ears, close lips, a dumb relentless Nay.
And, as to mingle mockery with mourning,
A tinsel crown his royal head adorning.

Now on the earth at grey of dawn descended,
They pause to rest beside a mountain-brook;
Along the path, with years his shoulders bended,
An old man totters feebly—by his look
Wishful of swift release from life's Forever;
He halts, he groans, panting in sore endeavour.

"Companion of my sorrows, welcome hither!"
The disthroned god salutes that age-worn one.
"When youth and strength are past, and muscles wither,
Existence is but grief—as well have done.

Be comforted! We all must pay for living.
Speak! Let me hear your wish without misgiving."

Ungraciously the old man frowns to hear him,
Twitching his toothless mouth malignantly;
Then coming on, but never looking near him,
Sneering he says: "Whoever you may be,
Keep your fine gifts! The spring will flow unheeded
Of him by whom no water thence is needed.

"If you would give, if bounties you would scatter,
Ask of the youth, whose ripening ardour glows,
Ask of the child, whom toys and gewgaws flatter,
Whose greedy hands are stretched for life's gay shows;
What this world has to give, to me was given—
My cup is full, my bonds are well-nigh riven.

"If now from Heaven miraculously descending,
Kronos the All-Creative came, and told
The tale of those my sires, the strains that, blending,
Are kith and kin to me that now am old,
More grateful to my heart were that for pleasure
Than land or gold or any earthly treasure."

Gazing upon his fettered hands pathetic,
The prisoner mused a moment, deep in thought;
Then closed his lids, those heavy lids prophetic,
And lifted up his voice in song that wrought
For that astonied listener the long story
Of days gone by, vast æons dim and hoary.

With giant steps it bridged the endless ages,
Finding the things that Memory's self had lost—
Things all too deep for humbler mortal sages
It brought from out their cave of dark and frost;
It sang to him of those that gave him being,
The Unknown knowing, and the Unseen seeing.

No name, no recollected face was wanting,
Dropped was no link, though close the chain and long,
And kindness glowed in all those lips were chanting,
And everything they touched was turned to song;
The life he knew, the lives he apprehended,
By scents of home into one dream were blended.

Forgotten all of pain and all of grieving,
As if on spirit-wings the old man flew.
Listening with lips apart—their places leaving,
The guards lay round the car, and listened too;
The brook with silver tinkle kept the measure;
Pale Morn stood still, the hours obeyed her pleasure.

But hark! a cock's shrill crow—the sunlight beaming!
Down from the peak bright Day advances red.
The guards affrighted wake from out their dreaming,
Duty is here, and poesy is fled;
There's tumult—scolding—strife—harsh orders spoken;
"Onward!" The steeds are lashed, the spell is broken.

But lo!—what magic on the old man playeth,
His eyes aflame, his head uplifted high?
He strives to stay the car—for none it stayeth,
He rushes panting after—fain would fly—
Of whirling wheels awhile the paces keeping,
He clings now here, now there, with piteous weeping.

"One word—O yet one unremembered matter!
Hear me—have mercy—stop! You will not go!"
Replies the whistling whip, the chariot's clatter;
The old man in the dust is fallen low,
And swifter, swifter, hoofs are onward flying,
And all his words of supplication dying.

E. C. M.

THE HOLIDAY FOR DEATH

While Saturn still of all the earth was King,
Death had but once a year his harvesting;
Man yielded not alone his dying breath—
It was a people's holiday for death.

Unto a meadow all together came,
Brother and stranger, friend and foe, the same
In reverent awe, by fellow-feeling moved—
The chosen ones, by Death long since approved.

The King's voice first upon the silence fell:
"Children of Death! scan one another well!
Because ye now must die and vanish hence,
Leave on this earth all anger and offence,
Your bitterness, your suffering, your scorn,
Cast them behind as old heart's-ache outworn!
Your souls have heard—the call within obey.
Let none depart unreconciled to-day."

Shuddered the sacrificial group to hear,
Foe measured foe, and hesitant drew near—
The melting look, that melted his in turn,
Disarmed the self-willed pride that yet could burn;
They knew themselves through suffering kin at last,
Each found the other's hand, and held it fast.

The Queen spoke next, breaking the hush profound:
"Often in loss our dearest gain is found:
No earthly lot was e'er so steeped in woe
But Love could make some happiness to grow.
If here is one, who deep within his heart
Thinks on a maiden, silently, apart,
Let him now stand before her, and declare

His love, and comfort find, and answer fair.
For mighty Death lays low Life's customs all;
Death breathes—and rank and riches both must fall."

Then, as to springs refreshing, pure, and clear,
Joyful the thirsty traveller draws near,
So, by bright hope allured as by the sun,
To her, his heart's elect, rushed every one;
A cry of yearning, stammered words of bliss—
And chastity and joy met in a kiss.

Hark! there is music, there is psalmody!
And reverently each doth bend the knee;
Death's herald comes, with awful wreathèd blade,
Riding a horse in black of night arrayed:
"Greetings, O chosen heroes! Hear my call!
In the Olympian's name, come—follow all!
Stands fast for ever destiny's decree
Unchanged, unfaltering—what must be, must be."

O then the tossing farewell-sea moaned high,
With myriad names sobbed forth tumultuously;
The herald flung his mantle o'er his face
Till grief had wept its fill in that sad place;
Then motioned with his hand—the trumpet blared,
And hence the doomed procession slowly fared.
Their brethren went along with them awhile
Seeking the death-troop's anguish to beguile,
Until the boundary showed, where now the way
Across a bridge upon the mountain lay.
There they assembled all around the spring,
And up and down the banks went wandering;
From willows by the brookside growing thick
Each broke a fresh young wand, and stretched it quick
To his companion there athwart the brook;
So each an end within his fingers took,
And thus they formed a living ribbon green
That spanned the little rivulet between;

And then a thousand voices sang a song
In double chorus as they marched along:—

"Be comforted! Though Death's abyss divide,
We all are kindred, each to each allied;
Our God is one, and one our meeting-place
Where each shall see the other face to face.
No breath, no atom, in this world is vain,
No fallen stone but finds a niche again;
A clue through Nature's labyrinth runs clear—
Where'er thou standest, others once were near.
The drops run down the rock unwittingly,
But, blind, they still shall reach the distant sea.
God is the End—our pole-star shines above;
Farewell, farewell, O comrades that we love!"

In a vast maze of glaciers high and still
A dreary plain above the earth lay chill,
And men had given it the name of Woe,
For Death was bitter there as here below.
And there, the sickle in his hand, stood he,
The Slayer. No reprieve from his decree.

But when the dismal task was finished all,
And silence o'er the death-plain spread its pall,
They lowered all the dead, aye, every one,
Into a common grave, nor paused till done.
A single broad memorial-stone was made
For all the pale ones there together laid;
For all, for each and all, was every tear
By mortals shed for any buried here—
None was so poor, and none was so disdained,
But one bright little tear-drop on him rained.

E. C. M.

DIE WELTPOST

There stands a post-house on a hill,
  like none you ever knew;
No traveller comes to call there,
  no letter passes through.
The vasty rooms yawn empty—
  nor word nor cry they hear;
Man's mind, man's hand, are nowhere felt;
  there's naught but iron fear.
The pendulum swings to and fro,
  unwound the wheels rotate;
The throbbing, ticking, beating pulses
  endlessly create.
The telegraph hums busily;
  its murmur never fails.
Before the window, in the yard,
  gleam double lines of rails,
And on them going, coming,
  coaches from dawn to night,
And souls within the coaches,
  all dumb and deathly-white.

* * *

And now the wall-clock's finger
  the long dark midnight shows—
Peals out a little carillon,
  a cock struts forth and crows.
Stately, the Twelve Apostles march
  to measure dignified;
A herald waves his wand, and lo!
  a door is opened wide.
He shouts with lungs stentorian,
  he stamps, he strikes the ground:
"Arise! The Master cometh—
  let all be ready found!"

Oh then there's uproar through the house,
excited voices call,
And see! the wheels have stopped, and see!
the pulleys quiver all,
The coaches in the yard are scotched,
their iron feet stand still,
And breathless all, expectant all,
each waits the Master's will.
Now through the silent blackness
eleven strokes are heard,
And then the Twelfth. The wonder-clock
has said its final word.
But hark! a titter opposite—
so might a devil jeer—
The telephone shrills out . . .
What mocking Judas-cry is here?
"The Master lieth ailing—
ye look for him in vain!"
—The herald's wand is lowered,
the cock struts back again,
The carillon falls silent,
the wall sucks in the door,
The soul-train shudders through its length,
moves off. . . . And, as before,
The busy wheels go whirling,
the wires flash out their spark,
And on the world's post-office works,
phantasmal in the dark.

E. C. M.

THE THREE SPINNERS

Three spinsters old in the turret-room
Sit singing and spinning through storm and gloom.
When the first in her hand the shuttle takes,
Tremble the tapes, and the distaff shakes.

"The king would give battle
The shuttle must rattle,
Run upward, run downward,
Leap hither, leap thither.
The rain's on the slate,
The brooklet's in spate,
And called are the many,
No respite for any."

The second is waiting the pattern to set
Till her thumb from her hanging lip is wet.
"The gate is of iron, the castle of stone,
What stronger than heaven and earth is known?
In heaven above sits Odin, greater:
Good spirits laud him, the All-Creator.

"Now over, now under,
A crash as of thunder,
And Emperors fall,
And grooms from the stall."

The third with her fingers is plucking the skein:
"It's knotted, it's twisted, again and again.

"The yarn is caught in,
The thread will not spin,
The woof is criss-crossed,
The labour is lost.
Botched all that I see—
Alas! Woe is me!"

E. C. M.

THE DEAD EARTH

At the portal of Heaven twelve angels wait:
"Ye Watchers, ye Sentries, come down to the gate!"
—"What news are ye dear ones bringing?"—

"From the earthly star we have ridden here,
Swift as the wind with our news of cheer,
    And now the bells shall be ringing!"

And soon as the wicket open flew,
They set their shawms to their lips and blew,
    And their cheeks were round with the blowing:—
"Rejoice, O legions, be glad—huzza!
Come all and sing Alleluia,
    The joyful tidings knowing!

"Long have we prayed this hour to see,
Long have we sighed 'It will never be!'
    But now our prayers have their ending—
From the distant earth we have ridden to-day;
It is numb and cold, it is dead and grey,
    No breath from its corpse ascending."

Oh then was opened each window, each door,
And legions of angels, and more, and more,
    On foot and on horse came bearing
Their drums and tabors and harps of gold,
And with chatter and laughter light-hearted and bold,
    Down to that earth went faring.

But when in the glittering star-sown sky
They saw the earth extinguished lie,
    Ashen in cloud-rack sleeping,
The tabors fell silent, the breath came quick,
The tears in every eye stood thick,
    And the angels all were weeping.

And then they crept down on the giant tomb,
And whispered, stumbling through cold and gloom,
    In voices timid and quailing,
Of that old immemorial earthly life,
Of sickness and dying, of anger and strife,
    Of hoping and seeking and failing.

An altar of sacrifice there they built,
That priestly mass might atone for guilt;
　　And a dirge they set rising, falling,
A *requiem æternam* soft and low,
And they sprinkled the holy water, so
　　A benison earthward calling.

The benison came on the earth to brood,
And over the soil ran the sacred flood—
　　But lo! what means this happening?
The benison crouched like a frightened dove,
No inch would the curdling water move—
　　O say, what shall mean this happening?

The holy water said: "Nay, no spot
On all this earth where tears are not—
　　No soil for me is waiting."
And the benison said: "I see, oh, I see,
No least little nook from their rancours free,
　　From their bane of murderous hating."

E. C. M.

THE TRANSIT OF VENUS

Twelve hours the ether now, with fragrant hand,
Had held blue heaven o'er blue ocean spanned,
While Helios aimed incessant shafts of gold
Into the crystal caverns manifold—
For kindly chance, mayhap, might show him there
The young love-goddess with her rippling hair,
Her girlish beauty's budding harmony,
The shapely limbs, the firm well-knitted knee,
The proud lips' twin perfection, fair and wise,
And, crown of all, the deep expressive eyes.

Lo, where tall trees obscure a land-locked bay,
Lit briefly by the sun at dawn of day,

The water swells, and sows the beach with pearls.
A silver-shimmering billow landward swirls;
Then the spume parts—on coal-black steed of state
Rides Aphrodite through the water-gate.

Scarce has the barb's great hoof the shingle pressed
Ere softly-gripping thighs his course arrest;
Down to the turf she slips; she pats his neck
And grasps his forelock; then by word and beck
Urging him on, with gentle childlike hand
She leads the charger trampling up the strand,
Gives him his head, and he—he spurns the ground,
His whinnying wakes the solitude around,
And she is borne on air, as though by wings.
The blossoms kiss her feet as on she swings,
Her fingers in those russet ripples twine
That wet her nape and loins with ocean-brine;
So to the beechen-hedge she walks upright,
Nude as a diamond, pure, august as light.

And where, with leafage crowned, with violets pied,
The green turf swelled in waves the wood beside,
Noon's ardent breath around, the goddess laid
Her cool young limbs beneath a yew-tree's shade,
Enjoying sweet repose, drinking life's wine,
Glorying in youth, knowing herself divine.
Above her head the summer-day shone clear,
Doves fluttered by, and sheep were cropping near;
Through rock-strewn grass her courser wandered free,
The town, the world, were far across the sea,
Arched over all the broad majestic sky,
And the wood stirred, as though a storm were nigh.
Her eyes are dazzled; drowsily she blinks,
Lid falls on lid, the lashes' curtain sinks;
Woolgathering the fancy strays for her
In purple chaos, all the world a blur.
Now droops her head, her breath caressing sighs
Along her arm, that deep in blossoms lies;

The soul, unguarded, wanders where it will,
And false bright dreams the slumbering senses fill.

* * *

The bay is loud with gulls that wrangling scream—
Alert she leaps to life from out her dream,
And nimbly runs the vagrant barb to find,
Mounts him, and gallops inland like the wind.
Through leafy hazel-grove, through brake and bush,
On to a hill-surrounded plot they rush,
Whence a broad avenue, with gardens gay,
Sun-dappled to the city wends its way.
She stays her course, no farther need she fly,
Smooths her tossed hair, and rubs each lovely eye.

A vineyard path that climbed the summit sheer
Of that fair isthmus tempted her—though near
An irksome glacier-tract with snow-drifts wet,
By cloud obscured, by purply gloom beset,
Glowered menacingly the pass beside;
But this would serve as compass and as guide.
Plucking an early-budded spray, she wound
The branch for coronal her head around;
And toiling up that uncouth wall of wrack
Often she turned her face, often looked back
Where houses clustered in the valley lay,
Red in the stormy light of dying day.
They vanished in the gathering dusk ere long;
And she, her fair lips opening, sang a song:—
"Could ye but know what fortune gave this day!
Could ye but guess how near the boon ye pray!
Could ye but learn how dreams that mortals woo
In broad daylight before their eyes come true!
O fools of knowledge, still wise, still too late—
Fast come, fast gone; ye cannot bridle fate.
Chide not the gods, nor say your hopes they mock;
Who watches well needs no awakening shock.
To take and spend the bliss through æons grown

In one glad moment gods have ever known.
Unheralded the golden hour will come—
My foot is fleet, and none shall track me home."
So sang she, climbing where the vineyard sloped;
Upon her path a poor blind shepherd groped.
Across his face her beauty's lightning shot—
He met her gracious look, and saw it not;
Her hand she stretched in pitiful farewell,
His rough hair round her feet in ribbons fell.
Then to the wind-blown island-rock rode she,
Set like a dam 'twixt this and that wild sea;
There by the fierce outrageous blast assailed,
Dun coasts around by coming tempest paled,
While dark waves, whipped to foam with furious lash,
Hissing upon the granite boulders crash,
She laughs aloud, she bares her budding breast,
Luring the wind, a mænad half-confessed;
Her alabaster arms she flings on high,
From heart and lips breaks out her joyous cry:—
"Hephæstos, O my love, O spouse to be!
Uranos' scion, heroes' progeny!
Creation thrills at thy fierce hammer-blows,
Cold iron blossoms red, pale marble glows;
Thy thundered whisper porphyry obeys,
Opening her sealed, her adamantine ways.
They mocked me that thou haltest, jeered and cursed
—O fools, in Eros' primal law unversed!
Know ye not, Unbelievers, love makes whole,
And beauty bends before the heroic soul?
Learn that a woman's heart is full of guile,
Steeled by a frown, distrustful of a smile;
What though ye prank in beauty pink and white?
One only on the earth is my delight."

She calls, she listens—will the answer sound?
The earth vibrates. In mountain-caves profound
The anvil rings. A blast of fire, blood-red,
Belches black smoke and ashes from the shed.

The steed knows, trumpeting, his master's cry,
He rears, he paws the ground impatiently.
And now, on slippery footholds, pace by pace,
The sheer descent beyond they bravely face,
And reach ere long the rock-girt barren shores
Where venomously ocean spits and roars.
Thence, where a level boulder roofs the sea,
Into the vortex plunging joyously,
Deep in the brine they sink by evil chance,
And waves close over them in boisterous dance.
But soon, though hills of water on them rush,
Though myriad salty tongues malignant brush,
Though rudely Triton troops around them jeer,
One-hearted for Hephæstos' home they steer.
A towering cliff of bronze their landing stays—
The charger lifts his hoof, the rock obeys;
From out its heart gleam wedding-torches bright,
They enter, dancing, shouting, with delight;
Her lit exultant face is seen no more,
And mockingly swings-to the jealous door.

But Zeus, distraught by envy, grief, and ire,
Weighed in his mighty fist the bolt of fire!
With heel set firm against the throne, took aim
And hurled upon the rock flame, flame, and flame.
Roaring the thunder split, and splitting roared,
Over the hills the deluge broke and poured,
The hailstones danced—from Heaven's loftiest throne
Down through the valley swept the wild cyclone.
Howled through the din the frantic hurricane,
Vulcan hurled rocks on high like flinty rain,
Mute in the savage strife the mountains cowered,
And night behind the fiery chasms lowered.
But see! from out the town what throng is here,
Innumerable rushing, nearer, near!
They search the shore along, now up, now down:—
"Here from this arching shelf she sprang to drown."
Lost joy lies in the sea—they bend, they stare,

Then turn away with eyes that speak despair.
Hither centurions drag a blind old herd,
The panting mob swarms round, awaits his word:—
"Say on! She greeted thee? She spoke to thee?
Divine breath crossed him—nay, tell me, tell me!"
And ever new the throng about him pressed
To see, to touch, the man whom gods had blessed.
But hark! a sudden shout of glad surprise!
With one accord the gazers turned their eyes—
Joy! on the wind a curl of hair was borne
From her in that brave ride by Boreas torn;
Not one but snatched, for each would wrest the boon;
Fierce envious greed was turned to slaughter soon,
To clamorous Heaven pealed the battle-cry,
And red with blood the billows tossed on high.

But yonder, where the woodland fastness lay,
That flower-grown combe where first she left the bay,
Dipping white limbs in that celestial stream,
The wedding-guests held revelry supreme.
Great ardent surges rushed into the pond
As lovers might, for courtship fierce and fond;
Gentle Medusas, fish of every sort,
Mingled in silvery shoals for wanton sport;
As lightning flashed the leaping salmon bold,
And far away the thunder's organ rolled.

E. C. M.

THE WEDDING OF THESEUS

The sails were bellying proudly, filled by the morning breeze;
From the bow of the "Atalanta" young Theseus looks and sees
The crystal plain of ocean all blue and golden light,
And thinks of Ariadne, old Minos' daughter bright.

Nor rock nor reef was threatening, no cloud was in the skies;
Dancing upon the ripples, the white-winged vessel flies.
But now along the coast that skirts the blue Aegean Bay
The temple-groves cast shadows from gardens green and gay,
And through an oak-tree flitting, there falls a sunny beam
That woos the royal stripling to a gallant golden dream.

He dreamt the gods came sweeping down, divine, from Heaven's
gate,
And each and all brought wedding-gifts upon his choice to wait;
The gondola soon overflowed with precious golden store,
And the azure Pontus, strewn with fruits, was azure now no more.
"Come, choose a sponsor at the feast from us whom here you see."
The king looked in the eyes of them, and swiftly answered he:—
"I am Aegisthus' offspring, begat of princely blood,
Nor ever have I bargained, nor sought the lesser good.
He ne'er shall gain the utmost who ne'er the utmost tries;
For sponsor give me Zeus himself, the Lord of all the skies."

* * *

And now it is the wedding-day, and now the bonds are tied,
And all the folk are cheering round the bridegroom and the bride;
And see! above the nuptial throne where sit the happy pair
In splendid circling flight an eagle cleaves the waves of air.
And through the crowd a messenger arrayed in spotless white
Breathlessly makes his way, and stops the litter golden-bright.
"Turn back, O king exalted, O scion bravely born!
Unto Phaleros' harbour turn thy steps this happy morn;
Thence doth a ship come winging from the distant Chersonese,
It bears the boy called Hyllos, the son of Heracles,
Banished from home and throne, by coward murderers betrayed;
It was Eurystheus' envy—he flees to thee for aid.
Hark! over all that ocean his cries for help we hear!
Soon will he wholly perish, the enemy is near."

"To Jove was ever sacred a creature held at bay—
I thank Thee, Zeus, who grantest me such noble work to-day.
Compassion and protection are wedding-gifts of price—

Where now belongs my service I know, and will suffice."
Swiftly he sprang from off his throne and left his bride so fair,
And swiftly called his legions, and swiftly all were there;
Manned six triremes with sailors that never knew defeat,
And rowed with oars like lightning to battle ever sweet.
And when the foe outnumbered fled before his fierce onslaught
And with tattered sails and bloody their homeward journey sought,
The victor led exultantly the guest that God had sent,
The noble son of Heracles, within his palace tent,
With words of comfort soothed him, cheered his despairing soul,
And served him well with drink and food, and quickly made him whole.
Then in the bath he laved his wounds and washed the blood away,
And flew on wings of rapture to his bride of but a day.

"Alas, thou loveless, unloved! Eternal shame be thine!
Did ever new-made bride know any insult like to mine!
In Hymen's sacred hours, that even Hermes stays,
My lover rushes from me, on this the day of days;
Instead of sweet communings, instead of vow and kiss,
I have to hear the bruit of war, and murder's hateful hiss.
O that I never, never had left Ionia's coast
And the palace of my father where I was honoured most!"
"Enough of idle weeping! Is this the time for tears?
Behold me at thy feet, I'll pour repentance in thine ears!
If ease was thy desiring, and life without a care,
Thou never should'st have loved a King of Athens, O my fair!
Windless the marsh-land festers, while lightning whips the tower,
On peaks and crowns the tempest exults to wreak its power;
A feeble ray of passion burns with a steady wick,
Only in heroes' bosoms can feeling blaze and prick.
See how the golden morning dispels the murky night—
It knows that Ariadne can front the broad daylight.
Leave darkness to barbarians—they find contentment there;
But Hellenes on their wedding-day demand the sun and air.
Am I not glad with well-doing, heartened with deeds of might?
And in thy lap I pour Jove's blessings, pour his grace and light."

E. C. M.

DEATH OF CYRUS

The noble host of Cyrus was pent in narrow room
While round them Scythian missiles sang their shrill song of doom.

His doughty warriors lie stretched in heaps upon the plain;
His mail-clad janissaries have nearly all been slain.

Up rode a Persian satrap, a veteran old and tried:
"I come as humble mouthpiece of forty lords beside.

"Note that the wounds we show you are all upon the front.
Therefore I speak quite frankly; your anger cannot daunt.

"If our choice were a free one, no death we would not dare;
But our task is to save you, whom ill the world could spare.

"We cannot look for victory; their strength all hope denies.
Your only chance of safety is flight in humble guise.

"Your face is known and dreaded; it shines in hatred's light.
It is your blood they covet; the smaller fry they slight.

"See what a cloud of arrows is swarming round your brow.
Let us partake the danger that menaces you now.

"Lay by the signs of dignity that mark you as their prey;
Become just like your comrades in bearing and array.

"Your crown lend to another, likewise your royal chain;
Your purple robe and girdle be my reward and gain.

"Let each one who is worthy share in your pomp and state.
Retain alone your buckler, with trusty sword as mate.

"Then up with horse and chariot, to flee this fatal strife.
The rest of us may perish, if we but save your life."

With gloomy mien great Cyrus these manly words did hear.
Against the grain their import; their force was all too clear.

He lighted from his chariot, doffing his rich array;
A sorry steed he mounted, and charged into the fray.

Round him like wedge of iron pressed on his warriors brave;
Vain were their deeds of valour; their king they could not save.

Spite of their fiercest efforts, too strong the foeman's might.
Some twelve of them were captured; the rest were slain outright.

* * *

To palace of Tomyris, Queen of the Scythian race,
With news of glorious victory Orestes rode apace.

"O'erwhelmed in narrow valley lies Cyrus' proud array.
Save for a group of captives, not one survives the day."

"Peace be to Zeus Avenger, to whom this grace is due.
Now show the head of Cyrus, to prove your news is true."

"He lives, but as a prisoner," the Scythian made reply.
"He waits me at the stake, then, that I may see him die?"

"Forgive," said pale Orestes, to his vindictive Queen,
"A dozen Persian princes, alike in garb and mien,

"Exchanged with noble Cyrus their weapons and attire;
To die to save their master their last and fond desire.

"What boots it us to fancy the king must 'mid them be—
No one of them is traitor, to tell us which is he."

"These men are each one mortal. They may be slain, I ween?"
At her feet fell Orestes, in supplicating mien.

"We warriors, though desperate, still hold the Gods in awe;
To slay our gallant prisoners would outrage every law.

"In furious bloody conflict, we give them blow for blow;
But no magnanimous victor can slay a captive foe."

Then in his beard smiled slyly Tomyris' son and heir,
And placed himself before her, with reassuring air.

"Restrain the anger, Mother, that surges in your breast.
I surely can distinguish great Cyrus from the rest."

Thereon, with Scythian cunning, a banquet he prepares
To feast his noble captives; this honour shall be theirs.

Twelve damsels, kind and lovely, twelve boys of nurture fine,
Adorn their heads with garlands, and serve them with old wine.

Anon, with morn approaching, with wine and food well plied,
The revellers grew more jovial, all caution laid aside.

The wily Scythian, noting, brought in a Persian chained,
And showed him to the warriors that he had entertained.

"As pledge of my sincerity," he cried, "and honour too,
I'll let you fix the penalty that is this wretch's due.

"Ready and glib in tongue-talk, in fighting slow and shy,
This hound, to gain my favour, has not disdained to lie

"And blast the name of Cyrus, which ev'n his foes respect,
With foul and venomous slander. What must this man expect?"

Then rose a raucous clamour, with one consenting breath:
"There is no room for doubting; the answer must be death."

But one calm, noble captive was ready to forgive;
Smiled, as he shrugged his shoulders; "let the poor creature live."

The Scythian bowed before him, turned to his Mother-Queen—
"There stands the hero, Cyrus, it's easy to be seen.

"The rôle of lowly subject no monarch can sustain;
The lordly will to pardon reveals the royal strain.

"My power, brave King, avails not to save you from your fate
You know a tiger's cruelty is naught to woman's hate;

"Your sense of royal duty has led you to your doom;
But rightful pomp and homage shall tend you to the tomb."

J. F. M.

THE FALSE BEL

Spoke the king to bold Ben Hadad,
 The Lord of Nineveh:
"Two hundred thousand cowards all
 The men in my array.
On you alone I set my trust.
 Your hand will have the power,
Backed by courageous heart, to plant
 My flag on Tyre's proud tower."
And with these words he reaches him
 The golden image Bel:
"Oh, king, thy confidence in me
 Shall be requited well."

So answered bold Ben Hadad,
 Raising the emblem bright;
And after him the Syrian troops
 Rode fiercely to the fight.

The middle space 'twixt horde and horde
Grew narrow as they sped;
With battle yell and stamp of steed
Quivered the air o'erhead.
In tangled groups of furious men
Array fought with array
And through the living warp and woof
Death's sickle sheared its way.

Forward and backward swayed the tide
Of the wild battle dance
And high o'erhead hangs Bel the God,
Shining in sunlight's glance.
See how the swarming Syrians
Scale fast the lofty wall!
By dark the fight was over,
The tower was forced to fall.

* * *

But as in twilight's dusky hour
The king rode through the gate,
Through double lanes of slaughtered men,
Acclaimed by trumpet's state,
There lay just by the bloody breach
Ben Hadad, struck to death,
And he cursed his king and master
As he drew his latest breath.

"He who the eye of death has met
Need fear no living man!
Look at the standard that you gave,
To carry in the van!
The purple's sham, decayed the wood,
Tinsel the golden Bel!
Deceit grins in the idol's face.
The staff is but a shell.
I speak not of my loving wife,
Nor how my life is done.

When did I ever count my foes?
What danger did I shun?

"Pale death upon the bloody field
The warrior meets as due;
But fame must be of virgin gold,
His honour must be true."
He spake, and from the heaps of dead
He clutched a keen-edged sword;
And with one last convulsive blow
Struck down his sovereign lord.

J. F. M.

HILDEBRAND

The Canon of Palermo—his name was Polycarp—
Led all the convent brothers up the steep mountain scarp.

When they, with pious groanings, had reached the upper wood,
The Canon showed them, rev'rently, a man in monkish hood,
Who swung a wood-axe bravely, with all his heart and soul,
Polishing, cutting, pointing a hefty ashen-pole.

"Hosanna," called the Canon, "regard this sturdy man,
Mark well his busy toiling, and emulate his plan.
You see the Holy Father, the princely Hildebrand,
Exiled by Rome ungrateful to this far-distant land.
A Saracen or Paynim this wrong would quick resent.
Eheu! but wrath is pagan, and Christians must relent.
Ecce! The patient martyr, bowing to God's decree,
His enemy forgiving, makes vine-poles peacefully."

The saintly toiler wiped his brow and fetched his breath and said:—
"My friends, your words are foolishness—they've neither tail nor head.

It's true I've swallowed gladly full many a sparkling draught,
But as to vineyard-culture, I never learned the craft.
So please you, here's a lance now, a trifle rough, but strong;
God grant I'll see it sticking in my foe's back ere long.
He's but a caitiff Jebusite who, foiled by knavish trap,
Instead of fighting stoutly, lies down in David's lap.*
The church on Christ is builded, the Devil lieth low.
When to the dust I've borne him, I, too, forgive my foe."

J. F. M.

THE OCTOPUS

Methought I drifted lonely on the sea,
And crazy was the bark that carried me.
Then stirred the eastern waters—and behold!
An octopus with members manifold,
A face in every foot and every arm,
With eyes that hated me and wished me harm.
"Thou murderer!" I cried, "art not content?
See how my flesh by those vile fangs was rent!
Daily it bleeds, it festers ceaselessly;
And now wilt thou pursue me o'er the sea?"

In vain. For now it swooped upon the boat.
I seized the tiller, blindly, fiercely smote.
Then quivered that abominable beast
As though to death struck down, and from me ceased,
Fled the wind across the ocean wide
And, fleeing, shed a limb on every side—
Destroyed it was. And from the loathsome form,
O wonder! rose a woman, sweet and warm,
Radiant with colours, gleaming, flashing bright—
She smiled, and in a dance she circled light,
Crossing her arms to keep her balance true,
Her raiment wing-like spread against the blue;

* The reference is to II Samuel, v, 6–10.

And farther, farther, fairer, fairer still—
Serpentine grace that made my pulses thrill.

I could not turn my eyes from that display,
Sorcery it was, sweet horror on me lay,
And when at last she vanished quite away,
I thought to shout exultant: "Victor I!"—
But from my breast there broke a deep-drawn sigh.

E. C. M.

A WOMAN'S VOICE

In dream it was. A pilgrim-troop
Of men and women hand-in-hand
Marched through a place I knew for home,
Singing sweet chants of thanksgiving;
And I, far in the rear, kept pace,
Happy to feel them all my kin.

Then soared above the harmonious choir,
Among the leaders, hid from me,
One voice—and young it was, and fresh
And clear; the distant hill and vale
With sunlight of that song were turned to gold—
But the exultant voice rang false,
Both time and tune it failed to keep.

And I, to hear the wondrous voice,
So lovely, so devout, so false,
Flung myself sobbing on the path—
My teeth in my clenched hand I sank,
My forehead in my native dust.

E. C. M.

THE LIFE AND WORKS OF CARL SPITTELER

By CHARLES BAUDOUIN

THE LITTLE TOWN of Liestal, Switzerland, a center of humanism associated with the names of Erasmus, Holbein, Burckhardt, and Böcklin, was the place of Carl Spitteler's birth on April 24, 1845.

From his work *Meine frühesten Erlebnisse* (My Earliest Experiences, 1914) it is obvious that, even as a small child, he was endowed with superior qualities of mind. Surely his senses and his mental capabilities must have been nearly perfect for him to retain such sharp, accurate impressions of his second year of life. Spitteler's mental makeup was a marvelous artist's instrument, a sensitive lyre responsive to the touch of the psyche, which soon was to awaken under the impact of the first emotions of adolescence and Switzerland's prodigious natural beauties. Unquestionably, Spitteler had a painter's eye which delighted unreservedly in a rapture of light and color. He had a great talent for drawing and seriously considered taking up painting.

At the impressionable ages of fifteen and seventeen, he made two visits to the little town of Winterthur in the canton of Zurich, where he stayed with a young aunt, the woman he called Eugenia, his good genius. On Spitteler's first visit, his aunt played a composition by Bach on the piano and he discovered music. He also was introduced to metaphysics through the gift from his aunt of a small book written by Feuchtersleben. It was a magic book, Spitteler tells us, "for one year I was playing with toy soldiers; a year later I was a serious thinker." He discovered Beethoven during his second visit with his aunt. Thus, his richly endowed nature with its all-'round talents began to take shape.

Painter, philosopher, and composer—the young Spitteler was all these things. But he felt his talents as a musician and a painter had come to light too late for him to acquire the necessary techniques (he was seventeen years old when he used the words "too late").

Nevertheless, he sustained a boundless respect for the arts and the craft of the artist. He now decided to be a poet.

No other medium was so well suited as poetry for the combination and fusion of all his various gifts.

His outward life was uneventful—the life of a man who was not of the times and who went unnoticed among his contemporaries. At eighteen, on reading Ariosto, his eyes were opened to his own potentialities and he fixed a goal to become an epic poet.

In 1863, he began studying law at the University of Zurich. From 1865 through

1870 he studied theology in Zurich, Heidelburg, and Basle. After taking and passing his theological examinations, he was appointed to a pastorship in 1871, but gave it up immediately. In August of the same year, he left Switzerland to take a post as tutor in St. Petersburg where he stayed until 1879. This was, in fact, the period when the idea of *Prometheus,* on which Spitteler worked for thirteen years, was taking shape. It was a period of meditation, during which he led a pure, retired life, an inward-looking life.

Prometheus und Epimetheus was published at his own expense by a small firm in the little town of Aarau in 1881, soon after Spitteler returned to Switzerland. The book went against everything to which readers were accustomed and it aroused astonishment, but not enough to attract public attention. It had all the attributes required for it to remain ignored. The manner in which it had been published alone was enough to make it pass unnoticed. Spitteler was a "beginner," but he was thirty-five years old and he had put his whole self into this work. Understandably, the silence which greeted the book was a deep disappointment for him. This discouragement was, indeed, "the time of thirst for life and of wounded faith."

For Spitteler, it also was a period of disagreeable duties. On returning from Russia, he accepted a teaching post at a girls' school in Berne. In 1881, he married one of his pupils, a Dutch girl, set up house in Neuveville on the lake of Biel, and continued to teach at the Progymnasium, where he taught German, Latin, Greek and French thirty hours a week. In 1885 he moved to Basle for a short time, writing for the newspaper *Grenzpost* until 1886, and then moved to Zurich where he wrote for *Neue Zürcher Zeitung* from 1890 to 1892. In both these positions he dealt with the literature of the day in essays which outshone it and which were republished in *Lachende Wahrheiten* (*Laughing Truths,* 1898). In 1892 Spitteler retired to Lucerne, where he remained until his death in 1924, and where, with his wife and two daughters, he led the life of a hospitable recluse.

Spitteler was unappreciated by the multitude, but he always was held in high regard by the select few. Nietzsche sensed his greatness from the start, as did Gottfried Keller and Jacob Burckhardt. In 1920 the award of the Nobel Prize set the seal to the sterling quality of his works. Most of Spitteler's prose, such as *Imago* (1908), takes its full value when seen as a commentary on his great poems. In his lyric poems the true Spitteler is less elusive than in his novels. The main interest of one book, *Schmetterlinge* (Butterflies, 1889) really lies in showing how a great poet ennobles everything he touches, even those things which would, in other hands, be merely finicky. In this book the butterfly becomes a sylvan power, a fairy, a goddess. Some of the poems are myths, legends about how things were created, and in these poems the essential characteristic of Spitteler's genius, brooking no restraint, contrives to insinuate itself into a subject which seems the least suited to the purpose.

Spitteler wondered whether ballads should rightly be regarded as lyric or as epic poetry. His own ballads are certainly of a very decidedly epic cast.

But in all his volumes of short poems, the verses are in the nature of exercises, as their author was the first to proclaim. The first *Prometheus* was not written in ordinary poetic form, but in long verses of rhythmic prose (similar to the verses in the Bible). No doubt before plunging into the composition of the great verse epic *Olympischer Frühling* (Olympian Spring, 1900–1906), Spitteler was experimenting.

Although he was on the wrong side of thirty-five when he first began to publish, this great workman still regarded himself as only an apprentice. In each of the small volumes of poetry he tackled every aspect of his craft. In *Glockenlieder* (Bell Songs, 1906) he combined chords in wondrous harmonies and orchestrated rich sounds, and in the *Balladen* (1896) he practiced writing narrative poetry. He was not in a hurry. Just as Hercules resolutely makes his way toward his task on earth with tranquillity and measured tread, so did Spitteler himself make his way toward his great work. He was not to fulfill himself creatively until he reached his fifties. However, his target was set and there could no longer be any doubt about the true nature of his poetic art—the mythical epic was his element and when he departed from it, it was by way of practice and amusement.

It was in connection with *Prometheus und Epimetheus* that the question of the relations between Spitteler and Nietzsche arose. The fact is that Spitteler and Nietzsche, both solitary men, rubbed shoulders at Basle University, where the former was completing his studies and the latter held a professorship, but they did not actually become acquainted. Later they corresponded. It is interesting to note that Nietzsche tried to find a publisher for Spitteler's works on esthetics at a time when he despaired of finding one for his own works. Subsequently, when *Ecce Homo* was published (Neitzsche was then on the brink of madness) Spitteler was one of the two persons to whom Nietzsche, the megalomaniac genius, deigned to send a copy.

In his own work, Spitteler retained nothing of the old Prometheus fable, only the names and the pure essence they express. Prometheus remains the strong hero who has rebelled against official divinity, the exiled benefactor of mankind. Still, Spitteler's myth remains faithful to the ancient one for the most part in its subconscious content, and this fact, more than any other, is proof of the profound, organic truth in Spitteler's creation. The entire external plot is his own invention. The episodes have nothing in common with those relating to the Prometheus of antiquity and the reader will look in vain for Prometheus's most classic attributes—there is no stolen fire, no Caucasus, and no vulture.

This treatment of myths found wider application in the great work of his late maturity, *Olympian Spring,* which established his worldwide fame. In this work all the gods have names found in classical antiquity, but they are new gods. Spitteler had little respect for mythological tradition. No doubt he retained the beautiful Greek names because they pleased his ear. In addition, they served to guide the reader's mind effortlessly toward the meaning—they were the poet's interpreters.

Spitteler's gods belong to him and to his native country, just as the Virgins of the Flemish painters are Flemish. Spitteler's Olympus is undoubtedly not in Greece. At every turn we recognize landscapes from the Jura or the Alps, transfigured by the legendary light which we become familiar with in *Prometheus.* At the same time, the endless, heavy, rolling sweep of the rhythmic prose verses in *Prometheus* has given place to regular, brisk, taut, impassioned verse in the form of iambic hexameters, which Spitteler discovered during his groping attempts in the *Balladen.* He considered that iambic hexameters could become the great epic verse form. No doubt the poet who would often reread one of Racine's tragedies before writing a canto had the satisfaction of finding a counterpart of the French alexandrine in this meter. His chosen verse form, however, is more rigorous than the alexandrine; while it also is based on lines of twelve syllables, it has, in addition, an accentual meter with the stress necessarily falling on the even-numbered syllables.

Afterward came another Prometheus—*Prometheus der Dulder* (*Prometheus the Sufferer,* 1924). This work of the poet's old age, is not—as Spitteler has explained—a mere improved version of the first *Prometheus.* Nor is it an expanded epilogue to the first one; rather it is in a sense complementary to the first *Prometheus,* in the same way the second *Faust* was complementary to the first, for the inner drama has not stood idle between the two works.

This second version treats the same theme, but in a different mode. First of all, the respective lengths of the sections are very different. The form, too, is different. The second *Prometheus* is not written in rhythmic prose verses as is the first; rather, it has the same regular meter, the iambic hexameter, as *Olympian Spring.* But the tone is airy; extraordinarily rich-hued verse has given place to a more solid-sounding music of granitelike hardness.

As though his testamentary work left nothing more to be said or done, Spitteler died two weeks after its appearance, just as Goethe after completing his second *Faust.*

Spitteler's works themselves, in the wake of Hugo, Richard Wagner, and Symbolism, provide more effective proof than any argument of the vitality of his epic, mythical art. And although this art is equal to the expression of all modern ideas, it displays an eternal youth sparkling with creation and freshness.

Spitteler was no esthete, or a man swayed by fine words. He could not be satisfied with a purely esthetic "Apollonian" solution to the problem of evil. On many occasions attention has been drawn to his uprightness, his fundamental straightforwardness, and his courage to stand up to people. These are qualities he shared with his principal heroes, giving them an essential, rocklike firmness of character. "Old Swiss granite" was the very apt comment of a graphologist who studied a specimen of Spitteler's handwriting. And reference has been made on more than one occasion to his love of a challenge, his manly stubbornness which became even more dogged in the face of opposition.

Spitteler was a man who had high principles, very high ones. He had an unswerving sense of probity and justice. In 1914 he made a courageous protest against public opinion in his own country and, as a result, he was boycotted in Germany from then on. He said in his famous protest speech that he remembered his youth had been nurtured on "certain principles," continuing: "Are the words *republic, democracy, liberty, tolerance,* etc., of minor importance to the Swiss? There was a time—I lived through it myself—when these words meant everything in Europe. Today they mean next to nothing. Everything may have been too much, but nothing is not enough."

Charles Baudouin is professor of literature at the University of Geneva.
Translated by Annie Jackson.

THE 1918 PRIZE

By KJELL STRÖMBERG

WITH Carl Spitteler, Switzerland for the first time carried off the honors of the Nobel Prize for Literature. In fact, he is the only Swiss writer whose name appears on the roll of honor, except for the poet and novelist Hermann Hesse, who was German by birth but had become a Swiss citizen some time before he received the Prize in 1946. The greatest name in contemporary Swiss literature in the French language, that of Charles-Ferdinand Ramuz, did not get the award: he was proposed as candidate several times, but died without the Prize in 1947. Little Switzerland has been awarded a considerable number of scientific Nobel Prizes, and no less than three Helvetic citizens appear among the earliest laureates to get the Prize for Peace; one of them was Henri Dunant, founder of the International Red Cross.

Carl Spitteler's name had been sent in to the Nobel Committee of the Swedish Academy well before World War I, and had been very seriously considered. His two master works, *Prometheus und Epimetheus* in prose, and *Olympischer Frühling* in verse, date from the distant past, the first from the 1880s and the second from the first years of the new century. They had been more or less forgotten, the more so because they had never reached the general public.

The Nobel Committee first asked for an analytical report on Spitteler's work in 1912. Karl Warburg, holder of the chair of literary history at Stockholm University, drew up the report and came to the conclusion that his work was entirely worthy of a Nobel Prize. "It is not necessary to compare the author with Homer, Dante, or Ariosto, and one may doubt whether the future will proclaim him their equal," he says, after having stated that Spitteler belongs well and truly to the line of these great narrative poets. In addition, Spitteler was not only the "great man" of Swiss literature, but he was also the bearer of one of the great names in all contemporary literature in the German language. Gottfried Keller, the old master writer of Swiss literature, had been struck by Spitteler's originality, which had also gradually aroused the interest of eminent critics abroad. The report quotes, among others, the Frenchman Maurice Muret, who had recently written a long and very flattering essay on him in the *Revue de Paris.* In conclusion, Warburg formally contradicted his German colleague, Richard M. Meyer, the author of a manual on literary history which was considered a work of authority in German universities, in which he describes Spitteler as following in the wake of Nietzsche, who had also lived in Basle for a long time. Warburg maintained that the contrary was true: Nietzsche's *Zarathustra* was published several years after Spitteler's first masterpiece, and Nietzsche was influenced by *Prometheus and Epimetheus*.

It was not until 1920, when Spitteler's name acquired a certain interest because of the warm tributes he received on his seventy-fifth birthday, that the Swedish Academy decided to reward a work which, by its general tenor and its notably idealistic tendencies, thoroughly satisfied the literally interpreted demands of the Nobel will. This did not happen until after lengthy tergiversations, because the 1919 Prize (which was the one which he was awarded a year later) had at first been "reserved."

Spitteler got his Prize at the same time as the Norwegian Knut Hamsun, who was awarded the Prize for 1920. He must have been thankful for this because, if he had been given it the year before and if he had gone to Stockholm to receive it personally as well, he would have found himself in bad company: the German professor, Fritz Haber, the inventor of poison gas, was the Nobel Prize laureate for Chemistry in 1919. The unusualness of this award, which obviously had other less shocking purposes, provoked general indignation in the Allied countries, particularly in France. Because of this, the diplomatic representatives in Stockholm refused to appear at the Prizegiving ceremony. The Royal family fortunately had another valid reason for abstaining, which was the full mourning imposed by the death of Princess Margareth, niece of King Edward VII of England and first wife of King Gustavus Adolphus VI of Sweden. Incidentally, it should be noted that this was the first and only time when this ceremony took place in summer, on June 1, instead of on December 10, the anniversary of Nobel's death. This was the result of general opinion in the press, which felt that the laureates and their usual following of journalists from all over the world should make the acquaintance of Sweden, not shrouded in winter fog, but in the lovely season of mild, light nights, when sunset melts into dawn.

Spitteler had rivals. One was Georg Brandes, the great Danish critic and historian, who was already world famous. Juhani Aho, the excellent Finish novelist, was proposed by von Heidenstam, who pleaded his cause with the same ardor as he did that of Spitteler. Some of the other candidates: the Englishman Galsworthy; the Pole Ladislas Reymont, who was added to the list later; and Hugo von Hofmannsthal, the delightful Viennese poet and dramatist.

The Swedish press, with very few exceptions, was reserved in its judgment, noting the learned but old-fashioned character of a work that was practically unknown even in literary circles outside the laureate's own country. The answer was quickly forthcoming from Anders Österling, who at that time was literary critic of the Conservative paper *Svenska Dagbladet*. "Carl Spitteler," he said, "is not only a genius of originality and a fine intellect, but also a wise personality who inspires deep respect. There is nobody who fits the requirements of the award in a more proper sense, and this choice should give all the more satisfaction because the laureate, far from being spoilt by easy popularity, could rather be entitled one of the Kings without a kingdom in the world of poetry."

Translated by Camilla Sykes.